Instructor's Resource Manual

Charles R. B. Wright

Discrete Mathematics
FOURTH EDITION

D1489690

Kenneth A. Ross ▪ Charles R. B. Wright

PRENTICE HALL, Upper Saddle River, NJ 07458

Executive Editor: George Lobell
Editorial Assistant: Gale A. Epps
Special Projects Manager: Barbara A. Murray
Production Editor: Barbara A. Till
Supplement Cover Manager: Paul Gourhan
Supplement Cover Designer: PM Workshop Inc.
Manufacturing Buyer: Alan Fischer

Printed in the United States of America

10 9 8 7 6 5 4 3 2

ISBN 0-13-083892-6

Prentice-Hall International (UK) Limited, London
Prentice-Hall of Australia Pty. Limited, Sydney
Prentice-Hall Canada, Inc., Toronto
Prentice-Hall Hispanoamericana, S.A., Mexico
Prentice-Hall of India Private Limited, New Delhi
Prentice-Hall (Singapore) Pte. Ltd.,
Prentice-Hall of Japan, Inc., Tokyo
Editora Prentice-Hall do Brazil, Ltda., Rio de Janeiro

Contents

PREFACE

This manual contains answers for all of the exercises in the text that call for explicit responses. In a number of instances we have elaborated on the answers that appear in the back of the text. Many exercises can be answered correctly in more than one way, and you may want to remind students who are grading homework for you of this fact, lest they think that only the manual answers should receive credit. [This is the voice of experience.]

We have preceded the solutions for each chapter by some suggestions and comments that we hope will be helpful to the instructor. In writing the text we have tried to divide the material so that each section corresponds to a single class period, but experience has shown that some sections really deserve two days, either because they contain a lot of new ideas or because students will need more than the usual amount of expert guidance. We have indicated in our chapter suggestions those sections that we think could use extra time. For quick reference, they are: §§ 1.1 and 1.2 together [getting started], 4.2 [induction], 5.3 and 5.4 [inclusion-exclusion, binomial methods and partitions], 7.3 [depth-first search], 8.3 [shortest path algorithms], 10.1 [partial orders] if you skip Chapter 9, and 10.2 [special linear orders]. Section 4.3 [big-oh notation] might also warrant an extra day.

Chapter 1

The first two sections of the chapter are meant to give students a gentle start toward thinking about mathematics in a new way, but they also contain ideas, notation and terms that will be used later on. It's a good idea to allow three class meetings to cover these sections, particularly if there are "beginning of term" mechanics that take class time at the start. Even then, you can get at least half way through Section 1.1 on the first day. Tell the students to read over the "To the Student Especially" part of the Preface and Sections 1.1 and 1.2 before the second class meeting. Some of the material in Section 1.2 may be familiar to a number of students, but the discussion of it should be thorough enough that the ideas and notation of divisors and primes can be used from now on. Don't get bogged down on the Euclidean Algorithm material. We'll come back later and prove everything we need, but at this point the idea is just to show how the algorithm would be useful if we had it.

This chapter also goes over elementary properties of sets, and establishes notation for sets and sequences. Much of the material will be old news for the students, and it may be hard to convince them that they don't know it all already. One of the aims of this chapter is to set the tone of the book by emphasizing the absolute necessity of careful definitions of even the most common terms.

In § 1.3 students have trouble with $\mathcal{P}(S)$ and Σ^*, both of which will be important later on. Now is the time to look at lots of examples, to get comfortable with the notation and to see how natural the ideas are.

Examples 4 and 5 in § 1.4 quietly include some proofs, but mostly this section relies on common sense and Venn diagrams. In the exercises, "determine" means list or describe the set unambiguously.

Section 1.5 is pretty standard. We tend to think of functions as rules, but from time to time also want to consider them as sets of ordered pairs, especially later on in Chapter 3 when we look at relations. Some of the examples seem more like the functions encountered in calculus than those associated with discrete mathematics, but we've also included floor and ceiling functions, as well as characteristic functions, to give a discrete flavor too. It also helps to have students think of functions in terms of hand-held calculators. If the square-root function were two-valued, what would the calculator display do? And how about inverse trigonometric functions?

The basic ideas of sequences in § 1.6 seem not to cause trouble. We've used this section to work in sigma notation and introduce the idea of growth rate, using some popular sequences for illustration.

In § 1.7 it is not necessary to prove the theorem in class; just give plenty of examples. Experience tells us that students have trouble with both the notation and the concept of preimage. The notion of inverse also seems slippery for some. To keep the two concepts distinct, we have introduced the notation $f^{\leftarrow}(B)$ for non-invertible functions f. Examples help. Examples 8 and 9 are important for later work on equivalence relations in Chapter 3. The last paragraph in this section is deceptively innocent. We do want students to think of this powerful observation as completely natural. It will get fairly heavy use later on.

1.1 Answers

---

1. (a) 20   (b) 20   (c) 19

   (d) 56   (e) 11   (f) 41

   (g) 10   (h) $2 \times 10^{30} + 1$ (i) $10^{30} - 10^{29} + 1$

2. (a) 9000   (b) 9000   (c) 9000   (d) 9000

3. (a) 0   (b) 1265   (c) −5   (d) −4

4. (a) 1   (b) 0   (c) 6   (d) 1

   (e) 0

5. (a) 10   (b) 40   (c) 40   (d) 501

   (e) 54   (f) 465

6. (a) 10   (b) 40   (c) 41   (d) 500

7. (a) 17   (b) 493   (c) 7   (d) 667

8. (a) 8   (b) 11   (c) 296   (d) 4

   (e) 9001   (f) 401

9. One could divide n by k to get n/k. If the answer is positive, then $\lfloor n/k \rfloor$ is the part of it to the left of the decimal point. If the answer is negative, then $\lfloor n/k \rfloor$ is the part of it to the left of the decimal point [a negative integer] minus 1.

   For example, $\lfloor 73/17 \rfloor = \lfloor 4.294 \cdots \rfloor = 4$, and $\lfloor -73/17 \rfloor = \lfloor -4.294 \cdots \rfloor = -4 - 1 = -5$.

10. (a) Any situation in which you want to consider floors of various numbers or do some algebraic manipulations with them is a natural candidate for using the compact $\lfloor \ \rfloor$ notation.

    (b) You might prefer to use words in talking to a mathematically unsophisticated audience.

11. (a) If t is an integer, then $\lceil x + t \rceil = \lceil x \rceil + t$ for every number x.

    (b) If t is an integer, then so is $\lceil x \rceil + t$. Since $\lceil x \rceil \geq x > \lceil x \rceil - 1$, we have $\lceil x \rceil + t \geq x + t > \lfloor x \rfloor + t - 1$. But $\lceil x + t \rceil$ is the only integer k with $k \geq x + t > k - 1$, so $\lceil x \rceil + t$ must be $\lceil x + t \rceil$.

12. $\lfloor 9999/y \rfloor - \lfloor 999/y \rfloor$, where y is your age.

13. (a) 11 [They are 2, 3, 5, 7, 11, 13, 17, 19, 23, 29, 31.]

    (b) $33/\ln 33 \approx 9.44$, which is pretty close.

    (c) Maybe. It turns out that the number of such primes is 470, and $3333/\ln 3333 \approx 410.89$. Not very close. Indeed, $470/3333$ and $1/\ln 3333$ differ by about 14%.

14. (a) and (b) Here are three possible answers, where m, n, j and k are integers:

    How many integers between 1 and n are multiples of k but not multiples of $2k$?

    How many integers between m and n are multiples of 5 but not of 10?

    How many integers between m and n are multiples of k but not multiples of jk?

    (c) 500

15. (a) $10^{30}/30 \ln 10 \approx 1.45 \times 10^{28}$ (b) $10^{29}/29 \ln 10 \approx 1.50 \times 10^{27}$

    (c) (a) $-$ (b) $\approx 1.3 \times 10^{28}$

    (d) $100 \times$ (c)$/(10^{30} - 10^{29}) \approx 1.4\%$

16. By Fact 1 there are n integers between 1 and n, and $m - 1$ integers between 1 and $m - 1$. The difference, $n - (m - 1)$, is the number of them between m and n.

17. Add $-m + 1$ to everything. The number of integers between m and n is the number of them between $m + (-m + 1)$ and $n + (-m + 1)$, i.e., between 1 and $n - m + 1$. Apply Fact 1 or Fact 2.

18. The integers between x and y are at most as big as $\lfloor y \rfloor$ and at least as big as $\lceil x \rceil$, so they are the integers between $\lceil x \rceil$ and $\lfloor y \rfloor$. Apply Fact 3, with $m = \lceil x \rceil$ and $n = \lfloor y \rfloor$.

19. (a) One example is $x = y = 1.5$.

    (b) Any two integers will do.

    (c) By definition, $\lfloor x \rfloor \leq x$ and $\lfloor y \rfloor \leq y$, so $\lfloor x \rfloor + \lfloor y \rfloor \leq x + y$. Since $\lfloor x + y \rfloor$ is the largest integer less than or equal to $x + y$, and since $\lfloor x \rfloor + \lfloor y \rfloor$ is an integer, $\lfloor x \rfloor + \lfloor y \rfloor \leq \lfloor x + y \rfloor$.

1.2   Answers

1. (a) False, since $\frac{4}{8}$ is not an integer.

   (b) False, since $\frac{15}{4}$ is not an integer.

   (c) True, since $374 = 17 \cdot 22$.

   (d) True, since $1001 = 91 \cdot 11$.

   (e) False. The only primes that divide $10^{400} = 2^{400} \cdot 5^{400}$ are 2 and 5.

2. (a) False. In general $\frac{1}{n}$ is not an integer.

   (b) True, since $\frac{n}{n} = 1$.

   (c) True, since $\frac{n^2}{n} = n$, an integer.

3. (a) 1, 2, 15, 1, 13   (b) 756, 60, 30, 432, 91

4. $1 \cdot 756 = 27 \cdot 28$, $2 \cdot 60 = 6 \cdot 20$, $15 \cdot 30 = 15 \cdot 30$, $1 \cdot 432 = 16 \cdot 27$, $13 \cdot 91 = 13 \cdot 91$.

5. (a) $4 = 2^2$, $4 = 2^2$, $22 = 2 \cdot 11$, $14 = 2 \cdot 7$,   37.

   (b) $24 = 2^3 \cdot 3$, $1248 = 2^5 \cdot 3 \cdot 13$, $374 = 2 \cdot 11 \cdot 17$, $504 = 2^3 \cdot 3^2 \cdot 7$,   37.

6. (a) False. See (b).   (b) True. Just check.

7. (a) 10, 1, 10.

   (b) Since n is a divisor of 0 and n is the largest divisor of itself, n is the largest common divisor. I.e., $\gcd(0, n) = n$.

   (c) The only multiple of 0 is 0, so $\mathrm{lcm}(0, n)$ must be 0.

8. We think that "evenly" might suggest some connection with the prime 2.

9. (a) They must be relatively prime, since $\gcd(m, n) = mn/\mathrm{lcm}(m, n) = 1$.

   (b) Since $n = \mathrm{lcm}(m, n)$ is a multiple of m, this is true if and only if $m | n$.

   (c) Since $\gcd(m, n)$ is a divisor of n, this is true if and only if $m | n$.

10. In this case $\gcd(p, q) = 1$ and $\mathrm{lcm}(p, q) = pq$.

11. (a) Relatively prime, since $64 = 2^6$ and 729 is odd.

    (b) Relatively prime, since $27 = 3^3$ and 31 is prime.

    (c) Relatively prime, since $45 = 3^2 \cdot 5$ and $56 = 2^3 \cdot 7$.

    (d) Not relatively prime, since both are multiples of 3.

12. No, since 2 is a common divisor.

13. (a) These are the odd ones, i.e., the ones that are not even.

    (b) These are the positive integers that are not multiples of 3.

    (c) The same as (a).

    (d) The same as (e).

    (e) These are the ones that are not multiples of p.

14. (a) We have $lm = (la) \cdot d$, a multiple of d.

    (b) We have $m + n = (a + b) \cdot d$ and $m - n = (a - b) \cdot d$.

    (c) Yes, since $17m - 72n = (17a - 72b) \cdot d$.

15. (a) $\gcd(m, n)$ is a divisor of m and n, so it's a divisor of their difference.

    (b) By part (a), $\gcd(m, m+2)$ divides $(m+2) - m = 2$, so all common divisors of m and $m + 2$ divide 2.

    (c) 2 and 1.

    (d) 1 and 5.

16. (a) 1, 7, 11, 13, 17, 19, 23, 29.

    (b) 1, 5, 7, 11, 13, 17, 19, 23, 25, 29, 31, 35.

17. (a) Since $1 \le k^2 \le kl = n$, we have $k \le \sqrt{n}$.

    (b) One example is $n = 4 = 2 \cdot 2$.

    (c) Since n is not prime, there are integers k and l with $1 \le k < n$, $1 \le l < n$ and $n = kl$. Say $k \le l$, and let p be a prime factor of k. By part (a), $p \le k \le \sqrt{n}$.

    (d) This follows from part (c).

18. (a)   (b)   (c)

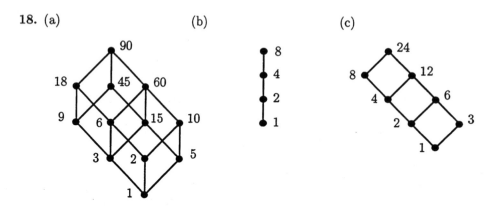

19. Since m, n and $\gcd(m,n)$ are positive, s and t cannot both be negative. They can't both be positive, because if they were we'd have

$$\gcd(m,n) \geq 1 \cdot m + 1 \cdot n = m + n \geq \gcd(m,n) + \gcd(m,n) = 2 \cdot \gcd(m,n),$$

which clearly cannot hold.

20. If $x \leq y$, then $\min\{x,y\} = x$ and $\max\{x,y\} = y$, so $\min\{x,y\} + \max\{x,y\} = x + y$. If $x > y$, then $\min\{x,y\} = y$ and $\max\{x,y\} = x$, so $\min\{x,y\} + \max\{x,y\} = y + x = x + y$. The equation holds in either case.

21. (a) 1,   1,   1,   7

(b) It helps to name $a = \gcd(m,n)$, $b = \gcd(l,a)$ and $c = \gcd(l,m,n)$. Our task is to show $b = c$.

First, note that $b \mid l$. Also $b \mid a$ and $a \mid m$, so $b \mid m$. Since $b \mid a$ and $a \mid n$, we also have $b \mid n$. Thus b is a common divisor of l, m and n. Hence $b \leq \gcd(l,m,n) = c$.

For the opposite inequality, observe first that $c \mid m$ and $c \mid n$. So c is a common divisor of m and n; hence $a = \gcd(m,n)$ is a multiple of c, as noted in the discussion following Example 6. Thus $c \mid a$. Since also $c \mid l$, c is a common divisor for l and a. Therefore $c \leq \gcd(l,a) = b$.

22. Because $0 \cdot m = 0$.

1.3   Answers

---

1. (a) 0, 5, 10, 15, 20, say.   (b) 3, 5, 7, 9, 11, say.

(c) $\emptyset$, $\{1\}$, $\{2,3\}$, $\{3,4\}$, $\{5\}$, say.   (d) 1, 2, 4, 8, 16, say.

(e) 1, 1/2, 1/3, 1/4, 1/73, say.

(f) 1/2, 1/3, 1/4, 1/5, 17/73, say.   (g) 1, 2, 4, 16, 18, say.

2. (a) 1, 1/2, 1/3, 1/4.   (b) 0, 2, 6, 12.

    (c) 1/4, 1/16, 1/36, 1/64, 1/100.   (d) 1, 3.

3. (a) λ, a, ab, cab, ba, say.

    (b) $\{\lambda, a, b, aa, ab, ba, bb\}$ is the complete set.

    (c) $aaaa$, $aaab$, $aabb$, etc.

The sets in parts (a) and (b) contain the empty word λ.

4. (a) $\{3\}$.   (b) $\{-3, 3\}$.

    (c) $\{-3, 3\}$.   (d) $\{4, 5, 6\}$.

    (e) $\{-6, -5, -4, 4, 5, 6\}$.   (f) $\varnothing$.

5. (a) $\varnothing$.   (b) $\varnothing$.   (c) $\varnothing$.

    (d) $\{1, 4, 7, 10, 13, 16, 19\}$.   (e) $\{2, 3, 5, 7, 11, 13\}$.

6. (a) $\{1, 2, 3, 4, 6, 12\}$ (b) $\varnothing$

    (c) $\{24, 25, 26\}$ (d) $\{15, 16\}$

7. (a) $\{0, 4, 8, 12, 16, 20\}$ (b) $\{1, 2, 4\}$

    (c) $\{0, 1, 2, 3, 4\}$ (d) $\{14, 15, 16, 17, 18, 19, 20\}$

8. (a) 0.   (b) 74.   (c) 138.   (d) 67.

    (e) 73.   (f) ∞.   (g) 0.   (h) 2.

9. (a) ∞.   (b) $2^4 = 16$.   (c) ∞.   (d) ∞.

    (e) ∞.   (f) 1.   (g) ∞.

10. (a) 2.   (b) ∞.   (c) ∞.   (d) 3.   (e) ∞.

    (f) $1 + 3 + 9 + 27 + 81 = 121$.

11. $A \subseteq A$, $B \subseteq B$, C is a subset of A, and C, D are subsets of A, B and D.

12. (a) False.   (b) True.   (c) True.   (d) True.   (e) False.

    (f) False.   (g) False.   (h) True.   (i) True.

13. (a) aba is in all three and has length 3 in each.

    (b) bAb is in Σ_3^* and has length 2.

    (c) cba is in Σ_1^* and length(cba) = 3.

    (d) cab has length 3 in Σ_1^* and length 2 in Σ_2^*.

    (e) $caab$ is in Σ_1^* with length 4 and is in Σ_2^* with length 3.

    (f) $baAb$ has length 3 in Σ_3^*.

14. In the first case there would be infinitely many words before ba: all the words beginning with a and then b. In the second case there would be $1 + 2 + 4 + 8 + 16 = 31$ words beginning with a, and then b before ba.

15. (a) Yes.

   (b) Not necessarily. If $\Sigma = \{a, b, Ab\}$ then $abAb$ is a word in Σ^*, but abA is not.

   (c) Delete first letters from the string until no longer possible. If λ is reached, the original string is in Σ^*. Otherwise, it isn't.

1.4   Answers

1. (a) $\{1, 2, 3, 5, 7, 9, 11\}$.   (b) $\{3\}$.   (c) $\{1, 5, 7, 9, 11\}$.

   (d) $\{1, 9\}$.   (e) $\{3, 6, 12\}$.

   (f) $\{3, 4, 5, 7, 8, 11\}$.   (g) 16.

2. (a) $\{2\}$, $\varnothing$, $\mathbb{P}$, $\mathbb{P}$.

   (b) $\varnothing$, $\{1\}$, $\{2\}$, $\{3\}$, $\{1, 2\}$, $\{1, 3\}$, $\{2, 3\}$, $\{1, 2, 3\}$.

   (c) $A \oplus B$, $A \oplus C$, $C \setminus A$.

3. (a) $[2, 3]$.   (b) $[0, 6]$.   (c) $[0, 2)$.

   (d) $[0, 2) \cup (3, 6]$.   (e) $(-\infty, 0) \cup (3, \infty)$.   (f) $\varnothing$.

   (g) $\mathbb{N}$.   (h) $[0, 2]$.   (i) $\varnothing$.

4. (a) $\{a, b, aa, bb\}$, $\{aaa, bbb\}$, $\{\lambda, ab, ba\}$, $\{\lambda, ab, ba, aaa, bbb\}$.

   (b) $\{aa, bb, aaa, bbb\}$, $\{aa, ab, ba, bb\}$, Σ^*, the set of words of length 2 or more, except for aa, bb, aaa and bbb.

   (c) $\{\lambda, a, b\}$, $\{a, b\}$, $\varnothing$.   (d) $\varnothing$, $\{a\}$, $\{b\}$, $\{a, b\}$.   (e) 4.

5. (a) $\varnothing$.

   (b) All words whose length is not 2.

   (c) $\varnothing$.   (d) Same as part (b).

   (e) $\{\lambda, ab, ba\}$.   (f) $\{\lambda\}$.

   (g) $B^c \cap C^c$ and $(B \cup C)^c$ are equal by a DeMorgan law [or by calculation] as are $(B \cap C)^c$ and $B^c \cup C^c$.

6. (a) Any pair of sets A, B where $A \neq B$ will work.

   (b) Any nonempty set A will work, since $A \cap \varnothing = \varnothing$.

   (c) Any example with $C \nsubseteq A$ will work, for instance $A = \varnothing \neq C$.

7. $A \oplus A = \varnothing$ and $A \oplus \varnothing = A$.

8. (a) 6   (b) 5   (c) 7   (d) $6 + 5 - 4 = 7$

   (e) In general, $|A| + |B|$ counts members of A and B, but members in $A \cap B$ get counted twice. For more, see the discussion about the Union Rule (b) on page 266.

9. (a) Make A very small, like $A = \emptyset$.

   (b) Make A "large", like $A = B \cup C$. For example, $B = \{1\}$, $C = \{2\}$ and $A = \{1, 2\}$ will work.

   (c) Try $A = B \cup C$ with B and C disjoint.

10. (a) Any example with $A \neq B$ shows the failure.

    (b) Any example with $A \cap C \neq \emptyset$ shows the failure.

11. (a) $(a, a), (a, b), (a, c), (b, a)$, etc. There are nine altogether.

    (b) $(a, a), (a, b), (a, d), (b, a), (b, b), (b, d), (c, a), (c, b), (c, d)$.

    (c) $(a, a), (b, b)$.

12. (a) 15, 15.

    (b) (0,2), (0,4), (1,2), (1,4), (2,4), (3,4).

    (c) (0,1), (0,2), (0,3), (0,4), (2,3), (2,4).

    (d)
    ```
    4  •  •  •  •  •
    2  o  •  •  •  •
    0  o  o  o  •  •
       0  1  2  3  4

          S × T
    ```

    (e)
    ```
    4  o  •  •
    3  o  •  •
    2  o  •  •
    1  o  o  •
    0  o  o  o
       0  2  4

        T × S
    ```

    (f) There are none.

13. (a) $(0,0), (1,1), (2,2), \dots , (6,6)$, say.

    (b) The set is infinite. $(0,2), (6,5), (2,3)$ are examples.

    (c) $(6,1), (6,2), (6,3), \dots , (6,7)$, say.

    (d) The set is infinite. $(3,5), (73,3), (3,3)$ are examples.

    (e) $(1,3), (2,3), (3,3), (3,2), (3,1)$.

    (f) The set is infinite. $(1,1), (0,0), (10,100)$ are examples.

14.

See *Mathematics Magazine 58* (Sept. 1985), p. 251 for five rectangles forming a Venn diagram.

1.5 Answers

1. (a) $4, -6$. (b) $7, -1$. (c) $12, 4$.

   (d) $19, 9$. (e) $28, 14$.

   (f) Yes. This can be seen in different ways. One is to note that $f(n) + g(n) = n^2 + 5n - 8$, so it suffices to argue that $n^2 + 5n$ is always even. But $n^2 + 5n = n(n+5)$ and when one of n, $n+5$ is odd, the other one is even.

2. For $n = 1, 2, 3, 4, 5, 6$ the answers are $1, 2, 2, 3, 2, 4$. The remaining answers are $2, 4, 3, 4, 2$.

3. (a) 3. (b) 8. (c) 0.

   (d) $\mathbb{N}$. For any $n \in \mathbb{N}$, there is a string of a's, for example, of length n.

4. (a) $\{\lambda\}$. (b) $\{\lambda, a, b\}$.

   (c) $\{\lambda, a, b, aa, ab, ba, bb\}$. (d) Yes.

   (e) Any infinite subset of Σ^*, like Σ^* itself, will do. There are many finite examples too, like $\{a\}$.

5. (a) $1, 1, 1, 0, 0$. See the answer to part (b).

   (b) $f(n, n) = 1$ for even n, and $f(n, n) = 0$ for odd n. This can be checked by calculation or by applying Theorem 1 on page 5, with $k = 2$.

6. (a) $7, 14, 1001$. (b) n.

   (c) $\mathbb{P}$. This can be seen using part (b). Of course, the identity $\gcd(n, n) = n$ also shows this.

7. (a) $f(3) = 27$, $f(1/3) = 1/3$, $f(-1/3) = 1/27$, $f(-3) = 27$.

   (b)

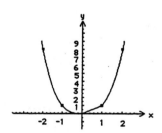

   (c) $\text{Im}(f) = [0, \infty)$.

8. (a)

$$
\begin{array}{rl}
1_S : & \{(1,1), (2,2), (3,3), (4,4), (5,5)\}, \\
f : & \{(1,5), (2,4), (3,3), (4,2), (5,1)\}, \\
g : & \{(1,3), (2,3), (3,3), (4,4), (5,5)\}, \\
h : & \{(1,1), (2,1), (3,2), (4,3), (5,4)\}.
\end{array}
$$

(b)

```
5  ○ ○ ○ ○ •    5  • ○ ○ ○ ○    5  ○ ○ ○ ○ •    5  ○ ○ ○ ○ ○
4  ○ ○ ○ • ○    4  ○ • ○ ○ ○    4  ○ ○ ○ • ○    4  ○ ○ ○ ○ •
3  ○ ○ • ○ ○    3  ○ ○ • ○ ○    3  • • • ○ ○    3  ○ ○ ○ • ○
2  ○ • ○ ○ ○    2  ○ ○ ○ • ○    2  ○ ○ ○ ○ ○    2  ○ ○ • ○ ○
1  • ○ ○ ○ ○    1  ○ ○ ○ ○ •    1  ○ ○ ○ ○ ○    1  • • ○ ○ ○
   1 2 3 4 5       1 2 3 4 5       1 2 3 4 5       1 2 3 4 5
      1_S              f               g               h
```

9. $\{n \in \mathbb{Z} : n \text{ is even}\}$.

10. (a) $A \cap B$, because for $x \in S$ the product $\chi_A(x) \cdot \chi_B(x)$ is 1 if and only if each factor is 1.

(b) $A \cup B$, since $\chi_A(x) + \chi_B(x) - \chi_{A \cap B}(x) = 1$ for $x \in A \cup B$. The case that x belongs to both A and B needs separate consideration.

(c) $A \oplus B$, since $\chi_A(x) + \chi_B(x) - 2 \cdot \chi_{A \cap B}(x) = 1$ if and only if $x \in (A \setminus B) \cup (B \setminus A) = A \oplus B$. Note that the sum is $1 + 1 - 2 = 0$ for $x \in A \cap B$.

11. (a) The answers for $n = 0, 1, 2, 3, 4, 5$ are $0, 0, 1, 2, 3, 3$. The remaining answers are $5, 5, 6, 7, 8, 60$.

(b) The set of odd integers.

12. Both equal 2.

13. (a) $f \circ f(x) = (x^3 - 4x)^3 - 4(x^3 - 4x)$.

(b) $g \circ g(x) = (x^2 + 1)^2 / [1 + (x^2 + 1)^2]$.

(c) $h \circ g(x) = (x^2 + 1)^{-4}$.

(d) $g \circ h(x) = (x^8 + 1)^{-1}$.

(e) $f \circ g \circ h(x) = (x^8 + 1)^{-3} - 4(x^8 + 1)^{-1}$.

(f) $f \circ h \circ g(x) = (x^2 + 1)^{-12} - 4(x^2 + 1)^{-4}$.

(g) $h \circ g \circ f(x) = [(x^3 - 4x)^2 + 1]^{-4}$.

14. (a) $f \circ f(x) = x^4$.

(b) $g \circ g(x) = \sqrt{x^2 + 2}$.

(c) $h \circ g(x) = 3\sqrt{x^2 + 1} - 1$.

(d) $g \circ h(x) = \sqrt{9x^2 - 6x + 2}$.

(e) $f \circ g \circ h(x) = 9x^2 - 6x + 2$.

(f) $f \circ h \circ g(x) = 9x^2 + 10 - 6\sqrt{x^2 + 1}$.

(g) $h \circ g \circ f(x) = 3\sqrt{x^4 + 1} - 1$.

15. (a) $1, 0, -1$ and 0.

(b) $9, 10, 1, 0$.

(c) $g \circ f$ is the characteristic function of $\mathbb{Z} \setminus E$. $f \circ f(n) = n - 2$ for all $n \in \mathbb{Z}$.

(d) $g \circ g(2m) = g(g(2m)) = g(1) = 0 = g(2m - 1) = g \circ f(2m)$, and also $g \circ g(2m + 1) = g(0) = 1 = g(2m) = g \circ f(2m + 1)$. Thus $g \circ g = g \circ f$. Also $f \circ g(2m) = f(1) = 0 = -0 = -g(2m - 1) = -g \circ f(2m)$, and $f \circ g(2m + 1) = f(0) = -1 = -g(2m) = -g \circ f(2m + 1)$. Hence $f \circ g = -g \circ f$.

16. The values of the function $1_\mathbb{R}$ can be calculated by doing nothing at all. They can also be considered as produced by keying in entries.

1.6   Answers

1. (a) 42.   (b) 210.   (c) 1.   (d) 1680.
   (e) 154.   (f) 360.

2. (a) n.   (b) $n/(n + 1)$.

3. (a) 3, 12, 39 and 120.   (b) 27, 91, 216.   (c) 3, 9 and 45.

4. (a) 0.   (b) 18.   (c) 15.   (d) 10,395.   (e) 2520.

5. (a) -2, 2, 0, 0 and 0.   (b) 2, 3, 4, $m + 1$.

6. (a) 3, 7, 15, 31, 63.   (b) $\sum_{k=0}^{n} 2^k = 2^{n+1} - 1$.

7. (a) 0, 1/3, 1/2, 3/5, 2/3, 5/7.   (b) 1/3, 1/6, 1/10.
   (c) Note that $a_{n+1} = \frac{(n+1)-1}{(n+1)+1} = \frac{n}{n+2}$ for $n \in \mathbb{P}$. Hence $a_{n+1} - a_n = \frac{n}{n+2} - \frac{n-1}{n+1} = \frac{2}{(n+1)(n+2)}$ for $n \in \mathbb{N}$.

8. (a) 1, 0, 1, 0, 1, 0, 1.   (b) $\{0,1\}$.

9. (a) 0, 0, 2, 6, 12, 20, 30.
   (b) Just substitute the values into both sides.
   (c) Same comment.

10. (a) 1, 5, 14, 55.
    (b) By definition of $\textsc{ssq}(n)$.
    (c) $\textsc{ssq}(74) = 132,349 + (74)^2 = 137,825$; $\textsc{ssq}(72) = 132,349 - (73)^2 = 127,020$.

11. (a) 0, 0, 1, 1, 2, 2, 3, 3, ...   (b) 0, 1, 1, 2, 2, 3, 3, ...
    (c) (0,0), (0,1), (1,1), (1,2), (2,2), (2,3), (3,3), ...

12. $\log_2 16 = 4 = \sqrt{16}$; $\log_2 64 = 6 < 8 = \sqrt{64}$; $\log_2 256 = 8 < 16 = \sqrt{256}$; $\log_2 4096 = 12 < 64 = \sqrt{4096}$. As in Example 4(a), it appears that $\log_2 n$ grows more slowly than $\sqrt{n}$.

13. (a)

n	n^4	4^n	n^{20}	20^n	$n!$
5	625	1024	$9.54 \cdot 10^{13}$	$3.2 \cdot 10^6$	120
10	10^4	$1.05 \cdot 10^6$	10^{20}	$1.02 \cdot 10^{13}$	$3.63 \cdot 10^6$
25	$3.91 \cdot 10^5$	$1.13 \cdot 10^{15}$	$9.09 \cdot 10^{27}$	$3.36 \cdot 10^{32}$	$1.55 \cdot 10^{25}$
50	$6.25 \cdot 10^6$	$1.27 \cdot 10^{30}$	$9.54 \cdot 10^{33}$	$1.13 \cdot 10^{65}$	$3.04 \cdot 10^{64}$

(b) The relative growth rates are not obvious from this table. For example, in the long run 4^n will grow faster than n^{20}; in fact, even 2^n will grow faster than n^{20} and n^{200}. These facts will be clarified in the next section.

14. (a)

n	$\log_{10} n$	$\sqrt{n}$	$20 \cdot \sqrt[4]{n}$	$\sqrt[4]{n} \cdot \log_{10} n$
50	1.70	7.07	53.18	4.52
100	2.00	10.00	63.25	6.32
10^4	4.00	100.00	200.00	40.00
10^6	6.00	1000.00	632.46	189.74

(b) As in Exercise 13, the relative growths of these sequences are not clear. $\log_{10} n$ does grow the slowest and $\sqrt{n}$ does grow the fastest. But in the long run $\sqrt[4]{n} \cdot \log_{10} n$ will grow faster than $20 \cdot \sqrt[4]{n}$.

15. $2^n = 10^{n \cdot \log_{10} 2}$. Why? The table values look a little different because the exponents $n \cdot \log_{10} 2$ are not integers.

1.7 Answers

1. (a) No; S is bigger than T.

   (b) Yes. For example, let $f(a) = 1$, $f(b) = 2$, $f(c) = 3$, $f(d) = 4$.

   (c) Yes. For example, let $f(1) = a$, $f(2) = b$, $f(3) = c$, $f(4) = f(5) = d$.

   (d) No. T is smaller than S.

   (e) No. This follows from either part (a) or part (d).

2. (a) f_1, f_2, f_{11}, f_{12}.

   (b) $f_1, f_4, f_5, f_6, f_7, f_9, f_{11}, f_{12}$.

   (c) f_1, f_{11}, f_{12}.

3. (a) $f(2,1) = 2^2 3^1 = 12$, $f(1,2) = 2^1 3^2 = 18$, etc.

   (b) If not, $2^m 3^n = 2^{m'} 3^{n'}$ for some $(m,n) \neq (m',n')$. Then $m \neq m'$ [why?]. Say $m < m'$. Divide both sides by 2^m to get a number that is both odd and even, a contradiction.

   (c) Consider 5, for instance. 5 is not in $\text{Im}(f)$.

(d) For example, $g(2,0) = g(0,1)$. In general, $g(m,n) = g(m',n')$ if and only if $m + 2n = m' + 2n'$.

4. (a) $1_{\mathbb{N}}$, f, g.   (b) $1_{\mathbb{N}}$, g, k.

5. (a) $f(0) = 1$, $f(1) = 2$, $f(2) = 3$, $f(3) = 4$, $f(4) = 5$, $f(73) = 74$.

   (b) $g(0) = 0$, $g(1) = 0$, $g(2) = 1$, $g(3) = 2$, etc.

   (c) For one-to-oneness, observe that if $f(n) = f(n')$, then $n = f(n) - 1 = f(n') - 1 = n'$. f does not map onto $\mathbb{N}$ because $0 \notin \mathrm{Im}(f)$.

   (d) g maps onto $\mathbb{N}$ because $g(n + 1) = n$ for each $n \in \mathbb{N}$. g is not one-to-one because $g(0) = g(1) = 0$.

   (e) $g(f(n)) = \max\{0, (n+1) - 1\} = n$, but $f(g(0)) = f(0) = 1$.

6. (a) $L(w_1) = 3$, $L(w_2) = 6$ and $L(w_3) = 0$. Note that w_3 is the empty word λ which uses no letters at all and so has length 0.

   (b) No. For example, $cab \neq abc$ but $L(cab) = L(abc)$.

   (c) Yes. $0 = L(\lambda)$, $1 = L(a)$, $2 = L(aa)$, $3 = L(aaa)$, etc. Indeed, $n = L(a^n)$ where a^n stands for the string of n a's.

   (d) There are nine: aa, ab, ac, ba, bb, bc, ca, cb, cc.

7. (a) $f^{-1}(y) = (y - 3)/2$.   (b) $g^{-1}(y) = \sqrt[3]{y + 2}$.

   (c) $h^{-1}(y) = 2 + \sqrt[3]{y}$.   (d) $k^{-1}(y) = (y - 7)^3$.

8. (a) $(0, \infty)$, $\mathbb{R}$, $[0, \infty)$, $(-\infty, 0) \cup (0, \infty)$.

   (b) The function $f(x) = 1/x$ is its own inverse. The inverse of the square-root function is the square function with domain $[0, \infty)$, but not with domain $\mathbb{R}$.

   (c) The functions given by x^2, $\sqrt{x}$ and $1/x$ commute with each other on their common domain $(0, \infty)$, but not with $\log x$.

   (d) $\mathbb{R}$, $\mathbb{R}$, $\mathbb{R} \setminus \{(2n + 1)\pi/2 : n \in \mathbb{Z}\}$; none; none.

9. (a) $(f \circ f)(x) = 1/(1/x) = x$.

   (b) and (c) are similar verifications.

10. $\chi_A^{\leftarrow}(1) = A$; $\chi_A^{\leftarrow}(0) = S \setminus A$.

11. (a) All of them; verify this.

    (b) Each has the same values on both (m, n) and (n, m), for example.

    (c) $\mathrm{SUM}^{\leftarrow}(4)$ has 5 elements, $\mathrm{PROD}^{\leftarrow}(4)$ has 3 elements, $\mathrm{MAX}^{\leftarrow}(4)$ has 9 elements, and $\mathrm{MIN}^{\leftarrow}(4)$ is infinite.

12. For $(x, y) \in \mathbb{R} \times \mathbb{R}$, we have $f^{-1} \circ f(x, y) =$

$$f^{-1}(x+y, x-y) = (\frac{(x+y) + (x-y)}{2}, \frac{(x+y) - (x-y)}{2}) = (x, y),$$

and for $(a, b) \in \mathbb{R} \times \mathbb{R}$, we have $f \circ f^{-1}(a, b) =$

$$f(\frac{a+b}{2}, \frac{a-b}{2}) = (\frac{a+b}{2} + \frac{a-b}{2}, \frac{a+b}{2} - \frac{a-b}{2}) = (a, b).$$

13. Since f and g are invertible, the functions $f^{-1} \colon T \to S$, $g^{-1} \colon U \to T$ and $f^{-1} \circ g^{-1} \colon U \to S$ exist. So it suffices to show $(g \circ f) \circ (f^{-1} \circ g^{-1}) = 1_U$ and $(f^{-1} \circ g^{-1}) \circ (g \circ f) = 1_S$.

14. To show that f^{-1} is invertible we must show that there is a function $(f^{-1})^{-1}$ such that $(f^{-1})^{-1} \circ f^{-1} = 1_T$ and $f^{-1} \circ (f^{-1})^{-1} = 1_S$. The function $(f^{-1})^{-1} = f$ has these two properties, since $f \circ f^{-1} = 1_T$ and $f^{-1} \circ f = 1_S$. If some function $g \colon S \to T$ satisfies $g \circ f^{-1} = 1_T$, then $g = g \circ 1_S = g \circ (f^{-1} \circ f) = (g \circ f^{-1}) \circ f = 1_T \circ f = f$. Thus f is the only candidate for $(f^{-1})^{-1}$. [Inverses, when they exist, are always unique.]

Chapter 2

This chapter introduces logic, both formal logic with its truth tables, tautologies and formal proofs, and logical thinking and proof methods as they are used in practice to give convincing arguments. Truth table methods come up again in the Boolean setting of Chapter 9. Logical thinking is expected from this point on, no matter what the context.

Section 2.1 is a gentle introduction to logical terms and symbols; § 2.2 gets down to business, with truth tables for the connectives and for compound propositions. Students seem to have special trouble with $p \rightarrow q$ in the cases in which p is false. One possible justification, which we do not give in the text, is that the other ways those entries could be filled in correspond to the legitimate propositions $p \wedge q$, q and $p \leftrightarrow q$, whose meanings are different from what $p \rightarrow q$ should mean. Give lots of examples.

Don't let students get hung up on Tables 1 and 2 on pages 85 and 86. They should be able to use the tables, but don't need to memorize them. Discuss Example 7 on page 87, and explain why some rows of the truth table can be ignored.

Section 2.3 is a new one in this edition, designed to help students with that old question, "How do I start a proof?" It's unusual in having exercises scattered along the way, as well as at the end. Students who usually just flip through the book to find template examples may find this section especially frustrating, but with luck you can persuade them to read it as intended, from beginning to end, with a hand over the answers until they've honestly tried to come up with what's called for by themselves.

Section 2.4, which continues the discussion more formally, is important. Not all students will pick these ideas up the first time. Encourage students to refer back to this section as the need arises. Example 12 slips in an infinite-finite pigeonhole principle without fanfare and then applies it to looking at remainders. The application foreshadows modular arithmetic in § 3.6. You may want to give students your own reaction to Office Hours 2.4, which, after all, is simply our view of the situation and may not match what you're trying to emphasize in your course.

The substitution rules in § 2.5 just formalize two obvious ways of getting new equivalences from old. To paraphrase: Rule (b) says you can always replace a proposition by an equivalent one, while Rule (a) says you can replace a variable p

by a proposition in a tautology **provided** you replace it with the same proposition everywhere.

Students [and instructors] often wonder why we spend time on formal proofs, with their ritualistic format. Our main concern is to develop logical reasoning, not to build facility with formal proofs. We include the formalism to illustrate that there is a bedrock not far below the level at which we normally work. In previous editions we scared some students by asking them to construct formal proofs. In this edition we just ask them to supply reasons. Exercises 16 to 18 have applications in circuit design. We usually do one of the three in class and assign one or both of the others as homework.

Section 2.6 begins with examples of translation between "real life" logic and formal proofs. Its main purpose is to give students practical guidance for constructing acceptable proofs and recognizing gaps and fallacies. This section is quite informal in spirit. You may want to draw examples from your own experience or get the class to volunteer sample arguments. Some of the exercises do ask for formal proofs, but the constructions are not complicated.

2.1 Answers

1. (a) $p \wedge q$. 　　　　　　(b) $p \to r$. 　　　　　　(c) $\neg p \to (\neg q \wedge r)$.

    (d) $q \leftrightarrow (\neg p)$. 　　　　　(e) $\neg r \to q$.

2. (a) If it is raining and the sun is shining, then there are clouds in the sky.

    (b) If it is raining only if there are clouds in the sky, then the sun is shining.

    (c) It is not raining if and only if [either] the sun is shining or there are clouds in the sky.

    (d) It is not true that it is raining if and only if [either] the sun is shining or there are clouds in the sky.

    (e) It is not true that it is raining or the sun is shining, and there are clouds in the sky.

    There are, of course, other ways to express these propositions in English.

3. (a) Parts (b) and (c) are true. The other three are false.

    (b) In Example 2, parts (a) and (b) are true.

4. (a) False. 　　　　　　　　　　(b) True.

    (c) Not a well-defined proposition. 　　(d) False.

    (e) Not a proposition. 　　　　　　(f) False; x might be 0.

    (g) True.

5. The proposition is true for all $x, y \in [0, \infty)$, but is false when applied to all $x, y \in \mathbb{R}$.

CHAPTER 2.

6. (a) $r \rightarrow q$.

(b) If I am rich, then I am smart.

(c) If $x = 0$ or $x = 1$, then $x^2 = x$.

(d) If $2 + 4 = 8$, then $2 + 2 = 4$.

7. (a) $\neg r \rightarrow \neg q$.

(b) If I am not rich, then I am not smart.

(c) If it is false that $x = 0$ or $x = 1$, then $x^2 \neq x$.

(d) If $2 + 4 \neq 8$, then $2 + 2 \neq 4$.

8. (a) $6 = 3 + 3$, $8 = 3 + 5$, $10 = 3 + 7$.

(b) $98 = 19 + 79$.

9. (a) $3^3 < 3^3$ is false.

(b) There are no other counterexamples.

10. (b) Any pair $(n, -n)$ will do, $n \neq 0$.

11. (a) $(-1 + 1)^2 = 0 < 1 = (-1)^2$. (b) Choose $x < -\frac{1}{2}$.

(c) No. If $x \geq 0$, then $(x + 1)^2 = x^2 + 2x + 1 > x^2$. In fact, if $x \geq -\frac{1}{2}$, then $2x + 1 \geq 0$ and $(x + 1)^2 \geq x^2$.

12. (a) $n = 6$. (b) $n = 3$. (c) $n = 7$.

13. (a) $(0, -1)$.

(b) Restrict x, y to be nonnegative.

14. (a) True by a commutative law for sets, Table 1 on page 34.

(b) False. Choose A and B with B not contained in A. For example, choose $A = \emptyset \neq B$.

(c) False. Choose A and B to overlap. For example, $A = B \neq \emptyset$.

(d) True by an associative law for sets.

15. (a) $p \rightarrow q$. (b) $p \rightarrow r$. (c) $\neg r \rightarrow p$. (d) $q \rightarrow p$. (e) $r \rightarrow q$.

(f) $r \rightarrow (q \vee p)$ or $(r \rightarrow q) \vee p$. Punctuation would help in part (f). For example, a comma after "$I = 0$" would yield $(r \rightarrow q) \vee p$.

16. (a) $r \rightarrow m$. (b) $\neg r \rightarrow p$. (c) $r \rightarrow m$. (d) $p \rightarrow m$.

(e) $r \vee (p \rightarrow m)$ or $p \rightarrow (r \vee m)$. Again punctuation would help.

17. (a) The probable intent is "If you touch those cookies, then I will spank you." It is easier to imagine p of $p \rightarrow q$ being true for this meaning than it is for "If you want a spanking, then touch those cookies."

(b) If you touch those cookies, then you will be sorry.

(c) If you do not leave, then I will set the dog on you.

(d) If you will, then I will.

(e) If you do not stop that, then I will go.

18. (a) "If I will not spank you, then you did not touch those cookies." In the other version, the contrapositive is "If you do not touch those cookies, then you do not want a spanking."

(b) If you will not be sorry, then you will not touch those cookies.

(c) If I will not set the dog on you, then you do leave.

(d) If I won't, then you won't.

(e) If you don't stop that, then I will go.

2.2 Answers

1. (a) Converse: $(q \wedge r) \to p$.
   Contrapositive: $\neg(q \wedge r) \to \neg p$.

   (b) Converse: If $x^2 + y^2 \geq 1$, then $x + y = 1$.
   Contrapositive: If $x^2 + y^2 < 1$, then $x + y \neq 1$.

   (c) Converse: If $3 + 3 = 8$, then $2 + 2 = 4$.
   Contrapositive: If $3 + 3 \neq 8$, then $2 + 2 \neq 4$.

2. (a) Converse: If $x^2 > 0$, then $x > 0$.
   Contrapositive: If $x^2 \leq 0$, then $x \leq 0$.

   (b) The proposition and its contrapositive are true. The converse is false.

3. (a) $q \to p$. (b) $\neg q \to \neg p$.

   (c) $p \to q$, $\neg q \to \neg p$, $\neg p \vee q$.

4. All but (a) and (g) are true.

5. (a) 0. (b) 1. (c) 1.

Note. For some truth tables, only the final columns are given.

6.

p	part(a)	part(b)	part(c)	part(d)
0	0	1	0	0
1	0	1	0	1

7.

p	q	part(a)	part(b)	part(c)	part(d)
0	0	1	1	1	1
0	1	1	0	0	1
1	0	1	0	0	1
1	1	0	0	0	0

8.

p	q	$(p \rightarrow q)$	$\rightarrow$	$[(p\vee$	$\neg q)$	$\rightarrow$	$(p \wedge q)]$
0	0	1	**0**	1	1	0	0
0	1	1	1	0	0	1	0
1	0	0	1	1	1	0	0
1	1	1	1	1	0	1	1

9.

p	q	r	final column
0	0	0	1
0	0	1	1
0	1	0	1
0	1	1	0
1	0	0	1
1	0	1	1
1	1	0	1
1	1	1	0

10.

p	q	r	final column
0	0	0	0
0	0	1	0
0	1	0	0
0	1	1	0
1	0	0	1
1	0	1	1
1	1	0	0
1	1	1	0

11.

p	q	r	part(a)	part(b)
0	0	0	0	0
0	0	1	1	0
0	1	0	1	1
0	1	1	1	0
1	0	0	1	1
1	0	1	1	0
1	1	0	1	1
1	1	1	1	0

12. (a) Exclusive; only one of soup or salad is offered.

(b) Inclusive; having both would be fine.

(c) The original intent was exclusive, but cynics might say it's inclusive.

(d) Same as (b).

(e) Exclusive; it can't be completed on both days.

(f) Exclusive.

(g) The intention is $\neg f \wedge \neg h \Longleftrightarrow \neg(f \vee h)$, so $\vee$ is inclusive.

(h) $\neg J \wedge \neg A \Longleftrightarrow \neg(J \vee A)$, so inclusive.

13. (b)

p	$p \oplus p$
0	0
1	0

(c)

p	q	r	$(p \oplus q) \oplus r$
0	0	0	0
0	0	1	1
0	1	0	1
0	1	1	0
1	0	0	1
1	0	1	0
1	1	0	0
1	1	1	1

(d)

p	$(p \oplus p) \oplus p$
0	0
1	1

14. (a) Make a 4-row truth table for $(p \wedge q) \vee (p \wedge \neg q)$, and observe that this proposition is true if and only if p is true.

(b)

p	q	r	$p \vee r$
0	0	0	0
0	0	1	1
0	1	0	0
0	1	1	1
1	0	0	1
1	0	1	1
1	1	0	1
1	1	1	1

(c)

p	q	$\neg q$
0	0	1
0	1	0
1	0	1
1	1	0

15. (a)

p	q	$p \sim q$
0	0	0
0	1	1
1	0	1
1	1	1

(b) $\sim$ is the same as (logically equivalent to) $\vee$.

(c) In view of part (b), it suffices to verify $p \vee q \iff \neg p \to q$ and $p \vee q \iff q \vee p$. These are Rules 11a and 2a in Table 1 on page 85. Or use truth tables.

16. (a) $\{[(p \wedge \neg q) \wedge \neg r] \vee [(\neg p \wedge q) \wedge \neg r]\} \vee [(\neg p \wedge \neg q) \wedge r]$ is one such proposition. So is $[(p \leftrightarrow \neg q) \wedge \neg r] \vee [\neg(p \vee q) \wedge r]$.

(b) $\{[(p \wedge q) \wedge \neg r] \vee [(p \wedge \neg q) \wedge r]\} \vee [(\neg p \wedge q) \wedge r]$ is one. So is $[p \wedge (q \leftrightarrow \neg r)] \vee [\neg p \wedge (q \wedge r)]$.

17. (a) No fishing is allowed and no hunting is allowed. The school will not be open in July and the school will not be open in August.

(b) No. $\neg(p \oplus q) \iff [(p \wedge q) \vee (\neg p \wedge \neg q)]$. For example, to negate Exercise 12(a) one would need something like "You must choose both soup and salad or else neither soup nor salad."

18. (a) True. Both $p \to (q \to r)$ and $(p \to q) \to (p \to r)$ are false only for

p	q	r
1	1	0

(b) False. Consider

p	q	r
1	0	0

or

p	q	r
1	1	1

(c) The propositions are not equivalent, as can be verified by comparing the first or third rows of their truth tables.

(d) and (e) are true. It is probably easiest to verify them using truth tables.

21. (a) One need only consider rows in which $[(p \wedge r) \to (q \wedge r)]$ is false, i.e., $(p \wedge r)$ is true and $(q \wedge r)$ is false. This leaves one row to consider:

p	q	r
1	0	1

(b) It's easiest to show that $p \to q$ has truth value 0 whenever $(q \to r) \to (p \to r)$ has truth value 0. Now $(q \to r) \to (p \to r)$ is false precisely if $q \to r$ is true and $p \to r$ is false, i.e., if p is true, r is false and q is false, in which case $p \to q$ is false, as desired. That is, the only row that matters is

p	q	r
1	0	0

(c) One need only consider rows in which $[(p \wedge r) \rightarrow (q \wedge s)]$ is false, i.e., $(p \wedge r)$ is true and $(q \wedge s)$ is false. This leaves three rows to consider:

p	q	r	s
1	0	1	0
1	0	1	1
1	1	1	0

22. (a) False. consider $q = 0$.

(b) False. consider $p = 1$, $q = 0$.

(c)

p	q	$(p \wedge q)$	$\rightarrow$	$(p \vee q)$
0	0	0	1	0
0	1	0	1	1
1	0	0	1	1
1	1	1	1	1

Thus $(p \wedge q) \rightarrow (p \vee q)$ is a tautology, so $(p \wedge q) \Longrightarrow (p \vee q)$ is true.

23. Let $p =$ "He finished dinner" and $q =$ "He was sent to bed." Then p is true and q is true, so the logician's statement $\neg p \rightarrow \neg q$ has truth value True. She was logically correct, but not very nice.

24. (a) If concrete grows, then you do water it. [The original statement is "If you do not water concrete, then it does not grow."]

(b) If concrete does not grow, then you do not water it.

(c) If you water concrete, then it grows.

(d) The original and its contrapositive are true. The statements in (b) and (c) are false.

25. (a) Consider the truth tables. B has truth value 1 on every row that A does, and C has truth value 1 on every row that B does, so C has truth value 1 on every row that A does.

(b) Since $P \Longleftrightarrow Q$, $P \Longrightarrow Q$. By (a), $P \Longrightarrow R$. Since $R \Longleftrightarrow S$, $R \Longrightarrow S$. By (a), $P \Longrightarrow S$. Or consider truth tables.

(c) We are given that $P \Longrightarrow Q$. Since $Q \Longrightarrow R$ and $R \Longrightarrow P$, by (a) $Q \Longrightarrow P$. Thus $P \Longleftrightarrow Q$.

2.3 Answers

1. For each part, test about five examples [i.e., consecutive sequences of integers], unless you run into a counterexample, in which case you can stop. Why?

2. (a) See the discussion in Example 2.

(b) See the discussion after Exercise 7.

3. (a) Fine. One can use other variables, perhaps k and l, or i and j.

   (b) This is fine if there's no need to name the original odd integers. It will depend on the situation, but it's always preferable to avoid unnecessary notation.

   (c) This is bad. The integers m and n are probably different, so the same variable k cannot be used for both of them.

   (d) This is just another way of writing part (a), and is fine.

   (e) This is technically correct, but bad practice and confusing, because the notation x and y suggest that x and y can be more general real numbers. It is traditional to use letters in the middle of the alphabet for integers.

   (f) Providing several examples is *not* sufficient to give a proof. See the discussion following the Silly Conjecture.

4. (a) There is nothing wrong here, but this sentence doesn't distinguish between rationals and irrationals. A second sentence is needed, as in part (b).

   (b) This is fine.

   (c) Though technically correct, this is a bad start because it doesn't distinguish between rationals and irrationals *and* because the choice of variables p and q is confusing. Rationals are often written $\frac{p}{q}$ [or $\frac{m}{n}$ or even $\frac{a}{b}$], but arbitrary real numbers are never written p or q. It wouldn't be illegal, but it would be confusing.

   (d) This is pretty good. It would be better to specify what p and q are, as in part (b), though most readers would guess correctly that they are integers with $q \neq 0$. Still, it's better to be specific. This improves the communication between the writer and the reader.

   (e) This is terrible and suggests confusion. The first half of the sentence specifies x, so the second half just tells us that $x \neq y$. This is what the sentence really says. Presumably, the author meant to tell us that the irrational number y satisfies $y \neq \frac{m}{n}$ for all choices of m and n in $\mathbb{Z}$ with $n \neq 0$. This is true, and helpful, but this isn't what is stated in the clause, "let $y \neq \frac{p}{q}$ be an irrational number."

5. By the Division Algorithm, we can write $n = 3k + r$ where $r = 0, 1, 2$. Then $n^2 - 2 = 9k^2 + 6rk + r^2 - 2$. Since $9k^2 + 6rk$ is divisible by 3, it suffices to show that $r^2 - 2$ is *not* divisible by 3. Now we are reduced to three cases involving r. Since $r^2 - 2$ is either $-2, -1$ or 2 for $r = 0, 1, 2$, we are done.

6. n^2 is odd by Example 1, so $n^2 - 2$ is also odd.

7. (a) We can write $n = 7k + r$ where $r = 0, 1, 2, \ldots, 6$. Then $n^2 - 2 = 49k^2 + 14rk + r^2 - 2$. Since $49k^2 + 14rk$ is divisible by 7, it suffices to show that $r^2 - 2$ is *not* divisible by 7. For $r = 0, 1$ and 2, we get $r^2 - 2 = -2, -1$ and 2. None are divisible by 7; so far so good. Alas, for $r = 3$ we see that $r^2 - 2 = 7$ which is certainly divisible by 7.

(b) Any number which, when divided by 7, leaves remainder 3 will give a counterexample. Thus 3, 10, 17, etc. are counterexamples. If in part (a), we had continued we would have discovered that $r = 4$ also does not work: $r^2 - 2 = 14$ is divisible by 7. So other counterexamples are 4, 11, 18, etc.

(c) The smallest three odd counterexamples are 3, 11 and 17.

8. Let x be a rational number, and let y be an irrational number. We can write $x = \frac{p}{q}$ where $p, q \in \mathbb{Z}$ and $q \neq 0$. We want to show that $x + y$ is irrational, i.e., that $x + y \neq \frac{m}{n}$ for all $m, n \in \mathbb{Z}$ and $n \neq 0$. This would be tough, perhaps impossible, to do directly. The way to tackle this is to give a proof by contradiction.

Assume that $x + y$ is rational, say $x + y = \frac{m}{n}$ for some $m, n \in \mathbb{Z}$ where $n \neq 0$. Then we have $\frac{p}{q} + y = \frac{m}{n}$. Solving for y gives $y = \frac{m}{n} - \frac{p}{q} = \frac{mq-np}{nq}$, so y is a rational number, contradicting our assumption on y. Hence $x + y$ must be irrational.

9. If m and n are even integers, then there exist j and k in $\mathbb{Z}$ so that $m = 2j$ and $n = 2k$. Then $mn = 4jk$, which is a multiple of 4.

10. The even integer is $2j$ and the odd integer is $2k + 1$ for some j and k in $\mathbb{Z}$. Their product $2j(2k + 1) = 2[j(2k + 1)]$ is even. [Indeed, it's irrelevant that the second integer is odd.]

11. As in Example 4, an integer n has the form $5k + r$ where $k \in \mathbb{Z}$ and r is in $\{0, 1, 2, 3, 4\}$. Then $n^2 - 3 = 25k^2 + 10kr + r^2 - 3$. It suffices to show that $r^2 - 3$ is not divisible by 5. To check this, calculate $r^2 - 3$ for $r = 0, 1, 2, 3$ and 4.

12. If $p|m$, then $m = pk$ for some $k \in \mathbb{Z}$. So $j = m - pl = p(k - l)$, so $p|j$. Similarly, $p|j$ implies $p|m$.

13. (a) Factor $n^4 - n^2$ into $(n - 1)n^2(n + 1)$ and note that one of the three consecutive integers $n - 1, n, n + 1$ is divisible by 3. Or treat three cases: $n = 3k$, $n = 3k + 1$, $n = 3k + 2$.

(b) If n is even, then so are n^4, n^2 and $n^4 - n^2$. If n is odd, then n^2 and $n^4 = (n^2)^2$ are odd by Example 1, so their difference is even. Or note that both $n - 1$ and n divide $n^4 - n^2 = (n - 1)n^2(n + 1)$, and one of $n - 1$ and n is even.

(c) Apply parts (a) and (b).

14. (a) Let $x = \frac{p}{q}$ be the rational number, with $p, q \in \mathbb{Z}$ and $q \neq 0$. Note that $p \neq 0$, since $x \neq 0$. Let y by an irrational number. We prove by contradiction that xy is irrational. Assume that the product $xy = \frac{p}{q} \cdot y$ is rational. Then $\frac{p}{q} \cdot y = \frac{m}{n}$ for $m, n \in \mathbb{Z}$, $n \neq 0$. Since $p \neq 0$, we can write $y = \frac{qm}{pn}$ where $pn \neq 0$. Thus y is rational, a contradiction to the hypothesis that y is irrational. We conclude that, in fact, xy is irrational.

(b) For one thing, the statement is false without it: $0 \cdot \sqrt{2} = 0$ is rational even though 0 is rational and $\sqrt{2}$ is irrational. In the proof of part (a), we certainly used the fact that the rational was nonzero.

15. (a) This statement is true and depends on the unique factorization of a number as a product of primes. If m and n are written as products of primes, then mn is a product of primes using only the primes used by m and n. Thus, if 3 is among the primes used by mn, it must have been used by m or n, or both. So $3|m$ or $3|n$. [Note that we've described the products of primes in words to avoid complicated notation: $m = p_1^{k_1} \cdots p_l^{k_l}$, $n = q_1^{j_1} \cdots q_m^{j_m}$ where $p_1, \ldots, p_l, q_1, \ldots, q_m$ are primes, $k_1, \ldots, k_l, j_1, \ldots, j_m$ are positive integers, etc. etc.]

   (b) 4 is not a prime, so the argument in part (a) doesn't carry over. In fact, the statement in part (b) is false. Select any m and n so that *exactly one* 2 appears in each of their prime factorizations, such as 6, 10, 14, etc. or even 2 itself. Then 4 will divide mn, as noted in Exercise 9, but not m or n.

   (c) The statement holds if and only if d is a prime or $d = 1$.

2.4 Answers

1. (a) Give a direct proof, as in Exercise 9 on page 98.

   (b) True. Write the three odd integers as $2k+1$, $2l+1$ and $2m+1$. Then the sum is $2(k+l+m+1)+1$, which is odd. This is a direct proof.

   (c) False. Try $2+3$ or $2+5$ or $2+11$, for instance.

2. Imitate the proof in Example 3, using the fact that if p is not divisible by 3 then p^2 is not divisible by 3. See Exercise 15 on page 99 and its answer. The proof is by contradiction.

3. (a) True. Say the integers are n, $n+1$ and $n+2$. Their sum is $3n+3 = 3(n+1)$. This is a direct proof.

   (b) False. Finding an example will be easy; the sum of four consecutive integers is **never** divisible by 4.

   (c) True; $n + (n+1) + (n+2) + (n+3) + (n+4) = 5n + 10$. Alternatively, $(n-2) + (n-1) + n + (n+1) + (n+2) = 5n$. This is a direct proof.

4. Imitate the proof in Example 3. Assume $x = \frac{m}{n}$ with $m \in \mathbb{Z}$, $0 \neq n \in \mathbb{Z}$ and $x^3 = 2$. We may suppose m and n have no common factors. Then $m^3 = 2n^3$. Since $(2j+1)^3 = 8j^3 + 12k^2 + 6j + 1$ is odd, m cannot be odd. I.e., $m^3 = 2n^3$ and m odd lead to a contradiction. So m is even, say $m = 2k$. Then $8k^3 = 2n^3$, so $4k^3 = n^3$. By the same reasoning, n must be even. But then m and n have a common factor, namely 2, and this is a contradiction.

   This proof is by contradiction.

5. This can be done using four cases: see Example 7.

6. Suppose $xy = 0$. Then either $x = 0$ or $y = 0$. Say $x = 0$. Then $x^n = 0^n = 0$ and $(x + y)^n = (0 + y)^n = y^n = 0 + y^n = x^n + y^n$. The argument for $y = 0$ is similar. This is a direct proof involving two simple cases.

7. Example 5 on page 97 shows that the set of primes is infinite. An argument like the one in Example 12 shows that some two primes give the same last six digits. This proof is nonconstructive.

8. (a) Some examples: (17,19), (29,31), (41,43), (1997,1999).

   (b) Consider three cases: $k = 3m$, $k = 3m + 1$ and $k = 3m + 2$ [or $3m - 1$]. For example, if $k = 3m$, then $2k + 3 = 6m + 3 = 3(2m + 1)$ is divisible by 3.

9. (a) None of the numbers in the set

$$\{k \in \mathbb{N} : (n + 1)! + 2 \le k \le (n + 1)! + (n + 1)\}$$

   is prime, since if $2 \le m \le n + 1$, then m divides $(n + 1)!$ and so m also divides $(n + 1)! + m$. The proof is direct.

   (b) Yes. Since $7! = 5040$, the proof shows that all the numbers from 5042 to 5047 are nonprime.

   (c) Simply adjoin 5048 to the list obtained in part (b). Another sequence of seven nonprimes starts with 90.

10. Each p_i divides $p_1 p_2 \cdots p_k$, so it can't divide $1 + p_1 p_2 \cdots p_k$. [If it did, it would divide their difference, which is 1.] So every prime factor of $1 + p_1 p_2 \cdots p_k$ must be different from $p_1, p_2, \ldots, p_k$. [At this writing, the problem of factoring an arbitrary integer is conjectured to be NP-hard. Thus there may be no effective algorithm for carrying out the method of this exercise to construct new large primes.]

11. (a) $14 = 2 \cdot 7$ and 7 is odd. So $14 = 2^1 \cdot 7$.

    (b) 73 is odd, so $73 = 2^0 \cdot 73$.

    (c) $96 = 2 \cdot 48 = 2 \cdot 2 \cdot 24 = 2 \cdot 2 \cdot 2 \cdot 12 = 2 \cdot 2 \cdot 2 \cdot 2 \cdot 6 = 2 \cdot 2 \cdot 2 \cdot 2 \cdot 2 \cdot 3$, so $96 = 2^5 \cdot 3$.

    (d) Answer $= 2^4 \cdot 73$.

12. (a) $2^4 - 1 = 15$ works.

    (b) This is already a lot harder, but the last paragraph of Example 12 suggests trying various numbers $2^n - 1$. One finds $2^{10} - 1 = 1023 = 93 \cdot 11$. [There is a general principle at work here; can you guess it?]

13. (a) We prove this by cases: n has the form $3k$, $3k + 1$ or $3k + 2$ for some $k \in \mathbb{N}$. If $n = 3k$, then

$$\left\lfloor \frac{n}{3} \right\rfloor + \left\lceil \frac{2n}{3} \right\rceil = \lfloor k \rfloor + \lceil 2k \rceil = k + 2k = 3k = n;$$

if $n = 3k + 1$, then

$$\left\lfloor \frac{n}{3} \right\rfloor + \left\lceil \frac{2n}{3} \right\rceil = \left\lfloor k + \frac{1}{3} \right\rfloor + \left\lceil 2k + \frac{2}{3} \right\rceil = k + (2k + 1) = 3k + 1 = n;$$

and if $n = 3k + 2$, then

$$\left\lfloor \frac{n}{3} \right\rfloor + \left\lceil \frac{2n}{3} \right\rceil = \left\lfloor k + \frac{2}{3} \right\rfloor + \left\lceil 2k + \frac{4}{3} \right\rceil = k + (2k + 2) = 3k + 2 = n.$$

(b) If m is even, then $m = 2k$ for some integer k, so

$$\left\lfloor \frac{m}{2} \right\rfloor + \left\lceil \frac{m}{2} \right\rceil = \lfloor k \rfloor + \lceil k \rceil = k + k = 2k = m.$$

If m is odd, then $m = 2k + 1$ for some integer k, so

$$\left\lfloor \frac{m}{2} \right\rfloor + \left\lceil \frac{m}{2} \right\rceil = \left\lfloor k + \frac{1}{2} \right\rfloor + \left\lceil k + \frac{1}{2} \right\rceil = k + (k + 1) = m.$$

This is a proof by cases.

14. (a) Trivially true.

(b) True, because $p \rightarrow p$ is a tautology.

(c) Vacuously true.

2.5 Answers

1. (a) Rule 2a and Substitution Rule (b).

(b) Rule 8a and Rule (b).

(c) Rules 10a and 1 and Rule (b).

(d) First apply Rule (a) to rule 2a to get $s \vee p \Longleftrightarrow p \vee s$. Then use Rule (b).

2. (a) Rule 5b and Substitution Rule (b).

(b) Rule 10a and Rule (b).

(c) Rules 2a [with a for p, b for q, using Substitution Rule (a)] and 8b, and Rule (b).

3. (a) Rule 10a [with s for q, using Rule (a)] and Rule 11a [with s for p and t for q, using Rule (a)] and Rule (b).

(b) Rule 3a [with $\neg p \vee s$ for p, s for q, t for r, using Rule (a)].

(c) Rule 3a [with $\neg p$ for p, s for q, s for r, using Rule (a)] and Rule (b).

(d) Rule 5a [with s for p, using Rule (a)] and Rule (b).

(e) Rule 3a again, using Rule (a).

(f) Rule 10 [with $s \vee t$ for q, using Rule (a)].

4. (a) Rule 10a and Rule (a).

(b) Rule 8a and Rules (a) and (b).

(c) Rule 8b [with Rule (a)] and Rule (b).

(d) Rule 2a with Rule (a).

(e) Rule 4a with Rule (a).

(f) Rules 2a [with Rule (a)] and 7a and Rule (b).

(g) Rule 6d with Rule (a).

(h) Rule 3a with Rule (a).

(i) Rules 2a and 7a and Rule (b).

(j) Rule 6b with Rule (a).

5.

$1, 2, 3$:   Hypothesis
     4:   Rule 16, a tautology
     5:   4, 1 and hypothetical syllogism (rule 33)
     6:   5, 3 and rule 33
     7:   6, 2 and modus tollens (rule 31)

6. All that matters is that 1 and 4 precede 5, 3 and 5 precede 6, and 2 and 6 precede 7. One possible order is:

1.	$s \vee g \rightarrow p$	
2.	$s \rightarrow s \vee g$	[old 4]
3.	$s \rightarrow p$	[old 5]
4.	$p \rightarrow a$	[old 3]
5.	$s \rightarrow a$	[old 6]
6.	$\neg a$	[old 2]
7.	$\neg s$	

7. (a) $\neg(p \rightarrow q) \rightarrow ((p \rightarrow q) \rightarrow p)$

(b) $[p \wedge (p \rightarrow (p \rightarrow q))] \rightarrow (p \rightarrow q)$

(c) $p \vee \neg p$

(d) $[(p \vee (p \rightarrow q)] \leftrightarrow [\neg(p \rightarrow q) \rightarrow p]$

8. For example, rule 23 corresponds to the rule of inference
$$\begin{array}{l} P \leftrightarrow Q \\ Q \leftrightarrow R \\ \hline \therefore \;\; P \leftrightarrow R \end{array}$$

26a corresponds to
$$\begin{array}{l} P \rightarrow Q \\ R \rightarrow S \\ \hline \therefore \;\; (P \vee R) \rightarrow (Q \vee S) \end{array}$$

27b corresponds to
$$\begin{array}{l} P \rightarrow Q \\ R \rightarrow S \\ \hline \therefore \;\; (\neg Q \wedge \neg S) \rightarrow (\neg P \wedge \neg R) \end{array}$$

9. (a) Rule 14 with $q \wedge r$ replacing q.

   (b) Rule 4a with $r \wedge s$ replacing r.

   (c) Rule 8a with $\neg p \wedge r$ replacing p, and $q \rightarrow r$ replacing q.

10. (a) Rule 22 with $\neg p \vee q$ replacing p.

    (b) Rule 27a with q replacing s.

    (c) Rule 20 with $p \rightarrow s$ replacing p, and $q \wedge s$ replacing q.

11. Interchange all $\vee$ and $\wedge$ in Example 8.

12. By rule 8c, $(p \vee q) \leftrightarrow \neg(\neg p \wedge \neg q)$ is a tautology. Use Substitution Rule (a) to replace each p by $\neg p$ and obtain another tautology:

$$(\neg p \vee q) \leftrightarrow \neg(\neg \neg p \wedge \neg q).$$

This has the same truth table as

$$(\neg p \vee q) \leftrightarrow \neg(p \wedge \neg q).$$

So this is a tautology and $(\neg p \vee q) \Longleftrightarrow \neg(p \wedge \neg q)$. Thus $(\neg p \vee q)$ and $\neg(p \wedge \neg q)$ have the same truth tables. Also $(p \rightarrow q)$ and $(\neg p \vee q)$ have the same truth tables by rule 10a, so $(p \rightarrow q)$ and $\neg(p \wedge \neg q)$ have the same truth tables. This implies rule 10b.

13. Consider the cases $\dfrac{p \quad q \quad r}{1 \quad 0 \quad 1}$ or $\dfrac{p \quad q \quad r}{1 \quad 1 \quad 0}$, and $\dfrac{p \quad q \quad r}{0 \quad 0 \quad 1}$ or

$\dfrac{p \quad q \quad r}{0 \quad 1 \quad 0}$.

14. Consider the row of the truth table where p is false and q is true.

15. (a) Take the original proof and change the reason for A from "hypothesis" to "tautology." I.e., the proof itself needs no change.

    (b) Let A be a tautology in the Corollary, and use (a). Specifically, if there is a proof of C from B, then there is a proof of C from $A \wedge B$, so by the Corollary there is a proof of $B \rightarrow C$ from A. Apply part (a).

16. (a) $\neg(\neg p \vee \neg q) \vee \neg(p \vee q)$.

   (b) $(\neg p \vee \neg q) \vee \neg(q \vee \neg r)$ or simply $(\neg p \vee \neg q)$.

   (c) $\neg[\neg(\neg p \vee q) \vee \neg(q \vee r)]$ or $q \vee \neg(p \vee \neg r)$.

   (d) $(p \wedge \neg q) \vee (\neg p \wedge q)$ leads to $\neg(\neg p \vee q) \vee \neg(p \vee \neg q)$.
   $(p \vee q) \wedge \neg(p \wedge q)$ leads to $\neg[\neg(p \vee q) \vee \neg(\neg p \vee \neg q)]$.

17. (a) See rules 11a and 11b.

   (b) $p \vee q \Longleftrightarrow \neg(\neg p \wedge \neg q)$, $p \to q \Longleftrightarrow \neg(p \wedge \neg q)$.

   (c) No. Any proposition involving only p, q, $\wedge$ and $\vee$ will have truth value 0 whenever p and q both have truth values 0. See Exercise 17 on page 414.

18.

p	q	$(p\|p)$	$\|$	$(q\|q)$	
0	0	1	0	1	gives (a) and (b).
0	1	1	1	0	
1	0	0	1	1	
1	1	0	1	0	

   (c) Since $p\|q \Longleftrightarrow \neg(p \wedge q)$ by inspection, $p \wedge q \Longleftrightarrow \neg(p\|q) \Longleftrightarrow (p\|q)\|(p\|q)$, by part (a).

   (d) $p \to q \Longleftrightarrow (\neg p) \vee q \Longleftrightarrow \neg(p \wedge (\neg q)) \Longleftrightarrow p\|(\neg q) \Longleftrightarrow p\|(q\|q)$.

   (e) $p \oplus q$ can be written out in very long form by using the results of parts (a) and (b). The shorter answer $[p\|(q\|q)]\|[q\|(p\|p)]$ comes from part (d) and the observation that $p \oplus q \Longleftrightarrow \neg[(p \to q) \wedge (q \to p)]$; see Exercise 13 on page 90.

19. Use truth tables.

2.6   Answers

1. The argument is not valid, since the hypotheses are true if C is true and A is false. The error is in treating $A \to C$ and $\neg A \to \neg C$ as if they were equivalent.

3. (a) and (b). See (c).

   (c) The case is no stronger. If C and all A_i's are false then every hypothesis $A_i \to C$ is true, whether or not C is true.

4. (a) No. B could be true but M, D and S false.

   (b) Same answer as (a).

5. (a) With suggestive notation, the hypotheses are $\neg b \to \neg s$, $s \to p$ and $\neg p$. We can infer $\neg s$ using the contrapositive. We cannot infer either b or $\neg b$. Of course, we can infer more complex propositions, like $\neg p \vee s$ or $(s \wedge b) \to p$.

(b) I did not pass both the midterm and the final. I.e., I failed at least one of them.

(c) The hypotheses are $(m \vee f) \rightarrow c$, $n \rightarrow c$ and $\neg n$. No interesting conclusions, such as m or $\neg c$, can be inferred.

6. (a) True if the only possibilities are bus, subway and cab, since of these three only the cab would make me on time. If there are other possibilities, a cab cannot be inferred.

(b) The answer is similar to that for part (a).

(c) Must follow. Since $b \vee s \rightarrow l$ and $\neg l$, $\neg(b \vee s)$ by modus tollens, so $\neg b \wedge \neg s$.

(d) The answer is similar to that for part (a). If a cab was taken, then the implication is true whether I become broke or not. If a cab was not taken, then the implication is true if and only if I didn't become broke.

(e) Must follow. From (c)'s answer and simplification (rule 29), $\neg b$ can be inferred. By addition (rule 28), $\neg b \vee n$ can be inferred, where n means "not broke." So $b \rightarrow n$ by implication (rule 10a). In fact, $b \rightarrow p$ can be inferred for any p.

7. (a) True. $A \rightarrow B$ is a hypothesis. We showed that $\neg A \rightarrow \neg B$ follows from the hypotheses.

(b) False. See (d) or check the case A, B, Y, L, N all true.

(c) True. Since $(B \vee \neg Y) \rightarrow A$ is given, $\neg Y \rightarrow A$ follows, or equivalently $\neg\neg Y \vee A$.

(d) True. By hypothesis $(B \vee Y) \rightarrow (L \wedge N)$. By (a) and substitution we have $(A \vee Y) \rightarrow (L \wedge N)$. Apply (c).

8. Pat did it. Here is the record from the trial, showing P from $P \vee Q$, $\neg(R \wedge Q)$ and R.

1.	$\neg(R \wedge Q)$	hypothesis
2.	$(\neg R) \vee (\neg Q)$	1; rule 8b
3.	R	hypothesis
4.	$\neg\neg R$	3; rule 1
5.	$\neg Q$	2,4; disjunctive syllogism rule 32
6.	$P \vee Q$	hypothesis
7.	$Q \vee P$	6; rule 2a (commutative law)
8.	P	7,5; rule 32

9. (a) Let $c :=$ "my computations are correct," $b :=$ "I pay the electric bill," $r :=$ "I run out of money," and $p :=$ "the power stays on." Then the theorem is:

$$\text{if } (c \wedge b) \to r \text{ and } \neg b \to \neg p, \text{ then } (\neg r \wedge p) \to \neg c.$$

1.	$(c \wedge b) \to r$	hypothesis
2.	$\neg b \to \neg p$	hypothesis
3.	$\neg r \to \neg(c \wedge b)$	1; contrapositive rule 9
4.	$\neg r \to (\neg c \vee \neg b)$	3; DeMorgan law 8b
5.	$p \to b$	2; contrapositive rule 9
6.	$(\neg r \wedge p) \to [(\neg c \vee \neg b) \wedge b]$	4,5; rule of inference based on rule 26b
7.	$(\neg r \wedge p) \to [b \wedge (\neg c \vee \neg b)]$	6; commutative law 2b
8.	$(\neg r \wedge p) \to [(b \wedge \neg c) \vee (b \wedge \neg b)]$	7; distributive law 4b
9.	$(\neg r \wedge p)$ $\to [(b \wedge \neg c) \vee \text{ contradiction}]$	8; rule 7b
10.	$(\neg r \wedge p) \to (b \wedge \neg c)$	9; identity law 6a
11.	$(\neg r \wedge p) \to (\neg c \wedge b)$	10; commutative law 2b
12.	$(\neg c \wedge b) \to \neg c$	simplification (rule 17)
13.	$(\neg r \wedge p) \to \neg c$	11,12; hypothetical syllogism

(b) If $d \to (h \vee s)$ and $s \leftrightarrow w$, then $\neg h \to (\neg d \vee w)$.

1.	$d \to (h \vee s)$	hypothesis
2.	$s \leftrightarrow w$	hypothesis
3.	$d \to (s \vee h)$	1; commutative law 2a
4.	$(s \to w) \wedge (w \to s)$	2; equivalence rule 13
5.	$s \to w$	4; simplification (rule 29)
6.	$(s \vee h) \to (w \vee h)$	5; rule of inference based on rule 25a
7.	$d \to (w \vee h)$	3,6; hypothetical syllogism (rule 33)
8.	$(\neg d) \vee (w \vee h)$	7; implication rule 10a
9.	$(\neg d \vee w) \vee h$	8; associative law 3a
10.	$h \vee (\neg d \vee w)$	9; commutative law 2a
11.	$\neg(\neg h) \vee (\neg d \vee w)$	10; double negation rule 1
12.	$\neg h \to (\neg d \vee w)$	11; implication rule 10a

(c) Let $j :=$ "I get the job," $w :=$ "I work hard," $p :=$ "I get promoted," and $h :=$ "I will be happy." Then the theorem is: if $(j \wedge w) \to p$, $p \to h$ and $\neg h$, then $\neg j \vee \neg w$.

1.	$(j \wedge w) \to p$	hypothesis
2.	$p \to h$	hypothesis
3.	$\neg h$	hypothesis
4.	$\neg p$	2,3; modus tollens (rule 31)
5.	$\neg(j \wedge w)$	1,4; modus tollens (rule 31)
6.	$\neg j \vee \neg w$	5; DeMorgan law 8b

(d) If $l \to m$, $a \to t$ and $(m \vee t) \to \neg d$, then $d \to (\neg l \wedge \neg a)$.

1.	$l \to m$	hypothesis
2.	$a \to t$	hypothesis
3.	$(m \vee t) \to \neg d$	hypothesis
4.	$(l \vee a) \to (m \vee t)$	1,2; rule of inference corresponding to rule 26a
5.	$(l \vee a) \to \neg d$	3,4; hypothetical syllogism (rule 33)
6.	$\neg(\neg d) \to \neg(l \vee a)$	5; contrapositive rule 9
7.	$d \to \neg(l \vee a)$	6; double negation rule 1
8.	$d \to (\neg l \wedge \neg a)$	7; DeMorgan law 8a

10. (a) Replace lines 8, 9 and 10 with:

8.	$\neg n$	hypothesis
9.	$\neg s$	5,8; modus tollens rule 31
10.	$s \wedge \neg s$	7,9; rule 34

(b) Replace as follows:

8.	p	3,7; modus ponens rule 30
9.	$\neg n$	hypothesis
10.	$\neg p$	4,9; modus tollens rule 31
11.	$p \wedge \neg p$	8,10; rule 34

11.

1.	$\neg\neg s$	negation of conclusion
2.	s	1; rule 1
3.	$s \to s \vee g$	addition
4.	$s \vee g$	2,3; modus ponens
5.	$s \vee g \to p$	hypothesis
6.	p	4,5; modus ponens
7.	$p \to n$	hypothesis
8.	n	6,7; modus ponens
9.	$\neg n$	hypothesis
10.	$n \wedge \neg n$	8,9; conjunction
11.	contradiction	10

12. (a) The theorem is false. Consider any choice of (p, q, r) in the set $\{(0,0,0), (0,0,1), (0,1,0)\}$.

(b) The theorem is false; suppose p is false and either q is true or r is false.

(c)

1.	$p \rightarrow (q \vee r)$	hypothesis
2.	$q \rightarrow s$	hypothesis
3.	$r \rightarrow \neg p$	hypothesis
4.	$(q \vee r) \rightarrow (s \vee \neg p)$	2,3; rule of inference corresponding to rule 26a
5.	$p \rightarrow (s \vee \neg p)$	1,4; hypothetical syllogism
6.	$\neg p \vee (s \vee \neg p)$	5; implication rule 10a
7.	$\neg p \vee (\neg p \vee s)$	6; commutative law 2a
8.	$(\neg p \vee \neg p) \vee s$	7; associative law 3a
9.	$\neg p \vee s$	8; idempotent law 5a
10.	$p \rightarrow s$	9; implication rule 10a

13. (a)

1.	$A \wedge \neg B$	hypothesis
2.	A	1; rule 29
3.	$A \rightarrow P$	hypothesis
4.	P	2,3; modus ponens
5.	$\neg B$	1; rule 29
6.	$P \wedge \neg B$	4,5; rule 34

(b)

1.	$H \wedge \neg R$	hypothesis
2.	H	1; rule 29
3.	$\neg \neg N$	negation of conclusion
4.	N	3; rule 1
5.	$H \wedge N$	2,4; rule 34
6.	$(H \wedge N) \rightarrow R$	hypothesis
7.	R	5,6; modus ponens
8.	$\neg R$	1; rule 29
9.	$R \wedge \neg R$	7,8; rule 34
10.	contradiction	9; rule 7b

14. He didn't regard yardwork worth doing.

Chapter 3

Relations are the unifying theme of this chapter, which also introduces graphs and digraphs, matrices and modular arithmetic. We want students to be able to think of relations geometrically as digraphs and algebraically as matrices.

Section 3.1 introduces the concept of relation as a set of ordered pairs, gives some examples, and suggests that pictures may be helpful. This is a good section to use for practice with definitions. What do these words really mean? What are some **nonexamples** of symmetric relations? Does every relation have to be either symmetric or antisymmetric? Etc.

Section 3.2 gives the basic definitions of graph theory. We take up digraphs first because of their link with relations in § 3.1. The reachable and adjacency relations will be important later on when we look at graphs as potential data structures. It's worth noting in class that one reason we study graphs is that they give us a conceptual geometric framework for modeling constructs, such as relations, that we have no inherent picture for. Computers don't draw graphs, but people do in order to visualize what the computers are dealing with.

Section 3.3 presents matrices as arrays. It's pretty standard stuff. Examples 4 to 7 tie matrices to relations and graphs. Matrices whose entries are given by formulas, such as the ones in Exercises 5 and 6, often cause students trouble. Assign one of these exercises and give some examples in class.

In § 3.4 we motivate the definition of matrix multiplication by counting paths in a digraph, and we then simply give the definition. Work out a couple of entries and exhibit the corresponding paths of length 2 in your digraph. Our own view is that the **right** way to see associativity of matrix multiplication is in the context of linear transformations, which we have no other reason to study here. So we simply say in a loud voice that multiplication is associative, and give examples. Exercises 5, 7 and 22 help convince students. Exercises 18 to 23 are fairly hard for many students. It's good to assign a few of them, though.

Section 3.5 gives the **whole story** on equivalence relations, which we view as another way of thinking about partitions. The characterization in Theorem 2 on page 172 is fundamental. Make sure students really understand Example 10 on page 172. It works well to take a few examples and view them from the three perspectives: relations between elements [still an intuitive idea at this point], par-

36

titions, and constant-value sets for functions.

Well-definedness of functions is a very slippery concept for many students. Since the question is always linked to some sort of equivalence relation, this is probably the first chance the students have had to really understand it, and this is the place to explain what's at issue.

Section 3.6 serves two purposes. Its main theme is modular arithmetic on the set $\mathbb{Z}(p)$ of congruence classes mod p, but it also gives a statement of the Division Algorithm on page 176 [or, as you may prefer to call it, the Division Property] on $\mathbb{Z}$. The treatment of $\mathbb{Z}(p)$ gives an important example of an equivalence relation and presents the mechanics of the DIV and MOD functions that students encounter in computer science. Even if you choose to soft-pedal $\mathbb{Z}(p)$ in a one-semester course, be sure to mention the Division Algorithm, since it forms the subject matter for the introduction to loop invariants in § 4.1.

3.1 Answers

1. (a) R_1 satisfies (AR) and (S).

   (b) R_2 satisfies (R), (S) and (T).

   (c) R_3 satisfies (R), (AS) and (T).

   (d) R_4 satisfies only (S).

   (e) R_5 satisfies only (S).

2. (a) {(0,0), (0,1), (0,2), (1,1), (1,2), (2,2)}.

   (b) {(0,1), (0,2), (1,2)}.

   (c) {(0,0), (1,1), (2,2)}.

   (d) {(0,0), (0,1), (0,2), (1,0), (2,0)}.

   (e) {(0,0), (0,1), (0,2), (1,1), (2,1)}.

   (f) {(0,0), (0,1), (0,2), (1,0), (1,1), (2,0)}.

   (g) {(1,1)}.

   (h) ∅.

   (i) {(1,0), (1,1), (2,2)}.

3. The relations in (a) and (c) are reflexive. The relations in (c), (d), (f), (g) and (h) are symmetric.

4. (a) {(0,5), (1,4), (2,3), (3,2), (4,1), (5,0)}.

   (b) {(0,2), (1,2), (2,2), (2,1), (2,0)}.

   (c) (2,2), (73,2) and (2,17) are some.

5. R_1 satisfies (AR) and (S). R_2 and R_3 satisfy only (S).

6. R satisfies (R), (S) and (T).

7. (a) The divides relation satisfies (R), (AS) and (T).

   (b) The converse relation $R^{\leftarrow}$ also satisfies (R), (AS) and (T).

   (c) $(m, n) \in R^{\leftarrow}$ if m is a multiple of n.

8. The relations R and $(R^{\leftarrow})^{\leftarrow}$ are the same.

9. (a) The empty relation satisfies (AR), (S), (AS) and (T). The last three properties hold vacuously.

   (b) U satisfies (R), (S) and (T).

10. (a) The relation $<$ on any set, say $\{1,2\}$.

   (b) The relation $\neq$ on any set, say $\{1,2\}$.

11. Yes. For (R) and (AR) observe that $(x, x) \in R \Longleftrightarrow (x, x) \in R^{\leftarrow}$. For (S) and (AS) just interchange x and y in the conditions for R to get the conditions for $R^{\leftarrow}$. There is no change in meaning.

12. If R satisfies (T), and if $(x, y) \in R^{\leftarrow}$ and $(y, z) \in R^{\leftarrow}$, then $(y, x) \in R$ and $(z, y) \in R$, so $(z, x) \in R$ and hence $(x, z) \in R^{\leftarrow}$. Thus $R^{\leftarrow}$ also satisfies (T). Either interchange R and $R^{\leftarrow}$ or apply Exercise 8 to get the reverse implication.

13. (a) If $E \subseteq R_1$ and $E \subseteq R_2$, then $E \subseteq R_1 \cap R_2$. Alternatively, if R_1 and R_2 are reflexive and $x \in S$ then $(x, x) \in R_1$ and $(x, x) \in R_2$, so $(x, x) \in R_1 \cap R_2$.

   (b) If R_1 and R_2 are symmetric and $(x, y) \in R_1 \cap R_2$, then $(x, y) \in R_1$ and $(x, y) \in R_2$, so $(y, x) \in R_1$ and $(y, x) \in R_2$.

   (c) Suppose R_1 and R_2 are transitive. If $(x, y), (y, z) \in R_1 \cap R_2$ then $(x, y), (y, z) \in R_1$ and so $(x, z) \in R_1$. Similarly $(x, z) \in R_2$.

14. (a) Yes. This is clear: if $E \subseteq R_1$ and $E \subseteq R_2$ then $E \subseteq R_1 \cup R_2$.

   (b) Yes. If $(x, y) \in R_1 \cup R_2$ then $(x, y) \in R_1$ or $(x, y) \in R_2$, and in either case $(y, x) \in R_1 \cup R_2$.

   (c) No. For a small example, let $S = \{a, b, c\}$, $R_1 = \{(a, b)\}$ and $R_2 = \{(b, c)\}$.

15. (a) Suppose R is symmetric. If $(x, y) \in R$, then $(y, x) \in R$ by symmetry and so $(x, y) \in R^{\leftarrow}$. Similarly $(x, y) \in R^{\leftarrow}$ implies $(x, y) \in R$ [check] so that $R = R^{\leftarrow}$. For the converse, suppose that $R = R^{\leftarrow}$ and show R is symmetric.

   (b) Suppose R is antisymmetric and $(x, y) \in R \cap R^{\leftarrow}$. Then $(x, y) \in R$ and $(y, x) \in R$, so $x = y$ and $(x, y) \in E$. Conversely, if $R \cap R^{\leftarrow} \subseteq E$ and if $(x, y) \in R$ and $(y, x) \in R$, then $(x, y) \in R \cap R^{\leftarrow} \subseteq E$ and so $x = y$.

16. (a) If $(t,s) \in (R_1 \cup R_2)^{\leftarrow}$ then $(s,t) \in R_1 \cup R_2$, so $(s,t) \in R_1$ or $(s,t) \in R_2$, whence $(t,s) \in R_1^{\leftarrow}$ or $(t,s) \in R_2^{\leftarrow}$ and thus $(t,s) \in R_1^{\leftarrow} \cup R_2^{\leftarrow}$. This argument is reversible, so $(R_1 \cup R_2)^{\leftarrow} \supseteq R_1^{\leftarrow} \cup R_2^{\leftarrow}$ as well.

(b) Replace "or" by "and" in the answer to part (a).

(c) Suppose $R_1 \subseteq R_2$ and $(t,s) \in R_1^{\leftarrow}$. Then $(s,t) \in R_1 \subseteq R_2$, so $(s,t) \in R_2$ and thus $(t,s) \in R_2^{\leftarrow}$.

17. (a)   (b)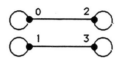

(c) See Figure 1(a).

(d) 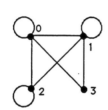   (e)

18. (a)

(b) Omit the loops from the answer to (a).

(c)   (d)

(e)   (f)

(g)   (h)

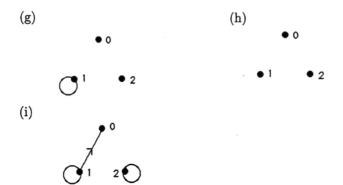

(i)

3.2 Answers

1. (a)

e	a	b	c	d	e	f
$\gamma(e)$	(x,v)	(v,x)	(v,w)	(w,y)	(w,y)	(y,x)

(b)

e	a	b	c	d	e	f	g	h
$\gamma(e)$	(u,v)	(u,x)	(v,w)	(v,y)	(x,w)	(x,y)	(w,z)	(y,z)

(c)

e	a	b	c	d
$\gamma(e)$	(x,w)	(w,x)	(y,z)	(z,y)

(d)

e	a	b	c	d	e
$\gamma(e)$	(x,x)	(y,y)	(z,z)	(x,y)	(y,z)

2.

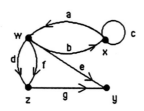

3. (a) Yes.   (b) Yes.

   (c) No. There is no edge from t to x.

   (d) No. There is no edge from y to s.

   (e) Yes.

   (f) No. There is no edge from u to x.

4. The shortest path is $x\,z\,w$, of length 2.

5. (a) $x\,w\,y$ or $x\,w\,v\,z\,y$.   (b) $y\,v\,z$ or $y\,x\,w\,v\,z$.

   (c) $v\,x\,w$ or $v\,z\,w$ or $v\,z\,x\,w$ or $v\,z\,y\,x\,w$.

   (d) $w\,v\,z$.

   (e) $z\,y\,x\,w\,v$ or $z\,w\,v$ or $z\,x\,w\,v$ or $z\,y\,v$.

6.

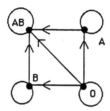

This digraph contains loops, so it is not acyclic.

7. Here is one:

8. (a) The reachability relation is the universal relation, i.e., all pairs of vertices.

   (c) $R = \{(w,w), (w,x), (x,x), (y,y), (y,z), (z,z)\}$.

   (d) $R = \{(x,x), (x,y), (x,z), (y,y), (y,z), (z,z)\}$.

9. (a) $(v,w), (v,y), (v,z)$. Note that (v,z) is in the reachability relation but not in the adjacency relation.

   (b) $(v,s), (v,t), (v,u), (v,w)$.

   (c) All of them. The reachability relation is the universal relation.

10. All describe paths except for parts (d) and (e). In (d), $\{z,z\}$ is not an edge. In (e), $\{w,z\}$ is not an edge.

11. (a) 2.   (b) 7.   (c) 3.   (f) 2.   (g) 3.

   Parts (d) and (e) are not vertex sequences for paths.

12. Parts (b) and (f) describe closed paths. Remember, (e) does not describe a path.

13. (a) Edges e, f and g are parallel.

   (b) Edges a and b are parallel. So are the loops e and f.

14. (a) 2.   (b) 3.

15. (a) $A = \{(w,w),(w,x),(x,w),(y,y),(w,y),(y,w),(x,z),(z,x)\}$, while R consists of all sixteen ordered pairs of vertices.

  (b) $A = \{(v,w),(w,v),(v,y),(y,v),(w,w),(z,z)\}$ and
  $R = \{(z,z),(v,v),(v,w),(v,y),(w,v),(w,w),(w,y),(y,v),(y,w),(y,y)\}$.

16. (a) de, df or dg. Each has vertex sequence $w\,x\,z$.

  (b) There are 90 possible answers. Two examples are $eddg$, with vertex sequence $z\,x\,w\,x\,z$, and $eefe$, with vertex sequence $z\,x\,z\,x\,z$.

  (c) There are 9 possible answers, all with vertex sequence $z\,x\,w\,w\,x\,z$.

  (d) There are 12 possible answers, such as bbd with vertex sequence $w\,y\,w\,x$.

17. (a) cad or cbd. Both have vertex sequence $y\,v\,w\,w$.

  (b) ccc with vertex sequence $v\,y\,v\,y$. There are 4 other such paths, each with vertex sequence $v\,w\,v\,y$.

  (c) There are 4 such paths, each with vertex sequence $v\,w\,w\,v\,y$.

  (d) There are 8 such paths, like eff. They all have vertex sequence $z\,z\,z\,z$.

3.3   Answers

---

1. (a) 1.   (b) 5.   (c) 2.   (d) 0.

2. (a) 2.   (b) 3.   (c) 1.   (d) 8.

3. (a) $\begin{bmatrix} -1 & 1 & 4 \\ 0 & 3 & 2 \\ 2 & -2 & 3 \end{bmatrix}$.   (b) $\begin{bmatrix} 1 & 2 & 5 \\ 3 & -4 & -2 \end{bmatrix}$.   (c) $\begin{bmatrix} 5 & 8 & 7 \\ 5 & 1 & 5 \\ 7 & 3 & 5 \end{bmatrix}$.

  (d) Does not exist.   (e) $\begin{bmatrix} 5 & 5 & 7 \\ 8 & 1 & 3 \\ 7 & 5 & 5 \end{bmatrix}$.   (f) $\begin{bmatrix} 5 & 5 & 7 \\ 8 & 1 & 3 \\ 7 & 5 & 5 \end{bmatrix}$.

  (g) $\begin{bmatrix} 12 & 12 & 8 \\ 12 & -4 & 8 \\ 8 & 8 & 4 \end{bmatrix}$.   (h) Does not exist.   (i) $\begin{bmatrix} 4 & 8 & 9 \\ 6 & 4 & 3 \\ 11 & 5 & 8 \end{bmatrix}$.

4. The answers to parts (a) - (d) are:

$$\begin{bmatrix} 1 & -1 & 1 \end{bmatrix}, \quad \begin{bmatrix} 2 & 0 & -1 \end{bmatrix}, \quad \begin{bmatrix} 1 & -1 & 0 \end{bmatrix}, \quad \begin{bmatrix} 2 & -1 & 1 \end{bmatrix}.$$

5. (a) $\begin{bmatrix} 1 & -1 & 1 & -1 \\ -1 & 1 & -1 & 1 \\ 1 & -1 & 1 & -1 \end{bmatrix}$.   (b) $\begin{bmatrix} 3 & 2 & 5 \\ 2 & 5 & 4 \\ 5 & 4 & 7 \\ 4 & 7 & 6 \end{bmatrix}$.   (c) Not defined.

(d) $\begin{bmatrix} 3 & 2 & 5 & 4 \\ 2 & 5 & 4 & 7 \\ 5 & 4 & 7 & 6 \end{bmatrix}$.

(e) $\begin{bmatrix} 3 & 2 & 5 & 4 \\ 2 & 5 & 4 & 7 \\ 5 & 4 & 7 & 6 \end{bmatrix}$.

(f) $\begin{bmatrix} 2 & -2 & 2 \\ -2 & 2 & -2 \\ 2 & -2 & 2 \\ -2 & 2 & -2 \end{bmatrix}$.

6. (a) $\begin{bmatrix} 3 & 7 & 13 \\ 5 & 10 & 17 \\ 7 & 13 & 21 \end{bmatrix}$. (b) 14. (c) $9 + 18 + 33 = 17 + 20 + 23 = 60$.

(d) $B[1,2] + B[1,3] + B[2,2] + B[2,3] = 5 + 10 + 6 + 11 = 32$;
$B[2,1] + B[3,1] + B[2,2] + B[3,2] = 3 + 4 + 6 + 7 = 20$.

(e) $(A[1,2] + A[1,3]) \cdot (A[2,2] + A[2,3]) = (2+3) \cdot (4+6) = 50$.

(f) Yes. (g) No.

7. (a) $\begin{bmatrix} 1 & 0 & 0 \\ 0 & 1 & 0 \\ 0 & 0 & 1 \end{bmatrix}$, $\begin{bmatrix} 1 & 0 & 0 \\ 0 & 0 & 1 \\ 0 & 1 & 0 \end{bmatrix}$, $\begin{bmatrix} 0 & 1 & 0 \\ 1 & 0 & 0 \\ 0 & 0 & 1 \end{bmatrix}$, $\begin{bmatrix} 0 & 1 & 0 \\ 0 & 0 & 1 \\ 1 & 0 & 0 \end{bmatrix}$,

$\begin{bmatrix} 0 & 0 & 1 \\ 1 & 0 & 0 \\ 0 & 1 & 0 \end{bmatrix}$, $\begin{bmatrix} 0 & 0 & 1 \\ 0 & 1 & 0 \\ 1 & 0 & 0 \end{bmatrix}$.

(b) Four of them equal their transposes.

8. All are true.

9. (a) $\begin{bmatrix} 1 & 0 \\ n & 1 \end{bmatrix}$.

(b) $\{0\}$.

(c) $\{n \in \mathbb{N} : n$ is odd$\}$.

(d) $\{n \in \mathbb{N} : n$ is even$\}$.

10. (a)

$$\begin{aligned}(\mathbf{A} - \mathbf{B}) + \mathbf{B} &= (\mathbf{A} + (-\mathbf{B})) + \mathbf{B} && \text{[definition of } \mathbf{A} - \mathbf{B}] \\ &= \mathbf{A} + ((-\mathbf{B}) + \mathbf{B}) && \text{[associative law]} \\ &= \mathbf{A} + \mathbf{0} && \text{[additive inverses]} \\ &= \mathbf{A} && \text{[additive identity]}.\end{aligned}$$

Or give an argument as in the answer to part (b) below.

(b) $(-(\mathbf{A} - \mathbf{B}))[i,j] = -((\mathbf{A} - \mathbf{B})[i,j]) = -((\mathbf{A} + (-\mathbf{B}))[i,j])$
$= -(\mathbf{A}[i,j] + (-\mathbf{B})[i,j]) = -(\mathbf{A}[i,j] - \mathbf{B}[i,j]) = -\mathbf{A}[i,j] + \mathbf{B}[i,j]$
$= \mathbf{B}[i,j] + (-\mathbf{A})[i,j] = (\mathbf{B} - \mathbf{A})[i,j]$ for all i,j.

(c) Any example with $\mathbf{C} \neq \mathbf{0}$ will work.

11. (a) The (i,j) entry of $a\mathbf{A}$ is $a\mathbf{A}[i,j]$. Similarly for $b\mathbf{B}$, and so the (i,j) entry of $a\mathbf{A} + b\mathbf{B}$ is $a\mathbf{A}[i,j] + b\mathbf{B}[i,j]$. So the (i,j) entry of $c(a\mathbf{A} + b\mathbf{B})$ is $ca\mathbf{A}[i,j] + cb\mathbf{B}[i,j]$. A similar discussion shows that this is the (i,j) entry of $(ca)\mathbf{A} + (cb)\mathbf{B}$. Since their entries are equal, the matrices $c(a\mathbf{A} + b\mathbf{B})$ and $(ca)\mathbf{A} + (cb)\mathbf{B}$ are equal.

(b) For all i, j we have $(-a\mathbf{A})[i,j] = -(a\mathbf{A})[i,j] = -(a\mathbf{A}[i,j]) = (-a)\mathbf{A}[i,j] = ((-a)\mathbf{A})[i,j]$ and also $-(a\mathbf{A}[i,j]) = a(-\mathbf{A}[i,j]) = a((-\mathbf{A})[i,j]) = (a(-\mathbf{A}))[i,j]$.

(c) The (j,i) entries of both $(a\mathbf{A})^T$ and $a\mathbf{A}^T$ equal $a\mathbf{A}[i,j]$. Here $1 \le i \le m$ and $1 \le j \le n$. So the matrices are equal.

12. (b) For all i, j, we have $(\mathbf{A}+\mathbf{B})[i,j] = \mathbf{A}[i,j] + \mathbf{B}[i,j] = \mathbf{B}[i,j] + \mathbf{A}[i,j] = (\mathbf{B}+\mathbf{A})[i,j]$.

(c) and (d) have similar proofs.

13. (a) $\begin{bmatrix} 0 & 0 & 1 & 0 \\ 0 & 0 & 1 & 0 \\ 0 & 0 & 0 & 0 \\ 0 & 0 & 1 & 0 \end{bmatrix}$.
(b) $\begin{bmatrix} 1 & 1 & 0 & 0 \\ 1 & 1 & 0 & 0 \\ 0 & 0 & 0 & 2 \\ 0 & 0 & 0 & 0 \end{bmatrix}$.
(c) $\begin{bmatrix} 0 & 0 & 0 & 0 \\ 0 & 0 & 0 & 2 \\ 0 & 0 & 1 & 0 \\ 0 & 1 & 0 & 0 \end{bmatrix}$.

14. (a) $\begin{bmatrix} 2 & 1 & 1 & 0 \\ 1 & 1 & 0 & 0 \\ 1 & 0 & 0 & 1 \\ 0 & 0 & 1 & 0 \end{bmatrix}$.
(b) $\begin{bmatrix} 0 & 1 & 1 & 1 & 0 \\ 1 & 0 & 0 & 0 & 1 \\ 1 & 0 & 0 & 1 & 1 \\ 1 & 0 & 1 & 0 & 1 \\ 0 & 1 & 1 & 1 & 0 \end{bmatrix}$.

(c) $\begin{bmatrix} 0 & 1 & 1 & 0 & 0 \\ 1 & 0 & 0 & 1 & 1 \\ 1 & 0 & 0 & 1 & 1 \\ 0 & 1 & 1 & 0 & 1 \\ 0 & 1 & 1 & 1 & 0 \end{bmatrix}$.
(d) $\begin{bmatrix} 0 & 1 & 0 & 0 \\ 1 & 1 & 0 & 0 \\ 0 & 0 & 1 & 0 \\ 0 & 0 & 0 & 0 \end{bmatrix}$.

15. (a)   (b)   (c)

16. (a)   (b)   (c)   (d)

17. (a) $\begin{bmatrix} 0 & 0 & 0 & 1 \\ 0 & 0 & 1 & 0 \\ 0 & 1 & 0 & 0 \\ 1 & 0 & 0 & 0 \end{bmatrix}$.
(b) $\begin{bmatrix} 1 & 0 & 1 & 0 \\ 0 & 1 & 0 & 1 \\ 1 & 0 & 1 & 0 \\ 0 & 1 & 0 & 1 \end{bmatrix}$.

(c) See Example 5(a) on page 152.

(d) $\begin{bmatrix} 1 & 1 & 1 & 1 \\ 1 & 1 & 1 & 1 \\ 1 & 1 & 1 & 0 \\ 1 & 1 & 0 & 0 \end{bmatrix}$.

(e) $\begin{bmatrix} 0 & 0 & 0 & 1 \\ 0 & 0 & 0 & 1 \\ 0 & 0 & 0 & 1 \\ 1 & 1 & 1 & 1 \end{bmatrix}$.

18.

19. (a) $\begin{bmatrix} 1 & 1 & 1 \\ 0 & 1 & 1 \\ 0 & 0 & 1 \end{bmatrix}$.

(b) $\begin{bmatrix} 0 & 1 & 1 \\ 0 & 0 & 1 \\ 0 & 0 & 0 \end{bmatrix}$.

(c) $\begin{bmatrix} 1 & 0 & 0 \\ 0 & 1 & 0 \\ 0 & 0 & 1 \end{bmatrix}$.

(d) $\begin{bmatrix} 1 & 1 & 1 \\ 1 & 0 & 0 \\ 1 & 0 & 0 \end{bmatrix}$.

(e) $\begin{bmatrix} 1 & 1 & 1 \\ 0 & 1 & 0 \\ 0 & 1 & 0 \end{bmatrix}$.

(f) $\begin{bmatrix} 1 & 1 & 1 \\ 1 & 1 & 0 \\ 1 & 0 & 0 \end{bmatrix}$.

(g) $\begin{bmatrix} 0 & 0 & 0 \\ 0 & 1 & 0 \\ 0 & 0 & 0 \end{bmatrix}$.

(h) $\begin{bmatrix} 0 & 0 & 0 \\ 0 & 0 & 0 \\ 0 & 0 & 0 \end{bmatrix}$.

(i) $\begin{bmatrix} 0 & 0 & 0 \\ 1 & 1 & 0 \\ 0 & 0 & 1 \end{bmatrix}$.

3.4 Answers

1. (a) $\begin{bmatrix} -8 & 13 \\ 2 & 9 \end{bmatrix}$.

(b) $\begin{bmatrix} 5 & 4 & 10 \\ -1 & -2 & -4 \\ 7 & -4 & -2 \end{bmatrix}$.

(c) $\begin{bmatrix} 31 & -16 & -6 \\ 29 & 4 & 26 \end{bmatrix}$.

(d) $\begin{bmatrix} 3 & 1 & 2 \\ 4 & 0 & 5 \end{bmatrix}$.

(e) $\begin{bmatrix} -1 & 7 \\ 8 & 0 \\ 16 & 0 \end{bmatrix}$.

(f) $\begin{bmatrix} 90 & 13 \\ 2 & 107 \end{bmatrix}$.

2. (a) $\begin{bmatrix} 5 \\ 5 \end{bmatrix}$.   (b) Not defined.   (c) Not defined.   (d) [2].

(e) $\begin{bmatrix} 1 & 0 & 1 \\ 0 & 0 & 0 \\ 1 & 0 & 1 \end{bmatrix}$.

(f) $\begin{bmatrix} 73 \\ 0 \\ 73 \end{bmatrix}$.

3. The products written in parts (a), (c) and (e) do not exist.

(b) $\begin{bmatrix} 2 & 1 & 1 \\ 1 & 6 & 1 \\ 1 & 1 & 2 \end{bmatrix}$.

(d) $\begin{bmatrix} -1 & 4 & -2 & -3 \\ 6 & -3 & 7 & -3 \\ 3 & -1 & -1 & -2 \end{bmatrix}$.

(f) $\begin{bmatrix} -1 & 6 & 3 \\ 4 & -3 & -1 \\ -2 & 7 & -1 \\ -3 & -3 & -2 \end{bmatrix}$.

4. (a) $\begin{bmatrix} -3 & 7 & -7 & -4 \end{bmatrix}$.   (b) $\begin{bmatrix} 3 & -1 & 2 \end{bmatrix}$.

(c) $\begin{bmatrix} 3 \\ -1 \\ 2 \end{bmatrix}$.   (d) $\begin{bmatrix} 3 \\ -1 \\ 2 \end{bmatrix}$.   (e) $\begin{bmatrix} 6 \\ -2 \\ 4 \end{bmatrix}$.

5. (a) $\begin{bmatrix} 1 & 10 \\ 11 & 19 \end{bmatrix}$.

(b) $\begin{bmatrix} 1 & 1 \\ 0 & 1 \end{bmatrix} \begin{bmatrix} 2 & 13 \\ 9 & 13 \end{bmatrix} = \begin{bmatrix} 11 & 26 \\ 9 & 13 \end{bmatrix} = \begin{bmatrix} 1 & 9 \\ 2 & 5 \end{bmatrix} \begin{bmatrix} 2 & -1 \\ 1 & 3 \end{bmatrix}$.

6. (a) $\mathbf{AB} = \begin{bmatrix} -1 & 3 \\ 2 & 7 \end{bmatrix}$ $\mathbf{BA} = \begin{bmatrix} 1 & 9 \\ 2 & 5 \end{bmatrix}$.

(b) $\mathbf{AC} = \begin{bmatrix} 2 & 13 \\ 9 & 13 \end{bmatrix}$ $\mathbf{CA} = \begin{bmatrix} -4 & 3 \\ 5 & 19 \end{bmatrix}$.   (c) $\begin{bmatrix} 9 & 16 \\ 8 & 33 \end{bmatrix}$.

7. (a) $\begin{bmatrix} 7 & 14 \\ 8 & 11 \\ 2 & -6 \end{bmatrix}$.

(b) $\begin{bmatrix} 3 & -1 \\ 2 & 1 \\ -2 & 4 \end{bmatrix} \begin{bmatrix} 1 & 4 \\ 0 & 1 \end{bmatrix} = \begin{bmatrix} 3 & 11 \\ 2 & 9 \\ -2 & -4 \end{bmatrix} = \begin{bmatrix} 3 & 5 \\ 2 & 5 \\ -2 & 0 \end{bmatrix} \begin{bmatrix} 1 & 2 \\ 0 & 1 \end{bmatrix}$.

9. (a) 2.   (b) 1.   (c) 2.   (d) 0.

10. (a) $a\,a$ and $g\,f$.   (b) $a\,g$.   (c) $a\,h$ and $g\,k$.

(d) There are none.

11. (a) $\mathbf{M}^3 = \begin{bmatrix} 3 & 20 & 2 & 3 \\ 0 & 8 & 0 & 0 \\ 2 & 9 & 1 & 2 \\ 0 & 4 & 0 & 0 \end{bmatrix}$.   (b) 9.

(c) $f\,a\,b,\ f\,a\,c,\ f\,b\,d,\ f\,b\,e,\ f\,c\,d,\ f\,c\,e,\ f\,h\,j,\ k\,j\,d,\ k\,j\,e$.

12. (a) Simply remove the arrows from Figure 1.

(b) $\mathbf{M}^2$ is given in Example 3 on page 161. So there are $\mathbf{M}^2[3,3] = 5$ paths of length 2 from v_3 to itself.

(c) $f\,f,\ g\,g,\ f\,g,\ g\,f,\ k\,k$.

(d) $\mathbf{M}^3$ is given in Example 3, so answer is $\mathbf{M}^3[3,3] = 8$.

(e) $f\,a\,f,\ g\,a\,g,\ f\,a\,g,\ g\,a\,f,\ f\,h\,k,\ g\,h\,k,\ k\,h\,f,\ k\,h\,g$.

13. (a) Simply remove the arrows from Figure 1.

(b) $\mathbf{M}^2$ is given in Example 3 on page 161. So the answer is $\mathbf{M}^2[2,2] = 9$.

(c) $d\,d,\ e\,e,\ d\,e,\ e\,d,\ b\,b,\ c\,c,\ b\,c,\ c\,b,\ j\,j$.

(d) $\mathbf{M}^3$ is given in Example 3, so the answer is $\mathbf{M}^3[2,2] = 36$.

14. If $ad - bc \neq 0$, then check that the suggested matrix $\mathbf{A}^{-1}$ is the inverse of $\mathbf{A}$. Conversely, suppose that $\mathbf{A}$ has an inverse; say

$$\begin{bmatrix} a & b \\ c & d \end{bmatrix} \begin{bmatrix} x & y \\ z & w \end{bmatrix} = \begin{bmatrix} 1 & 0 \\ 0 & 1 \end{bmatrix}.$$

Then $ax + bz = 1$ so a and b are not both 0. Moreover, we have $ay + bw = 0$ and $cy + dw = 1$, so $acy + bcw = 0$, $acy + adw = a$, and thus $(ad - bc)w = a$. Similarly, $ady + bdw = 0$ and $bcy + bdw = b$, so $(ad - bc)y = -b$. Since a and $-b$ are not both 0, $ad - bc \neq 0$.

15. (a) $\mathbf{I}^{-1} = \mathbf{I}$.   (b) $\mathbf{A}^{-1} = \begin{bmatrix} 1 & -1 \\ 0 & 1 \end{bmatrix}$ (c) Not invertible.

   (d) $\mathbf{C}^{-1} = \frac{1}{31} \begin{bmatrix} 8 & 3 \\ -5 & 2 \end{bmatrix}$ (e) $\mathbf{D}^{-1} = \mathbf{D}$.

16. Since $(\mathbf{A} + \mathbf{B})(\mathbf{A} - \mathbf{B}) = \mathbf{A}^2 + \mathbf{BA} - \mathbf{AB} - \mathbf{B}^2$, it is enough to find $\mathbf{A}$ and $\mathbf{B}$ where $\mathbf{BA} \neq \mathbf{AB}$.

17. (b) Correct guess $\mathbf{A}^n = \begin{bmatrix} 1 & 0 \\ n & 1 \end{bmatrix}$. Observe that

$$\mathbf{A}^n\mathbf{A} = \begin{bmatrix} 1 & 0 \\ n & 1 \end{bmatrix} \begin{bmatrix} 1 & 0 \\ 1 & 1 \end{bmatrix} = \begin{bmatrix} 1 & 0 \\ n+1 & 1 \end{bmatrix} = \mathbf{A}^{n+1}.$$

18. Here we need $m = n$. For all i, k, $((a\mathbf{A})\mathbf{B})[i,k] = \sum_{j=1}^{n}(a\mathbf{A})[i,j]\mathbf{B}[j,k] = $

$\sum_{j=1}^{n} a\mathbf{A}[i,j]\mathbf{B}[j,k] = a\sum_{j=1}^{n} \mathbf{A}[i,j]\mathbf{B}[j,k] = a(\mathbf{AB})[i,k] = (a(\mathbf{AB}))[i,k]$ and also

$a\sum_{j=1}^{n} \mathbf{A}[i,j]\mathbf{B}[j,k] = \sum_{j=1}^{n} \mathbf{A}[i,j]a\mathbf{B}[j,k] = \sum_{j=1}^{n} \mathbf{A}[i,j](a\mathbf{B})[j,k] = (\mathbf{A}(a\mathbf{B}))[i,k].$

19. For $1 \leq k \leq p$ and $1 \leq i \leq m$,

$$(\mathbf{B}^T\mathbf{A}^T)[k,i] = \sum_{j=1}^{n} \mathbf{B}^T[k,j]\mathbf{A}^T[j,i] = \sum_{j=1}^{n} \mathbf{B}[j,k]\mathbf{A}[i,j].$$

Compare with the (k,i)-entry of $(\mathbf{AB})^T$.

20. (a) If $\mathbf{A} + \mathbf{C} = \mathbf{B} + \mathbf{C}$, then $\mathbf{A}[i,j] + \mathbf{C}[i,j] = \mathbf{B}[i,j] + \mathbf{C}[i,j]$ for all i,j. So $\mathbf{A}[i,j] = \mathbf{B}[i,j]$ for all i,j by the cancellation law for real numbers. Thus $\mathbf{A} = \mathbf{B}$.

   (b) For example,

$$\begin{bmatrix} 1 & 1 \\ 1 & 1 \end{bmatrix} \begin{bmatrix} 1 & -1 \\ -1 & 1 \end{bmatrix} = \begin{bmatrix} 0 & 0 \\ 0 & 0 \end{bmatrix} = \begin{bmatrix} 0 & 0 \\ 0 & 0 \end{bmatrix} \begin{bmatrix} 1 & -1 \\ -1 & 1 \end{bmatrix},$$

   but $\begin{bmatrix} 1 & 1 \\ 1 & 1 \end{bmatrix} \neq \begin{bmatrix} 0 & 0 \\ 0 & 0 \end{bmatrix}$.

21. (a) In fact, $\mathbf{AB} = \mathbf{BA} = a\mathbf{B}$ for all $\mathbf{B}$ in $\mathfrak{M}_{2,2}$.

(b) $\mathbf{AB} = \mathbf{BA}$ with $\mathbf{B} = \begin{bmatrix} 1 & 0 \\ 0 & 0 \end{bmatrix}$ forces $\begin{bmatrix} a & 0 \\ c & 0 \end{bmatrix} = \begin{bmatrix} a & b \\ 0 & 0 \end{bmatrix}$, so $b = c = 0$. So $\mathbf{A} = \begin{bmatrix} a & 0 \\ 0 & d \end{bmatrix}$. Now try $\mathbf{B} = \begin{bmatrix} 0 & 1 \\ 0 & 0 \end{bmatrix}$.

22. (a)

$$\begin{bmatrix} a_1 & a_2 \\ a_3 & a_4 \end{bmatrix} \left\{ \begin{bmatrix} b_1 & b_2 \\ b_3 & b_4 \end{bmatrix} \begin{bmatrix} c_1 & c_2 \\ c_3 & c_4 \end{bmatrix} \right\}$$

$$= \begin{bmatrix} a_1 b_1 c_1 + a_1 b_2 c_3 + a_2 b_3 c_1 + a_2 b_4 c_3 & a_1 b_1 c_2 + a_1 b_2 c_4 + a_2 b_3 c_2 + a_2 b_4 c_4 \\ a_3 b_1 c_1 + a_3 b_2 c_3 + a_4 b_3 c_1 + a_4 b_4 c_3 & a_3 b_1 c_2 + a_3 b_2 c_4 + a_4 b_3 c_2 + a_4 b_4 c_4 \end{bmatrix}$$

$$= \left\{ \begin{bmatrix} a_1 & a_2 \\ a_3 & a_4 \end{bmatrix} \begin{bmatrix} b_1 & b_2 \\ b_3 & b_4 \end{bmatrix} \right\} \begin{bmatrix} c_1 & c_2 \\ c_3 & c_4 \end{bmatrix}$$

(b) Are you kidding? Actually, it's not so bad if you use summation notation.
$(\mathbf{A}(\mathbf{BC}))[i,l] = \sum_j \mathbf{A}[i,j](\mathbf{BC})[j,l] = \sum_j \mathbf{A}[i,j] \sum_k \mathbf{B}[j,k]\mathbf{C}[k,l]$
$= \sum_k \sum_j \mathbf{A}[i,j]\mathbf{B}[j,k]\mathbf{C}[k,l] = \sum_k (\mathbf{AB})[i,k]\mathbf{C}[k,l] = ((\mathbf{AB})\mathbf{C})[i,l]$,
but such manipulations with double sums haven't been discussed in this book.

23. (a) Consider $1 \le i \le m$ and $1 \le k \le p$ and compare the (i,k) entries of $(\mathbf{A} + \mathbf{B})\mathbf{C}$ and $\mathbf{AC} + \mathbf{BC}$.

(b) If $\mathbf{A}$ is $m \times n$, then $\mathbf{B}$ and $\mathbf{C}$ must both be $n \times r$ for the same r. For $1 \le i \le m$ and $1 \le k \le r$,

$$\begin{aligned}
(\mathbf{A}(\mathbf{B} + \mathbf{C}))[i,k] &= \sum_{j=1}^{n} \mathbf{A}[i,j](\mathbf{B} + \mathbf{C})[j,k] \\
&= \sum_{j=1}^{n} \mathbf{A}[i,j](\mathbf{B}[j,k] + \mathbf{C}[j,k]) \\
&= \sum_{j=1}^{n} \mathbf{A}[i,j]\mathbf{B}[j,k] + \sum_{j=1}^{n} \mathbf{A}[i,j]\mathbf{C}[j,k] \\
&= (\mathbf{AB})[i,k] + (\mathbf{AC})[i,k] = (\mathbf{AB} + \mathbf{AC})[i,k].
\end{aligned}$$

24. (a) For $1 \le i \le m$ and $1 \le k \le n$ we have

$$(\mathbf{I}_m \mathbf{A})[i,k] = \sum_{j=1}^{n} \mathbf{I}_m[i,j] \mathbf{A}[j,k].$$

Since $\mathbf{I}_m[i,j] = 0$ for $j \ne i$, the sum collapses to the single term $\mathbf{I}_m[i,i]\mathbf{A}[i,k] = 1 \cdot \mathbf{A}[i,k] = \mathbf{A}[i,k]$.

(b) Similarly to (a), we have

$$(\mathbf{A}\mathbf{I}_n)[i,k] = \sum_{j=1}^{n} \mathbf{A}[i,j]\mathbf{I}_n[j,k] = \mathbf{A}[i,k]\mathbf{I}_n[k,k] = \mathbf{A}[i,k] \cdot 1 = \mathbf{A}[i,k].$$

3.5 Answers

1. (a) is an equivalence relation.

   (b) $\perp$ is not reflexive or transitive.

   (c) There are lots of Americans who live in no state, e.g., the residents of Washington, D.C., so (R) fails for $\sim$.

   (d) As in (c), (R) fails, and $\approx$ is also not transitive.

   (e) is not an equivalence relation because $\approx$ is not transitive.

   (f) $\cong$ is an equivalence relation.

2. (a) $[L]$ is the family of all lines parallel to L, including L itself.

   (f) $[p]$ is the set of all people who have the same mother as p does.

   (b), (c), (d) and (e) do not give equivalence relations.

3. Very much so.

4. The relation $\equiv$ is an equivalence relation. Since $m - m = 0$ is even, $m \equiv m$. If $m - n$ is even, so is its negative $n - m$. Thus $m \equiv n$ implies $n \equiv m$. If $m - n$ and $n - p$ are even, so is $(m - n) + (n - p) = m - p$. Hence $m \equiv n$ and $n \equiv p$ imply $m \equiv p$.

5. (a) The possibilities are

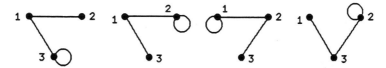

   (b) For (R) no relabeling is required; $f = 1_{\{1,\dots,n\}}$ works. For (S), if G can be labeled with f to become H, then reversing the labeling with f^{-1} turns H back into G. For (T), if f labels G to be H and g labels H to be K, then $g \circ f$ labels G to be K.

7. (a) Verify directly, or apply Theorem 2(a) on page 172 with $f(m) = m^2$ for $m \in \mathbb{Z}$.

   (b) There are infinitely many classes: $\{0\}$ and $\{n, -n\}$ for $n \in \mathbb{P}$.

8. Since $m - m = 0$, which is not odd, $m \sim m$ fails. If $m - n$ and $n - p$ are both odd, then $m - p = (m - n) + (n - p)$ is not odd.

9. (a) There are infinitely many classes: $\{0\}$ and the classes $\{n, -n\}$ for $n \in \mathbb{P}$.

   (b) There are two classes:

$$h^{\leftarrow}(2) = \{n \in \mathbb{Z} : n \text{ is even}\} \quad \text{and} \quad h^{\leftarrow}(0) = \{n \in \mathbb{Z} : n \text{ is odd}\}.$$

10. (a) Check (R), (S) and (T) or apply Theorem 2(a) on page 172 with $f(m, n) = m - n$.

   (b) $(m, n) \sim (k, l)$ if and only if $m - n = k - l$.

11. Apply Theorem 2, using the length function. The equivalence classes are the sets Σ^k, $k \in \mathbb{N}$.

12. Not always. One easily verifies (S) and (T), but the relation might not be reflexive if P has programs that reference uninitialized variables or items such as the time of day or if program behavior depends on external factors such as available memory.

13. (a) Use brute force or Theorem 2(a) with part (b).

   (b) Since $0 \notin \mathbb{P}$, $mq = np$ if and only if $m/n = p/q$.

14. No. Even if ν is one-to-one, so that ν^{-1} exists, ν^{-1} maps $[S]$ into S, not into $[S]$.

   The notation $\nu^{\leftarrow}([s])$ stands for $\{x \in S : \nu(x) = [s]\}$. More generally, if $\theta : A \to B$ is a function, then according to our definition preceding Example 8 on page 62, $\theta^{\leftarrow}(b) = \{a \in A : \theta(a) = b\}$ for each b in B. We can define a function, $\hat{\theta}$ say, from B to the set $\mathcal{P}(A)$ [but *not* to A itself] by $\hat{\theta}(b) = \theta^{\leftarrow}(b)$. In the present context, the equation $\nu^{\leftarrow}([s]) = [s]$ translates into $\hat{\nu}([s]) = [s]$ with $\hat{\nu} : [S] \to \mathcal{P}(S)$. Since $[S] \subseteq \mathcal{P}(S)$, $\hat{\nu}$ acts like the identity function on $[S]$. But $\hat{\nu}$ is not the same thing as ν^{-1}.

15. (a) Not well-defined: depends on the representative. For example $[3] = [-3]$ and $-3 \leq 2$. If the definition made sense, we would have $[3] = [-3] \leq [2]$ and hence $3 \leq 2$.

   (b) Trouble. For example, $[2] = [-2]$ but $(2)^2 + (2) + 1 \neq (-2)^2 + (-2) + 1$.

   (c) Nothing wrong. If $[m] = [n]$ then $m^4 + m^2 + 1 = n^4 + n^2 + 1$.

   (d) Not well-defined. For example, $[-1] = [1]$, but $[-1 + 1] = [0] \neq [2] = [1 + 1]$.

16. (a) Well-defined, since $f(x) = 1/x$ for $x \in \mathbb{Q}^+$.

(b) Not well-defined. For instance $1/2 = 3/6$, but $1^2 + 2^2 \neq 3^2 + 6^2$.

(c) Well-defined. Indeed, $h(m/n) = (m/n) + (n/m)$, so that $h(x) = x + 1/x$ for $x \in \mathbb{Q}^+$.

17. (a) $\cong$ is reflexive by its definition, and it's symmetric since equality "$=$" and R are. For transitivity, consider $u \cong v$ and $v \cong w$. If $u = v$ or if $v = w$, then $u \cong w$ is clear. Otherwise, (u,v) and (v,w) are in R, so (u,w) is in R. Either way, $u \cong w$. Thus $\cong$ is transitive.

(b) The equivalence class containing v consists of v and all the vertices reachable by a path from v.

18. One needs to show:

(R) For each (s_n), the set $\{n \in \mathbb{N} : s_n \neq s_n\}$ is finite, i.e., $(s_n) \sim (s_n)$.

(S) If $\{n \in \mathbb{N} : s_n \neq t_n\}$ is finite, so is $\{n \in \mathbb{N} : t_n \neq s_n\}$, i.e., $(s_n) \sim (t_n)$ implies $(t_n) \sim (s_n)$.

(T) If $\{n \in \mathbb{N} : s_n \neq t_n\}$ and $\{n \in \mathbb{N} : t_n \neq u_n\}$ are finite, so is $\{n \in \mathbb{N} : s_n \neq u_n\}$, i.e., $(s_n) \sim (t_n)$ and $(t_n) \sim (u_n)$ imply $(s_n) \sim (u_n)$.

19. For one-to-one, observe that $\theta([s]) = \theta([t])$ implies $f(s) = f(t)$ implies $s \sim t$, and this implies $[s] = [t]$. Clearly θ maps $[S]$ into $f(S)$. To see that θ maps onto $f(S)$, consider $y \in f(S)$. Then $y = f(s_0)$ for some $s_0 \in S$. Hence $[s_0]$ belongs to $[S]$ and $\theta([s_0]) = f(s_0) = y$. I.e., y is in $\text{Im}(\theta)$. We've shown $f(S) \subseteq \text{Im}(\theta)$, so θ maps $[S]$ onto $f(S)$.

3.6 Answers

1. (a) $q = 6$, $r = 2$.   (b) $q = 5$, $r = 0$.   (c) $q = -7$, $r = 1$.

   (d) $q = -5$, $r = 0$.   (e) $q = 5711$, $r = 31$.   (f) $q = -5712$, $r = 34$.

2. The answers are the same as for Exercise 1, with $m \,\text{DIV}\, n$ instead of q, and $m \,\text{MOD}\, n$ instead of r.

3. (a) $-4, 0, 4$.   (b) $-3, 1, 5$.   (c) $-2, 2, 6$.   (d) $-1, 3, 7$.   (e) $-4, 0, 4$.

4. (a) $[0]_4$, $[1]_4$, $[2]_4$, $[3]_4$.   (b) 73.

5. (a) 1.   (b) 3.   (c) 1.   (d) 2.   (e) 0.

6. (a) 1.   (b) 4.   (c) 2.   (d) k.   (e) k.

7. (a) 3 and 2.

   (b) $m +_{10} k$ is the last [decimal] digit of $m + k$.

   (c) $m *_{10} k$ is the last [decimal] digit of $m * k$.

8. (a) $A_0 = \{-9, -6, -3, 0, 3, 6, 9\}$, $A_1 = \{-8, -5, -2, 1, 4, 7, 10\}$ and $A_2 = \{-10, -7, -4, -1, 2, 5, 8\}$.

   (b) $A_3 = A_0$, $A_4 = A_1$, $A_{73} = A_1$.

9.

$+_4$	0	1	2	3
0	0	1	2	3
1	1	2	3	0
2	2	3	0	1
3	3	0	1	2

$*_4$	0	1	2	3
0	0	0	0	0
1	0	1	2	3
2	0	2	0	2
3	0	3	2	1

10. Solutions are 5, 4, 3, 2 and 1, respectively.

11. Solutions are 1, 3, 2 and 4, respectively.

12. (a) (R) and (S) are clear. If $m \sim n$ and $n \sim p$, then $m^2 - p^2 = (m^2 - n^2) + (n^2 - p^2)$ is a multiple of 3, so $m \sim p$. Thus (T) holds.

    (b) 0, 3, 6 and 72 are some.   (c) 1, 2 and 73 are some.

    (d) These are all there are, since $(3k)^2 - 0^2$ and $(3k \pm 1)^2 - 1^2$ are multiples of 3 and every number in $\mathbb{N}$ can be written in the form $3k$, $3k - 1$ or $3k + 1$.

13. (a) $m \equiv n \pmod{1}$ for all $m, n \in \mathbb{Z}$. There is only one equivalence class.

    (b) The conditions $m = (m \, \mathrm{DIV} \, 1) \cdot 1 + m \, \mathrm{MOD} \, 1$ and $0 \leq m \, \mathrm{MOD} \, 1 < 1$ force $m \, \mathrm{MOD} \, 1 = 0$ and $m \, \mathrm{DIV} \, 1 = m$.

    (c) $0 = 0 +_1 0$ and $0 = 0 *_1 0$.

14. (a) Suppose that $m \equiv n \pmod{p}$. Then $m - n$ is a multiple of p. Hence $(m - n)(m + n)$ is also a multiple of p. Thus $m^2 - n^2$ is a multiple of p, and so $m^2 \equiv n^2 \pmod{p}$. Or apply Theorem 2 to $m \equiv n \pmod{p}$ and $m \equiv n \pmod{p}$.

    (b) f is well-defined, by (a).

    (c) g is well-defined. If $m \equiv n \pmod{6}$, so that $m = n + 6k$ with $k \in \mathbb{Z}$, then $m^2 = n^2 + 12nk + 36k^2 \equiv n^2 \pmod{12}$.

    (d) h is not well-defined. For instance, $[1]_6 = [7]_6$ but $[1^3]_{12} = [1]_{12} \neq [7]_{12} = [7^3]_{12}$.

15. (a) $n = 1000a + 100b + 10c + d = a + b + c + d + 9 \cdot (111a + 11b + c) \equiv a + b + c + d \pmod{9}$, or use Theorem 2 together with $1000 \equiv 100 \equiv 10 \equiv 1 \pmod{9}$.

    (b) Sure. $10^k \equiv 1^k \equiv 1 \pmod{9}$ for every $k \in \mathbb{P}$; therefore, by Theorem 2,
$$\sum_{k=0}^{m} a_k 10^k \equiv \sum_{k=0}^{m} a_k \pmod{9}.$$

16. (a) $n = 1000a + 100b + 10c + d \equiv d \pmod{2}$ since $1000 \equiv 100 \equiv 10 \equiv 0 \pmod{2}$.

    (b) Like (a).

17. Like Exercise 15. Note that $1000 = 91 \cdot 11 - 1$, $100 = 9 \cdot 11 + 1$, $10 = 1 \cdot 11 - 1$, so $1000a + 100b + 10c + d \equiv -a + b - c + d \equiv 0 \pmod{11}$ if and only if $a - b + c - d \equiv 0 \pmod{11}$.

18. (a) If $n \operatorname{MOD} p = 0$ then $n = (n \operatorname{DIV} p) \cdot p$, so $-n = -(n \operatorname{DIV} p) \cdot p + 0$ and thus $(-n) \operatorname{DIV} p = -(n \operatorname{DIV} p)$ and $(-n) \operatorname{MOD} p = 0$.

    (b) If $0 < n \operatorname{MOD} p < p$, then $0 < p - n \operatorname{MOD} p < p$ and $-n = -[(n \operatorname{DIV} p) \cdot p + n \operatorname{MOD} p] = [-(n \operatorname{DIV} p) - 1] \cdot p + [p - n \operatorname{MOD} p]$.

19. We have $q \cdot p - q' \cdot p = r' - r$, so $r' - r$ is a multiple of p. But $-p < -r \le r' - r \le r' < p$, and 0 is the only multiple of p between $-p$ and p. Thus $r' = r$, so $0 = (q - q') \cdot p$ and $q = q'$.

20. (a) If $\theta(m) = \theta(n)$ with $m, n \in \mathbb{Z}(p)$ then $[m]_p = [n]_p$, so $m \equiv n \pmod{p}$ and $m = m \operatorname{MOD} p = n \operatorname{MOD} p = n$. Thus θ is one-to-one. Since $[m]_p = [m \operatorname{MOD} p]_p = \theta(m \operatorname{MOD} p)$ and $m \operatorname{MOD} p \in \mathbb{Z}(p)$, θ maps $\mathbb{Z}(p)$ onto $[\mathbb{Z}]_p$.

    (b) Using Example 6, we obtain $\theta(m) + \theta(n) = [m]_p + [n]_p = [m + n]_p = [(m + n) \operatorname{MOD} p]_p = [m +_p n]_p = \theta(m +_p n)$. The proof for $\cdot$ is similar.

21. (a) By Theorem 3(a)

$$
\begin{aligned}
(m \operatorname{MOD} p) +_p (n \operatorname{MOD} p) &= (m + n) \operatorname{MOD} p = (n + m) \operatorname{MOD} p \\
&= (n \operatorname{MOD} p) +_p (m \operatorname{MOD} p).
\end{aligned}
$$

Since $m, n \in \mathbb{Z}(p)$, $m \operatorname{MOD} p = m$ and $n \operatorname{MOD} p = n$.

    (b) As in part (a),

$$
\begin{aligned}
(m +_p n) +_p r &= (m \operatorname{MOD} p +_p n \operatorname{MOD} p) +_p r \operatorname{MOD} p \\
&= (m + n) \operatorname{MOD} p +_p r \operatorname{MOD} p = [(m + n) + r] \operatorname{MOD} p
\end{aligned}
$$

and similarly $m +_p (n +_p r) = [m + (n + r)] \operatorname{MOD} p$. But $m + (n + r) = (m + n) + r$.

22. (a) If $m \equiv n \pmod{p}$, then $m^2 \equiv n^2 \pmod{p}$ by Theorem 2. So it suffices to show that $n^2 \not\equiv 2 \pmod{3}$ for $n = 0, 1, 2$. This is evident, since $n^2 = 0, 1$ and 4 for these values of n.

    (b) As in part (a), it suffices to show $n^2 \not\equiv 2 \pmod{5}$ for $n = 0, 1, 2, 3, 4$.

Chapter 4

Our computer science colleagues tell us that from their point of view induction is the most important technique in the discrete math course. Experience shows that even some of the better students still have trouble with induction at the end of a year's course, especially if the instructor has not really insisted that they learn it. Be firm.

We base our account of induction on loop invariants. Since our treatment is not the old familiar one, you will probably want to read through the whole chapter before starting to teach any of it. The core facts about induction are in §§ 4.2 and 4.6, with big-oh notation and a recursive interlude between the two doses. The main innovations are our presentation of loop invariants and our careful account of recursion in its various aspects, which we begin in this chapter and continue in Chapter 7.

Section 4.1 introduces algorithm segments, called **while loops**, that occur in iterative algorithms. The main example of the section develops an algorithm for finding quotient and remainder in N. The algorithm terminates because of the Well-Ordering Property, which we simply state as a fact about N. The algorithm gives the right answer because "$q \cdot n + r = m$ and $r \geq 0$" is a loop invariant. We've learned from our students that computer science instructors use loop invariants a lot, often without explanation, so we've given both a careful definition and a clear statement of the fundamental theorem. The idea is completely natural and makes some of our algorithms easy to verify later on, too.

Section 4.2 introduces mathematical induction. One reason we started the chapter with loop invariants is so that we could use them to justify induction. If you want to give a more traditional justification based on the Well-Ordering Property you can do that instead, of course. We think it's wise to give some sort of mathematical justification just so students won't see induction as a trick out of the blue to use when you get stuck. An extra day spent on this section doing lots of examples [not just sums] might be a good idea.

Students need to understand that induction gives a framework or template for a proof, but it doesn't provide the details. Here is one way to present induction that seems to help many students. Think of a business letter format [perhaps produced by word processing software] with its date, address, salutation, body, closing and signature. Every letter has these parts, but what goes in the parts varies from letter to letter. Now draw the following on the blackboard:

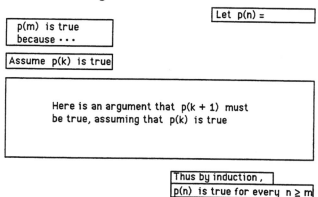

Induction works like this. It's a framework for a valid mathematical proof, and it produces a correct proof if each essential part of it is correctly written.

Section 4.3 contains a careful account of big-oh notation, which we use extensively later on to estimate algorithm complexity. Students may already have encountered this notation in their computer science classes, where the treatment is likely to have been off-hand and confusing. They may also have learned some tricks using limits to calculate estimates for sequences of the form $f(n)/g(n)$. Because we naturally want the smallest m such that $f(n) = O(n^m)$, students may think that $f(n) = O(n^m)$ means that $n^m = O(f(n))$ too. Try to watch for this misconception, and point out that Θ instead of O does what they want.

Emphasize that the big-oh and big-theta notations are very handy, but that they are not a license to be sloppy. Quite the contrary, they give a precise way of describing rough estimates. Exercises 13 and 14 illustrate the second way we use the notation. Exercise 19 connects $\log n$ with the number of digits in n, an important observation in computer science.

Section 4.4 introduces recursion in the context of definition and calculation of sequences. The Fibonacci sequence makes a good example for class discussion. We return to it in the next section. Observe the difference between Exercises 11 and 14. The students can use induction as presented in § 4.2 to give a proof in Exercise 11(b), but 14(b) is considerably harder right now. [See the treatment in Example 2 on page 247.] We give a much more complete answer to 14(b) than we expect from students. Exercise 22 is pretty hard.

Section 4.5 just gives a taste of solving recurrence relations. You may want to spend a moment in class discussing how the theorem for second order linear recurrences might extend to higher order recurrences with constant coefficients. To go much farther in solving recurrence relations takes some fairly fancy machinery, of course, and our students may not have seen calculus, let alone differential equations or complex power series. The account of divide-and-conquer recurrences is included because they occur so commonly. Don't prove Theorem 2 in class; just illustrate its use for some monotone sequence. Perhaps ask a student to bring an example from a computer science class. If you are pressed for time, Theorem 2 can be left as a reading assignment. Only Exercises 15–19 are concerned with the material of that theorem. If time is *really* short, you can omit this section altogether without paying a later penalty.

Present the Second Principle of Induction in § 4.6 as an improvement, as simple as the First Principle and more useful. Show how to do one of Exercises 6 to 9, before you start to prove inequalities.

Section 4.7 on the Euclidean Algorithm presents material that we referred to at the very beginning of the book in § 1.2. It's nice mathematics, and gives a beautiful illustration of how a loop invariant helps shape an algorithm. Any mathematics majors in the class will surely want to go through this section, even if you omit it from the syllabus. Computer science majors will almost certainly see a recursive version of this algorithm as a programming example, and we will present it that way ourselves at the end of § 7.2. The discussion of congruences ties this material back to our account of $\mathbb{Z}(p)$ in § 3.6.

4.1   Answers

1. (a) 0, 3, 9, 21, 45.   (b) 1, 5, 13, 29, 61.   (c) 1, 1, 1, 1, 1.

2. (a) $b = 7$.   (b) $b = 6$.

3. (a)

	m	n
initially	0	0
after first pass	1	1
after second pass	4	2
after third pass	9	3
after fourth pass	16	4

   (b) Replace 4 by 17.

4. (a) 0, 1, 4, 9, 16.   (b) 16.

5. (a) 4, 16, 36, 64.   (b) 9, 25, 49, 81, 121, ...

6. (a)   (b)

```
   i := 1                        k := 8
   while i < 18 do               while k > 0 do
       k := k + 2i                   i := i + 2k
       i := i + 1                    k := k - 1
```

7. (a) If $m + n$ is even, so is $(m + 1) + (n + 1) = (m + n) + 2$. Of course, we didn't need the guard $1 \leq m$ to see this.

   (b) If $m + n$ is odd, so is $(m + 1) + (n + 1)$.

8. (a) If $n^2 \geq m^3$ and $m \geq 1$, then $(3n)^2 = 9n^2 \geq 9m^3 > 8m^3 = (2m)^3$.

   (b) If $2m^6 < n^4$, then $2(2m)^6 = 64 \cdot 2m^6 < 64n^4 < 81n^4 = (3n)^4$.

9. (a) Yes. If $i < j^2$ and $j \geq 1$ then $i + 2 < j^2 + 2 < j^2 + 2j + 1 = (j+1)^2$.

   (b) Yes. The case $i < j^2$ and $j = 0$ cannot happen, and otherwise the answer for (a) applies.

   (c) No. Consider the case $i = j = 0$.

   (d) No. Consider the case $i = j = 1$, for example.

10. (a) Yes. Suppose $k \geq 1$ and $k^2 \equiv 1 \pmod 3$. Since $(2k)^2 = 3k^2 + k^2$ and since $3k^2 \equiv 0 \pmod 3$ and $k^2 \equiv 1 \pmod 3$, $(2k)^2 \equiv 1 \pmod 3$ by Theorem 2 on page 179.

    (b) No. If $k = 1$, $k^2 = 1 \equiv 1 \pmod 4$ but $(2k)^2 = 4 \not\equiv 1 \pmod 4$.

11. (a) $b \geq 2$. (b) $b \in \{2, 3, 5\}$. (c) $b \in \mathbb{N}$.

12. Change the guard to $m \leq n$. The initialization can remain the same or change to $m := 2$. The new loop invariant is FACT $= (m-1)!$.

13. No. The sequence "$k := k^2$, print k" changes the value of k. Algorithm A prints 1, 4 and stops. Algorithm B prints 1, 4, 9, 16, because "for" resets k each time.

14. No. Algorithm C prints 2, 4, 8. Algorithm D prints 2, 4.

15. (a) Yes. new $r < 73$ by definition of MOD.

    (b) No. If $r = 5 \equiv 0 \pmod 5$, for instance, then new $r = 9 \not\equiv 0 \pmod 5$.

    (c) This is an invariant vacuously, because $r \leq 0$ and $r > 0$ cannot both hold at the start of the loop.

16. (a) new $S = S + 2I + 1 = I^2 + 2I + 1 = (I+1)^2 = $ (new $I)^2$.

    (b) new $S = S + 2I + 1 = I^2 + 1 + 2I + 1 = (I+1)^2 + 1 = $ (new $I)^2 + 1$.

    (c) 73^2 since the Loop Invariant Theorem 4.1 on page 191 applies to $S = I^2$.

    (d) $73^2 + 1$ since the Loop Invariant Theorem applies to $S = I^2 + 1$.

17. The sets in (a), (c) and (f) have smallest elements, (f) because $n! > 80^n$ for all large enough n by Example 3(b) on page 216.

    The sets in (b) and (e) fail, because they aren't subsets of $\mathbb{N}$.

    The set in (d) fails because it is empty.

18. (a) We would get 1 in each case. No.

    (b) Same as (a).

19. (a) This is an invariant: if $r > 0$ and a, b and r are multiples of 5, then the new values b, r and $b \operatorname{MOD} r$ are multiples of 5. Note that $b \operatorname{MOD} r = b - (b \operatorname{DIV} r) \cdot r$.

(b) This is not an invariant. For example, if $r = 1$, $a = 5$ and $b = 3$ then $a = 3$ after execution of the loop.

(c) This is an invariant: If $r < b$ and $r > 0$ on entry into the loop then new $r <$ new b, i.e., $b \operatorname{MOD} r < r$, by definition of MOD.

(d) This is an invariant vacuously, because $r \leq 0$ and $r > 0$ cannot both hold at the start of the loop.

20. (a) Yes. If $4 \leq k$ and $5^k < k!$ then $5^{k+1} = 5 \cdot 5^k < 5 \cdot k! \leq (k+1) \cdot k! = (k+1)!$.

(b) No. For example, this fails for $k = 4$.

21. (a) If m is even, $2^{(\text{new } k)} \cdot (\text{new } m) = 2^{k+1} \cdot \frac{m}{2} = 2^k \cdot m = n$.

(b) If m is even, the loop replaces m by $m/2$ and tries again. The chain $n > n/2 > n/4 > \cdots$ is a decreasing chain of positive numbers, so its members cannot all be integers. During some pass $m/2$ cannot be an integer; i.e., m is odd. Then the algorithm exits the loop.

22. (a) Yes. If $p \wedge q$ holds at the start of the loop, then p is true and q is true. If g is also true, then since p and q are invariants of the loop they are both true at the end; hence $p \wedge q$ is also true at the end.

(b) Yes. If $p \vee q$ holds at the start then, say, p holds. If g is true, then p also holds after S, so $p \vee q$ holds.

23. (a)

$a = 2, n = 11$	p	q	i
initially	1	2	11
after first pass	2	4	5
after second pass	8	16	2
after third pass	8	256	1
after fourth pass	$256 \cdot 8$	256^2	0

(b) We need to show that if $q^i p = a^n$ then $(\text{new } q)^{(\text{new } i)}(\text{new } p) = a^n$. If i is odd, then $i = 2 \cdot (\text{new } i) + 1$, new $q = q^2$ and new $p = p \cdot q$, so

$$(\text{new } q)^{(\text{new } i)}(\text{new } p) = (q^2)^{(\text{new } i)} p \cdot q = q^{2 \cdot (\text{new } i) + 1} \cdot p = q^i \cdot p = a^n.$$

If i is even, then $i = 2 \cdot (\text{new } i)$, new $q = q^2$ and new $p = $ old $p = p$, so

$$(\text{new } q)^{(\text{new } i)}(\text{new } p) = (q^2)^{(\text{new } i)} \cdot p = q^i \cdot p = a^n.$$

Since i runs through a decreasing sequence of nonnegative integers, eventually $i = 0$ and the algorithm exits the loop. At this point $p = a^n$.

24. (a) On exit $m = 0$, so $x^n = x^0 \cdot y = y$.

(b) Yes; $x^{m-1} \cdot z = x^n = x^m \cdot y$ if and only if $z = x \cdot y$.

25. The Well-Ordering Principle fails for $\mathbb{R}$ because there are sets, like $(1,2)$, that have no least element. Similarly, the Well-Ordering Principle fails for $[0,\infty)$. In fact, the same example $(1,2)$ illustrates this.

4.2 Answers

Induction proofs should be written carefully and completely. These answers will serve only as guides, *not* as models.

1. This is clear, because both n^5 and n are even if n is even, and both are odd if n is odd.

2. (a) As in Exercise 1, each $n^3 - n$ is even, so it suffices to show that each $n^3 - n$ is a multiple of 3. This is an easy induction argument, where the inductive step uses

$$(k+1)^3 - (k+1) = k^3 + 3k^2 + 3k + 1 - k - 1 = (k^3 - k) + 3(k^2 + k).$$

One can also argue as follows, using $n^3 - n = (n+1) \cdot n \cdot (n-1)$. One of the three consecutive integers $n-1$, n, $n+1$ must be a multiple of 3, so the same is true for $n^3 - n$.

   (b) Each $8^k - 2^k$ has the form $n^3 - n$ where $n = 2^k$.

3. Check the basis. For the inductive step, assume the equality holds for k. Then

$$\sum_{i=1}^{k+1} i^2 = \sum_{i=1}^{k} i^2 + (k+1)^2 = \frac{k(k+1)(2k+1)}{6} + (k+1)^2.$$

Some algebra shows that the right-hand side equals

$$\frac{(k+1)(k+2)(2k+3)}{6},$$

so the equality holds for $k+1$ whenever it holds for k.

4. Let $p(n)$ be "$4+10+16+\cdots+(6n-2) = n(3n+1)$." Then $p(1)$ is "$4 = 1 \cdot (3+1)$" which is true by inspection. Assume that $p(k)$ is true for some $k \in \mathbb{P}$. Then

$$
\begin{aligned}
4 + 10 \ &+ \cdots + (6k - 2) + (6(k+1) - 2) \\
&= \ k(3k+1) + (6(k+1) - 2) \qquad \text{[since $p(k)$ is assumed true]} \\
&= \ 3k^2 + 7k + 4 \\
&= \ (k+1)(3k+4) \qquad\qquad\qquad \text{[algebra]} \\
&= \ (k+1)(3(k+1) + 1),
\end{aligned}
$$

so $p(k+1)$ is true. That is, $p(k) \Longleftrightarrow p(k+1)$. By induction, $p(n)$ is true for all $n \in \mathbb{P}$.

5. (a) Take $n = 37^{20}$ in Exercise 1.

(b) Take $n = 37^4$ in Exercise 1.

(c) By (a), (b) and Exercise 1, $(37^{500} - 37^{100}) + (37^{100} - 37^{20}) + (37^{20} - 37^4)$ is a multiple of 10.

(d) Calculate $37^4 - 1 = 1{,}874{,}160$ directly or observe that the difference $37^5 - 37 = 37 \cdot (37^4 - 1)$ is a multiple of 5 but 37 is not.

(e) By (c) and (d), as in (c).

6. The algebra in the inductive step is

$$\frac{k}{4k+1} + \frac{1}{(4k+1)(4k+5)} = \frac{k(4k+5)+1}{(4k+1)(4k+5)}$$

$$= \frac{4k^2 + 5k + 1}{(4k+1)(4k+5)} = \frac{(4k+1)(k+1)}{(4k+1)(4k+5)} = \frac{k+1}{4(k+1)+1}.$$

7. The basis is "$s_0 = 2^0 a + (2^0 - 1)b$," which is true since $2^0 = 1$ and $s_0 = a$. Assume inductively that $s_k = 2^k a + (2^k - 1)b$ for some $k \in \mathbb{N}$. The algebra in the inductive step is

$$2 \cdot [2^k a + (2^k - 1)b] + b = 2^{k+1}a + 2^{k+1}b - 2b + b.$$

8. (a) 1, 4, 9, 16.

(b) Let $p(n) = $ "$S = n^2$ at the start of the nth pass." For the inductive step use $k^2 + 2\sqrt{k^2} + 1 = (k+1)^2$.

9. Show that $11^{k+1} - 4^{k+1} = 11 \cdot (11^k - 4^k) + 7 \cdot 4^k$. Imitate Example 2(d).

10. (a) $m = 4$, $p(k) = $ "$2^k < k!$."

(b) The verification was given in Example 2(a).

(c) No. To get $p(k)$ true after each pass, we need first to know that $p(m)$ is true on entry into the loop. It turns out that m has to be at least 20.

11. (a) Suppose that $\sum_{i=0}^{k} 2^i = 2^{k+1} - 1$ and $0 \le k$. Then

$$\sum_{i=0}^{k+1} 2^i = (\sum_{i=0}^{k} 2^i) + 2^{k+1} = 2^{k+1} - 1 + 2^{k+1} = 2^{k+2} - 1,$$

so the equation still holds for the new value of k.

(b) Like (a).

(c) Yes. $\displaystyle\sum_{i=0}^{0} 2^i = 1 = 2^1 - 1$ initially, so the loop never exits and the invariant is true for every value of k in $\mathbb{N}$.

(d) No. The loop gets stuck at $k = 0$.

12. Basis: $2^2 = 4 > 3 = 2 + 1$. For the inductive step, if $k^2 > k + 1$ then $(k+1)^2 = k^2 + 2k + 1 > k + 1 + 2k + 1 \geq k + 2$ [since $k \geq 0$]. Simplest without induction: for $n \geq 2$ we have $n^2 \geq 2n = n + n > n + 1$.

13. (a) $1 + 3 + \cdots + (2n - 1) = n^2$.

(b) For the inductive step $k^2 + [2(k+1) - 1] = k^2 + 2k + 1 = (k+1)^2$.

14. If $n \geq 6$ then $n^2 - 4n - 7 = n(n - 4) - 7 \geq 6 \cdot (6 - 4) - 7 = 5 > 0$. No induction required. The inequality fails for $n \leq 5$ by calculation.

15. (a) Assume $p(k)$ is true. Then $(k+1)^2 + 5(k+1) + 1 = (k^2 + 5k + 1) + (2k + 6)$. Since $k^2 + 5k + 1$ is even by assumption and $2k + 6$ is clearly even, $p(k+1)$ is true.

(b) All propositions $p(n)$ are false. *Moral:* The basis of induction is crucial for mathematical induction. Also, see Exercises 10 and 11.

16. For the inductive step, if $\displaystyle\sum_{i=k}^{2k-1} (2i + 1) = 3k^2$, then

$$
\begin{aligned}
\sum_{i=k+1}^{2(k+1)-1} (2i + 1) &= \sum_{i=k}^{2k-1} (2i + 1) - [2k + 1] + [2 \cdot (2k) + 1] + [2 \cdot (2k + 1) + 1] \\
&= 3k^2 - 2k - 1 + 4k + 1 + 4k + 2 + 1 \\
&= 3k^2 + 6k + 3 = 3(k + 1)^2.
\end{aligned}
$$

Alternatively, we use Example 2(b): $\displaystyle\sum_{i=1}^{n} i = \frac{1}{2}n(n + 1)$. Thus

$$
\begin{aligned}
\sum_{i=n}^{2n-1} (2i + 1) &= 2 \cdot \sum_{i=n}^{2n-1} i + \sum_{i=n}^{2n-1} 1 \\
&= 2\left\{ \sum_{i=1}^{2n-1} i - \sum_{i=1}^{n-1} i \right\} + [(2n - 1) - (n - 1)] \\
&= 2\left\{ \frac{1}{2}(2n - 1) \cdot 2n - \frac{1}{2}(n - 1) \cdot n \right\} + n \\
&= 4n^2 - 2n - n^2 + n + n = 3n^2.
\end{aligned}
$$

For a third solution, note that $1+3+\cdots+(2n-1) = \sum_{i=0}^{n-1}(2i+1) = n^2$ by Exercise 13, and so $\sum_{i=n}^{2n-1}(2i+1) = \sum_{i=0}^{2n-1}(2i+1) - \sum_{i=0}^{n-1}(2i+1) = (2n)^2 - n^2 = 3n^2$.

17. *Hint:* $5^{k+1} - 4(k+1) - 1 = 5(5^k - 4k - 1) + 16k$.

18. If we use the formula $\sum_{i=1}^{n} i = \frac{1}{2}n(n+1)$ from Example 2(b), the algebra for the inductive step becomes

$$
\begin{aligned}
\sum_{i=1}^{k+1} i^3 &= \sum_{i=1}^{k} i^3 + (k+1)^3 = \left[\sum_{i=1}^{k} i\right]^2 + (k+1)^3 \\
&= \left[\frac{1}{2}k(k+1)\right]^2 + (k+1)^3 = \frac{k^2(k+1)^2}{4} + \frac{4(k+1)(k+1)^2}{4} \\
&= \frac{(k^2+4k+4)(k+1)^2}{4} = \left[\frac{1}{2}(k+2)(k+1)\right]^2 = \left[\sum_{i=1}^{k+1} i\right]^2.
\end{aligned}
$$

19. *Hints:*

$$\frac{1}{n+2} + \cdots + \frac{1}{2n+2} = \left(\frac{1}{n+1} + \cdots + \frac{1}{2n}\right) + \left(\frac{1}{2n+1} + \frac{1}{2n+2} - \frac{1}{n+1}\right)$$

and

$$\frac{1}{2n+1} + \frac{1}{2n+2} - \frac{1}{n+1} = \frac{1}{2n+1} - \frac{1}{2n+2}.$$

Alternatively, to avoid induction, let $f(n) = \sum_{i=1}^{n} \frac{1}{i}$ and write both sides in terms of f. The left-hand side is $f(2n) - f(n)$ and the right-hand side is

$$1 + \left(\frac{1}{2}\right) + \left(\frac{1}{3}\right) + \cdots + \left(\frac{1}{2n}\right) - 2 \cdot \left[\left(\frac{1}{2}\right) + \left(\frac{1}{4}\right) + \cdots + \left(\frac{1}{2n}\right)\right]$$

$$= f(2n) - 2 \cdot \frac{1}{2} \cdot f(n).$$

20. (a) To prove $\sqrt{k} + \frac{1}{\sqrt{k+1}} \geq \sqrt{k+1}$, for the inductive step observe that $\sqrt{k}\sqrt{k+1} > \sqrt{k \cdot k} = k$, so $\sqrt{k}\sqrt{k+1} + 1 > k+1 = \sqrt{k+1}\sqrt{k+1}$. Divide by $\sqrt{k+1}$.

(b) To prove $2\sqrt{k} - 1 + \frac{1}{\sqrt{k+1}} \leq 2\sqrt{k+1} - 1$, observe that

$$k(k+1) = k^2 + k < k^2 + k + \frac{1}{4} = (k + \frac{1}{2})^2,$$

so $\sqrt{k}\sqrt{k+1} < k + \frac{1}{2}$, $2\sqrt{k}\sqrt{k+1} + 1 < 2k + 2$ and thus

$$2\sqrt{k} + \frac{1}{\sqrt{k+1}} < \frac{(2k+2)}{\sqrt{k+1}} = 2\sqrt{k+1}.$$

21. *Hints:* $5^{k+2} + 2 \cdot 3^{k+1} + 1 = 5(5^{k+1} + 2 \cdot 3^k + 1) - 4(3^k + 1)$. Show that $3^n + 1$ is always even.

22. For the basis, $8^2 + 9 = 73$. For the inductive step, $8^{k+3} + 9^{2k+3} = 8 \cdot 8^{k+2} + 8 \cdot 9^{2k+1} - 8 \cdot 9^{2k+1} + 81 \cdot 9^{2k+1} = 8 \cdot (8^{k+2} + 9^{2k+1}) + (81 - 8) \cdot 9^{2k+1}$.

23. Here $p(n)$ is the proposition "$|\sin nx| \leq n|\sin x|$ for all $x \in \mathbb{R}$." Clearly $p(1)$ holds. By algebra and trigonometry,

$$\begin{aligned}|\sin(k+1)x| &= |\sin(kx + x)| = |\sin kx \cos x + \cos kx \sin x| \\ &\leq |\sin kx| \cdot |\cos x| + |\cos kx| \cdot |\sin x| \leq |\sin kx| + |\sin x|.\end{aligned}$$

Now assume $p(k)$ is true and show $p(k+1)$ is true.

4.3 Answers

1. (a) $k = 2$.

(b) $k = 6$ since f is a polynomial of degree 6.

(c) $k = 12$.

(d) $k = \frac{1}{2}$ since $\sqrt{n+1} \leq \sqrt{2n} = \sqrt{2} \cdot \sqrt{n}$.

2. (a) $k = 14$.

(b) $k = 1$ since $\sqrt{n^2 - 1} \leq \sqrt{n^2} = n$.

(c) $k = 1$. \qquad (d) $k = 7$.

3. (a) $n!$ Note that $3^n \neq O(2^n)$ but $3^n = O(n!)$; see Example 3(b) or Exercise 12.

(b) n^4. \qquad (c) $\log_2 n$.

4. (a) n.

(b) n^3 since $n \cdot \log_2 n = O(n \cdot \sqrt{n})$.

(c) n^n. Note that $(n+1)! \neq O(n!)$ since $(n+1)! \leq C \cdot n!$ for all large n would imply that $n + 1 \leq C$ for all large n.

5. (a) True. Take $C \geq 2$.

   (b) True. $(n+1)^2 = n^2 + 2n + 1$. Apply the result of Example 5(e).

   (c) False. $2^{2n} \leq C \cdot 2^n$ only for $2^n \leq C$, i.e., only for $n \leq \log_2 C$.

   (d) True. Take $C = 40,000$. Or apply Example 5(e).

   (e) True, since $2^{n+1} = 2 \cdot 2^n = O(2^n)$ and $2^n = \frac{1}{2} \cdot 2^{n+1} = O(2^{n+1})$.

   (f) True. $(n+1)^2 = n^2 + 2n + 1$, so $(n+1)^2 = O(n^2)$ by Example 5(e). Also $n^2 \leq (n+1)^2$, so $n^2 = O((n+1)^2)$. Or observe that $n+1 = \Theta(n)$ and apply Theorem 2(d).

   (g) False. It is false that $2^{2n} = O(2^n)$; see the answer to (c).

   (h) True, since $(200n)^2 = 200^2 \cdot n^2 = O(n^2)$ and $n^2 = \frac{1}{200^2} \cdot (200n)^2 = O((200n)^2)$.

6. (a) True. By Example 2(c), we have $\log_2 n = O(n^{1/146})$, so $(\log_2 n)^{73} = O((n^{1/146})^{73}) = O(\sqrt{n})$.

   (b) True because $\log_2(n^{73}) = 73 \cdot \log_2 n$.

   (c) False because $\log_2 n^n = n \cdot \log_2 n \leq C \cdot \log_2 n$ only for $n \leq C$.

   (d) True because $(\sqrt{n} + 1)^4 \leq (2\sqrt{n})^4 = 16 \cdot n^2$.

7. (a) False. If $40^n \leq C \cdot 2^n$ for all large n, then $20^n \leq C$ for all large n.

   (b) True since $(40n)^2 = 1600n^2$.

   (c) False. If $(2n)! \leq C \cdot n!$ for all large n, then $(n+1)! \leq C \cdot n!$ for large n and so $n + 1 \leq C$ for large n, which is impossible.

   (d) True because $(n+1)^{40} \leq (2n)^{40} = 2^{40} \cdot n^{40}$. Or apply Example 5(e).

8. (a) By Theorem 2(a) with $c = 73$ we have $73s(n) = O(s(n))$, and with $c = \frac{1}{73}$ we have $s(n) = \frac{1}{73} \cdot 73s(n) = O(73s(n))$.

   (b) We have $\lfloor s(n) \rfloor \leq s(n) < \lfloor s(n) \rfloor + 1 \leq 2\lfloor s(n) \rfloor$, so $\lfloor s(n) \rfloor = O(s(n))$, and $s(n) = O(\lfloor s(n) \rfloor)$.

9. (a) $k = 5$ (b) $k = 6.5$ (c) $k = 6$

   (d) $k = 4$. Observe that $s(n)$ is $n^4 + n^3 + n^2 + n + 1$ for $n > 1$.

   (e) $k = 2$. The sequence is the sequence t_n in Exercise 11(b).

10. (a) $a = 3$ (b) $a = 2^2 = 4$ (c) $a = \log_2 10$ (d) $a = 1$

11. (a) Clearly $t_n \leq n + n + \cdots + n$ [n terms] $= n^2$. In fact, $t_n = \frac{1}{2} \cdot n(n+1)$ as shown in Example 2(b) on page 204.

    (b) Clearly $s_n \leq n^2 + n^2 + \cdots + n^2$ [n terms] $= n^3$.

12. For $n > 2A$,

$$n! > n(n-1)\cdots(2A+1) > (2A)^{n-2A} = A^n\{2^n \cdot \frac{1}{(2A)^{2A}}\} > A^n$$

for $2^n > (2A)^{2A}$ or $n > 2A \cdot \log_2(2A)$.

13. We are given $s(n) = 3n^4 + a(n)$ and $t(n) = 2n^3 + b(n)$ where $a(n) = O(n)$ and $b(n) = O(n)$.

(a) Now $s(n)+t(n) = 3n^4 + [a(n)+2n^3+b(n)]$ and $a(n)+2n^3+b(n) = O(n^3)$ since $a(n)$, $2n^3$ and $b(n)$ are all $O(n^3)$ sequences. Theorem 2(b) with $a(n) = n^3$ is being used here twice.

(b) $s(n) \cdot t(n) = 6n^7 + [2n^3 \cdot a(n) + 3n^4 \cdot b(n) + a(n) \cdot b(n)]$. Theorem 2(d) shows that $2n^3 \cdot a(n) = O(n^4)$, $3n^4 \cdot b(n) = O(n^5)$ and $a(n) \cdot b(n) = O(n^2)$. So the sum in brackets is $O(n^5)$ by Theorem 2(b) with $a(n) = n^5$. Or apply Theorem 2(c).

14. (a) The product is $15n^7 + [5n^3 \cdot t(n) + 3n^4 \cdot s(n) + s(n) \cdot t(n)]$. Now $5n^3 = O(n^3)$ by Theorem 2(a), so $5n^3 \cdot t(n) = O(n^3 \cdot n^3)$ by Theorem 2(d). Similarly, $3n^4 \cdot s(n) = O(n^4 \cdot n^2) = O(n^6)$ and $s(n) \cdot t(n) = O(n^2 \cdot n^3) = O(n^5)$. The last observation implies that $s(n) \cdot t(n) = O(n^6)$. So the sum in brackets is $O(n^6)$ by Theorem 2(b). Hence the original product is $15n^7 + O(n^6)$.

(b) The argument is similar to that for (a).

15. (a) $s(n)/t(n) = n^4$ is not $O(n^3)$.

(b) For example, $s(n) = n^6$ and $t(n) = n$.

16. Since $\log_{10} n = \log_{10} 2 \cdot \log_2 n$ and $\log_{10} 2$ is a constant, this follows from two applications of Theorem 2(a) and the definition of big-theta.

17. (a) Algorithm B is more efficient if $5n \log_2 n \geq 80n$, i.e., if $n \geq 2^{16} = 65{,}536$.

(b) $n \leq 256$ (c) $n \geq 2^{32} \approx 4.3 \times 10^9$

18. (a) Algorithm A is more efficient if $1000\sqrt{n} \leq 5n$, i.e., if $n \geq 200^2 = 40{,}000$.

(b) $n \geq 160{,}000$ (c) $n \leq 10{,}000$

19. (a) Let $\text{DIGIT}(n) = m$. Then $10^{\text{DIGIT}(n)}$ is written as a 1 followed by m 0's, so it's larger than any m-digit number, such as n. And 10^{m-1} is a 1 followed by $m-1$ 0's so it's the smallest m-digit number.

(b) Since $n < 10^{\text{DIGIT}(n)}$ by part (a),

$$\log_{10} n < \log_{10} 10^{\text{DIGIT}(n)} = \text{DIGIT}(n) \text{ for every } n \in \mathbb{P}.$$

(c) Use part (a). In detail, $\text{DIGIT}(n) - 1 = \log_{10} 10^{\text{DIGIT}(n)-1} \leq \log_{10} n$, so $\text{DIGIT}(n) \leq 1 + \log_{10} n = O(\log_{10} n)$.

(d) follows from parts (b) and (c) and the definition of big-theta.

20. All the assertions in Exercise 19 hold with all occurrences of 10 replaced by 2 and with DIGIT replaced by DIGIT2. The proofs are the same. Thus $\text{DIGIT2}(n) = \Theta(\log_2 n)$. This fact also follows from the identity $\text{DIGIT2}(n) = 1 + \lfloor \log_2 n \rfloor$. The assertion $\text{DIGIT2}(n) = \Theta(\text{DIGIT}(n))$ now follows from Exercise 16, since in general $s(n) = \Theta(a(n))$ and $a(n) = \Theta(b(n))$ imply $s(n) = \Theta(b(n))$.

21. (a) Since i starts as n and is replaced by $\lfloor \frac{i}{2} \rfloor$ in each pass through the loop, we have $i \leq \frac{n}{2^k}$ at the end of the kth pass. The guard would fail for the next pass if $k > \log_2 n$, since then $i \leq \frac{n}{2^k} < 1$.

    (b) It makes 2, 101 and $101 + 2 = 103$ passes, respectively.

22. (a) Since i is n initially and decreases by 1 with each pass through the loop, the algorithm makes exactly n passes through the loop.

    (b) No! The algorithm in Exercise 21 is *much* faster for large n.

23. There are positive constants A, B, C and D so that

    $$s(n) \leq A \cdot n^5, \quad n^5 \leq B \cdot s(n), \quad t(n) \leq C \cdot n^2 \quad \text{and} \quad n^2 \leq D \cdot t(n)$$

    for sufficiently large n. Therefore

    $$\frac{s(n)}{t(n)} \leq \frac{A \cdot n^5}{n^2/D} = A \cdot D \cdot n^3$$

    for sufficiently large n, so $s(n)/t(n) = O(n^3)$. Similarly

    $$n^3 = \frac{n^5}{n^2} \leq \frac{B \cdot s(n)}{t(n)/C} = BC \cdot \frac{s(n)}{t(n)}$$

    for sufficiently large n, so $n^3 = O(s(n)/t(n))$. Hence $s(n)/t(n) = \Theta(n^3)$.

24. This follows from $\max\{a(n), a(n)\} = a(n)$.

25. (a) Assume $c \neq 0$ since the result is obvious for $c = 0$. There is a $C > 0$ so that $|s(n)| \leq C \cdot |a(n)|$ for large n. Then $|c \cdot s(n)| \leq C \cdot |c| \cdot |a(n)|$ for large n.

    (d) If $|s(n)| \leq C \cdot |a(n)|$ and $|t(n)| \leq D \cdot |b(n)|$ for large n, then we have $|s(n) \cdot t(n)| \leq C \cdot D \cdot |a(n) \cdot b(n)|$ for large n.

4.4   Answers

1. (a) 1, 2, 1, 2, 1, 2, 1, 2, ...   (b) $\{1, 2\}$.

2. 1, 1/2, 2/3, 3/5, 8/13.

3. (a) $\text{SEQ}(n) = 3^n$.

   (b) (B) $\text{SEQ}(0) = 1$,
   (R) $\text{SEQ}(n+1) = 3 \cdot \text{SEQ}(n)$ for $n \geq 1$.

4. (a) $\text{SEQ}(0) = 2$ and $\text{SEQ}(n+1) = \text{SEQ}(n)^2$ for $n \in \mathbb{N}$.

   (b) $\text{SEQ}(0) = 2$ and $\text{SEQ}(n+1) = 2^{\text{SEQ}(n)}$ for $n \in \mathbb{N}$.

5. No. It's okay up to $\text{SEQ}(100)$, but $\text{SEQ}(101)$ is not defined, since we cannot divide by zero. If, in (R), we restricted n to be ≤ 100, we would obtain a recursively defined *finite* sequence.

6. (a) $\text{SEQ}(9) = 315/128$.   (b) $\text{FIB}(12) = 144$.

   (c) $Q(19) = 2 \cdot Q(9) + 19 = 2[2 \cdot Q(4) + 9] + 19 = 4 \cdot Q(4) + 37 = 4[2 \cdot Q(2) + 4] + 37 = 8 \cdot Q(2) + 53 = 8[2 \cdot Q(1) + 2] + 53 = 16 \cdot Q(1) + 69 = 85$.

7. (a) 1, 3, 8.

   (b) $s_n = 2s_{n-1} + 2s_{n-2}$ for $n \geq 2$.

   (c) $s_3 = 22$, $s_4 = 60$.

8. (b) In the allowable words all b's precede all a's. The number of a's can be $0, 1, \ldots, n$, so $s_n = n + 1$ for $n \in \mathbb{N}$.

9. (a) 1, 1, 2, 4.

   (b) As in Example 5 we get $t_n = t_{n-1} + (2^{n-1} - t_{n-1}) = 2^{n-1}$ for $n \geq 1$, so no induction is required.

   (c) Ours doesn't, since $t_0 \neq \frac{1}{2}$.

10. (a) 1, 0, 1, 0, 1, 0, 1, 0, 1, 0, ...   (b) $\{0, 1\}$.

11. (a) $a_6 = a_5 + 2a_4 = a_4 + 2a_3 + 2a_4 = 3(a_3 + 2a_2) + 2a_3 = 5(a_2 + 2a_1) + 6a_2 = 11(a_1 + 2a_0) + 10a_1 = 11 \cdot 3 + 10 = 43$. This calculation uses only two intermediate value addresses at any given time. Other recursive calculations are possible that use more.

    (b) Use induction. By definition a_n is odd for $n = 0$ and $n = 1$. Assume that a_n is odd. Since $2a_{n-1}$ is even, $a_n + 2a_{n-1}$ is odd, but this is exactly a_{n+1}.

12. By computation, $\mathbf{M}_1 \cdot \mathbf{M}_1 = \mathbf{M}_2$. Since $\text{FIB}(k) + \text{FIB}(k-1) = \text{FIB}(k+1)$ for $k \geq 2$,

$$
\begin{aligned}
\mathbf{M}_1 \cdot \mathbf{M}_n &= \begin{bmatrix} 1 & 1 \\ 1 & 0 \end{bmatrix} \cdot \begin{bmatrix} \text{FIB}(n+1) & \text{FIB}(n) \\ \text{FIB}(n) & \text{FIB}(n-1) \end{bmatrix} \\
&= \begin{bmatrix} \text{FIB}(n+1) + \text{FIB}(n) & \text{FIB}(n) + \text{FIB}(n-1) \\ \text{FIB}(n+1) & \text{FIB}(n) \end{bmatrix} \\
&= \begin{bmatrix} \text{FIB}(n+2) & \text{FIB}(n+1) \\ \text{FIB}(n+1) & \text{FIB}(n) \end{bmatrix} = \mathbf{M}_{n+1}
\end{aligned}
$$

for $n \geq 2$.

13. Follow the hint. Suppose $S \neq \emptyset$. By the Well-Ordering Principle on page 190, S has a smallest member, say m. Since $s_1 = 2 = \text{FIB}(3)$ and $s_2 = 3 = \text{FIB}(4)$, we have $m \geq 3$. Then $s_m = s_{m-1} + s_{m-2} = \text{FIB}(m-1+2) + \text{FIB}(m-2+2)$ [since m was the smallest bad guy] $= \text{FIB}(m+2)$ [by recursive definition of FIB in Example 3(a)], contrary to $m \in S$. Thus $S = \emptyset$.

14. (a) 1, 1, 3, 7, 17, 41.

   (b) The first two terms are odd and if b_{n-2} is odd then b_n is an odd integer. A proof using our present version of induction is awkward, since if $p(n)$ is "b_n is odd," then $p(n) \rightarrow p(n+2)$ is fairly clear but $p(n) \rightarrow p(n+1)$ is not. We will cover a more general form of induction in § 4.6 that handles this situation. See Example 2 on page 247.

   If a proof is desired at this point, we can use the Well-Ordering Principle on page 190. Let $S = \{n \in \mathbb{N} : b_n \text{ is even}\}$ and suppose that S is not empty. Then S has a smallest member, say m. Now $m \neq 0$ and $m \neq 1$ since b_0 and b_1 are odd integers. Thus $m \geq 2$ so $m - 2$ is in $\mathbb{N}$. Since b_m is even, so is $b_{m-2} = b_m - 2b_{m-1}$, contradicting the choice of m. Hence S must be empty; i.e., b_n is odd for each $n \in \mathbb{N}$.

15. $\text{SEQ}(n) = 2^{n-1}$ for $n \geq 1$.

16. (a) 0, 1, 2, 1, 0, 1, 2, 1, 0, 1, ...   (b) $\{0, 1, 2\}$.

17. (a) $A(1) = 1$. $A(n) = n \cdot A(n-1)$.

   (b) $A(6) = 6 \cdot A(5) = 6 \cdot 5 \cdot A(4) = \cdots = 6! = 720$.

   (c) Yes.

18. (a) $B(1) = 1$. $B(n) = \dfrac{(2n)(2n-1)}{2} \cdot B(n-1)$ for $n \geq 2$.

   (b) $B(3) = \frac{6 \cdot 5}{2} \cdot B(2) = \frac{6 \cdot 5}{2} \cdot \frac{4 \cdot 3}{2} \cdot 1 = 90$.

   (c) $B(5) = 113,400$ [just for 10 children!].

   (d) $B(n) = (2n)!/2^n$.

19. (a) $\{1, 110, 1200\}$.   (b) $\{1, 2, 55, 120, 650\}$.

20. (a) $\text{SUM}(1) = a_1$ and $\text{SUM}(n+1) = \text{SUM}(n) + a_{n+1}$ for $n \in \mathbb{P}$.

   (b) $\text{SUM}(0) = 0$ and $\text{SUM}(n+1) = \text{SUM}(n) + a_{n+1}$ for $n \in \mathbb{N}$. The "empty sum" is 0. [Think of default content of a register.]

21. (a) (B) $\text{UNION}(1) = A_1$,
       (R) $\text{UNION}(n) = A_n \cup \text{UNION}(n-1)$ for $n \geq 2$.

   (b) The "empty union" is $\emptyset$.

   (c) (B) $\text{INTER}(1) = A_1$,
       (R) $\text{INTER}(n+1) = A_{n+1} \cap \text{INTER}(n)$ for $n \in \mathbb{P}$
       [or $\text{INTER}(n) = A_n \cap \text{INTER}(n-1)$ for $n \geq 2$].

   (d) Empty intersection should be the universe, in this case S.

22. Let $p(n)$ be "$x \in \text{SYM}(n)$ if and only if $\{k : x \in A_k$ and $k \leq n\}$ has an odd number of elements." Then $p(1)$ is "$x \in A_1$ if and only if $\{k : x \in A_k$ and $k \leq 1\}$ has an odd number of elements," by (B). Since $x \in A_k$ and $k \leq 1$ if and only if $k = 1$ and $x \in A_1$, $p(1)$ is true.

Assume inductively that $p(n)$ is true for some $n \in \mathbb{P}$. Consider x in $\text{SYM}(n+1) = A_{n+1} \oplus \text{SYM}(n)$. If $x \in A_{n+1}$, then $x \notin \text{SYM}(n)$, so by $p(n)$ the set $\{k : x \in A_k$ and $k \leq n\}$ has an even number of elements, say $2m$. Hence the set $\{k : x \in A_k$ and $k \leq n+1\}$ has $2m+1$ elements [including $n+1$]; i.e., it has an odd number of elements. If $x \in \text{SYM}(n)$, then $x \notin A_{n+1}$ and $\{k : x \in A_k$ and $k \leq n+1\} = \{k : x \in A_k$ and $k \leq n\}$, which has an odd number of elements, by $p(n)$. We have shown that if $x \in \text{SYM}(n+1)$ then $\{k : x \in A_k$ and $k \leq n+1\}$ has an odd number of elements. If $x \in S \setminus \text{SYM}(n+1)$ then either $x \notin A_{n+1} \cup \text{SYM}(n)$ or $x \in A_{n+1} \cap \text{SYM}(n)$. In the first case $\{k : x \in A_k$ and $k \leq n+1\} = \{k : x \in A_k$ and $k \leq n\}$, which has an even number of elements by $p(n)$. In the second case the set $\{k : x \in A_k$ and $k \leq n+1\} = \{n+1\} \cup \{k : x \in A_k$ and $k \leq n\}$, which has an even number of elements by $p(n)$. Thus if $x \in S \setminus \text{SYM}(n+1)$ then $\{k : x \in A_k$ and $k \leq n+1\}$ has an even number of elements. This fact and the result of the last paragraph show that $p(n+1)$ is true whenever $p(n)$ is true. It follows by induction that $p(n)$ is true for every $n \in \mathbb{P}$.

4.5   Answers

1. $s_n = 3 \cdot (-2)^n$ for $n \in \mathbb{N}$.

2. (a) $s_{2n} = 4^n$ and $s_{2n+1} = 4^n$ for $n \in \mathbb{N}$.

(b) $s_{2n} = 4^n$ and $s_{2n+1} = 2 \cdot 4^n$ for $n \in \mathbb{N}$; i.e., $s_n = 2^n$ for all $n \in \mathbb{N}$.

3. We prove this by induction. $s_n = a^n \cdot s_0$ holds for $n = 0$ because $a^0 = 1$. If it holds for some n, then $s_{n+1} = as_n = a(a^n \cdot s_0) = a^{n+1} \cdot s_0$, so the result holds for $n+1$.

4. $s_0 = 2^{0+1} + (-1)^0 = 3$. $s_1 = 2^{1+1} + (-1)^1 = 3$. For $n \geq 2$,

$$
\begin{aligned}
s_{n-1} + 2s_{n-2} &= 2^{(n-1)+1} + (-1)^{n-1} + 2[2^{(n-2)+1} + (-1)^{n-2}] \\
&= 2^n - (-1)^n + 2^n + 2(-1)^n \\
&= 2^{n+1} + (-1)^n = s_n.
\end{aligned}
$$

5. $s_0 = 3^0 - 2 \cdot 0 \cdot 3^0 = 1$. $s_1 = 3^1 - 2 \cdot 1 \cdot 3^1 = -3$. For $n \geq 2$,

$$
\begin{aligned}
6s_{n-1} - 9s_{n-2} &= 6[3^{n-1} - 2(n-1) \cdot 3^{n-1}] - 9[3^{n-2} - 2(n-2) \cdot 3^{n-2}] \\
&= 2[3^n - 2(n-1) \cdot 3^n] - [3^n - 2(n-2) \cdot 3^n] \\
&= 3^n[2 - 4(n-1) - 1 + 2(n-2)] \\
&= 3^n[1 - 2n] = s_n.
\end{aligned}
$$

6. Calculate $\dfrac{1}{\sqrt{5}}\left[\left(\dfrac{1+\sqrt{5}}{2}\right)^6 - \left(\dfrac{1-\sqrt{5}}{2}\right)^6\right].$

7. This time $c_1 = 3$ and $c_2 = 0$, so $s_n = 3 \cdot 2^n$ for $n \in \mathbb{N}$.

8. $c_1 = 0$, $c_2 = 3$, so $s_n = 3 \cdot (-1)^n$ for $n \in \mathbb{N}$.

9. Solve $1 = c_1 + c_2$ and $2 = c_1 r_1 + c_2 r_2$ for c_1 and c_2 to obtain $c_1 = (1+r_1)/\sqrt{5}$ and $c_2 = -(1+r_2)/\sqrt{5}$. Hence

$$s_n = \frac{1}{\sqrt{5}}(r_1^n + r_1^{n+1} - r_2^n - r_2^{n+1}) \text{ for all } n,$$

where r_1, r_2 are as in Example 3 on page 237.

10. (a) 3, 4, 7, 11, 18.

   (b) Solve $2 = c_1 + c_2$ and $1 = c_1 r_1 + c_2 r_2$ to obtain $c_1 = c_2 = 1$. So $s_n = r_1^n + r_2^n$ for $n \in \mathbb{N}$, where r_1, r_2 are as in Example 3 on page 237.

11. (a) $r_1 = -3$, $r_2 = 2$, $c_1 = c_2 = 1$ and so $s_n = (-3)^n + 2^n$ for $n \in \mathbb{N}$.

   (b) $s_n = 2 \cdot 5^n$ for $n \in \mathbb{N}$.

   (c) Here the characteristic equation has one solution $r = 2$. Then $c_1 = 1$ and $c_2 = 3$ and so $s_n = 2^n + 3n \cdot 2^n$ for $n \in \mathbb{N}$.

   (d) Here $r_1 = 2$, $r_2 = 3$. Solve $c = c_1 + c_2$ and $d = 2c_1 + 3c_2$ to obtain $c_1 = 3c - d$ and $c_2 = d - 2c$. So $s_n = (3c - d) \cdot 2^n + (d - 2c) \cdot 3^n$ for $n \in \mathbb{N}$.

   (e) $s_{2n} = 1$, $s_{2n+1} = 4$ for all $n \in \mathbb{N}$.

   (f) $s_{2n} = 3^n$ and $s_{2n+1} = 2 \cdot 3^n$ for $n \in \mathbb{N}$.

   (g) $s_n = (-3)^n$ for $n \in \mathbb{N}$.

   (h) $s_n = -(1/4)(-3)^n + (5/4)$ for $n \in \mathbb{N}$.

12. (a) $s_n = 0$ for $n \in \mathbb{N}$.

   (b) $s_n = 0$ for $n \in \mathbb{N}$.

   (c) $s_n = 5$ for $n \in \mathbb{N}$.

   (d) $s_n = 3 + 2n$ for $n \in \mathbb{N}$.

13. (a) By Theorem 1(a) there are constants C and D such that for $n \geq 2$ we have

$$s_n = Cr_1^n + Dr_2^n = (C + D(\frac{r_2}{r_1})^n)r_1^n \leq (|C| + |D|)r_1^n.$$

   (b) Any sequence $s_n = C2^n + Dn2^n$ with C and D different from 0 will work.

   (c) By Theorem 1(b) we have $s_n = O(nr_1^n)$.

14. The characteristic equation is $x^2 - b = 0$ and the solutions are $r_1 = \sqrt{b}$ and $r_2 = -\sqrt{b}$. Solving $s_0 = c_1 + c_2$ and $s_1 = c_1\sqrt{b} - c_2\sqrt{b}$ yields $c_1 = \frac{1}{2}(s_0 + s_1/\sqrt{b})$, $c_2 = \frac{1}{2}(s_0 - s_1/\sqrt{b})$. Now

$$s_n = \frac{1}{2}\left(s_0 + \frac{s_1}{\sqrt{b}}\right)(\sqrt{b})^n + \frac{1}{2}\left(s_0 - \frac{s_1}{\sqrt{b}}\right)(-\sqrt{b})^n$$

$$= (\sqrt{b})^n \cdot \frac{1}{2}\left[s_0 + \frac{s_1}{\sqrt{b}} + (-1)^n\left(s_0 - \frac{s_1}{\sqrt{b}}\right)\right].$$

So

$$s_{2n} = (\sqrt{b})^{2n} \cdot \frac{1}{2}\left[s_0 + \frac{s_1}{\sqrt{b}} + s_0 - \frac{s_1}{\sqrt{b}}\right] = b^n \cdot s_0$$

and

$$s_{2n+1} = (\sqrt{b})^{2n+1} \cdot \frac{1}{2}\left[s_0 + \frac{s_1}{\sqrt{b}} - s_0 + \frac{s_1}{\sqrt{b}}\right] = b^n \cdot s_1.$$

15. (a) $s_{2^m} = 2^m + 3 \cdot (2^m - 1) = 2^{m+2} - 3$.

(b) $s_{2^m} = 3 \cdot 2^m$. (c) $s_{2^m} = \frac{5}{2} \cdot 2^m \cdot m$.

(d) $s_{2^m} = 2^{m+1} + 3 \cdot (2^m - 1) + \frac{5}{2} \cdot 2^m \cdot m$.

(e) $s_{2^m} = 7 - 6 \cdot 2^m$. (f) $s_{2^m} = 7 - 2^{m+1}$.

(g) $s_{2^m} = (6 - m)2^{m-1}$. (h) $s_{2^m} = (10 - 7m)2^{m-1} - 5$.

16. (a) $s_{2^m} \le 2^m \cdot 7 + 2^m - 1 = 2^{m+3} - 1$.

(b) $s_{2^m} \le 2^m \cdot 7 + m \cdot 2^m = (7 + m)2^m$.

17. $s_{2^m} = 2^m[s_1 + \frac{1}{2}(2^m - 1)]$. Verify that this formula satisfies $s_{2^0} = s_1$ and $s_{2^{m+1}} = 2s_{2^m} + (2^m)^2$.

18. The inductive step is

$$s_{2^{m+1}} = 2s_{2^m} + A + B \cdot 2^m$$

$$= 2[2^m s_1 + (2^m - 1)A + \frac{B}{2} \cdot 2^m \cdot m] + A + B \cdot 2^m$$

$$= 2^{m+1}s_1 + [2 \cdot (2^m - 1) + 1] \cdot A + [2^m \cdot m + 2^m] \cdot B$$

$$= 2^{m+1}s_1 + [2^{m+1} - 1] \cdot A + \frac{B}{2} \cdot 2^{m+1}(m + 1).$$

19. (a) $t_{2^m} = b^m t_1 + b^{m-1} \cdot \sum_{i=0}^{m-1} \frac{f(2^i)}{b^i}$.

. (b) $t_{3^m} = 3^m t_1 + 3^{m-1} \cdot \sum_{i=0}^{m-1} \frac{f(3^i)}{3^i}$.

4.6   Answers

1. The First Principle is adequate for this. For the inductive step, use the identity $4n^2 - n + 8(n+1) - 5 = 4n^2 + 7n + 3 = 4(n+1)^2 - (n+1)$.

2. The First Principle on page 246 applies in both parts.

3. Show that $n^5 - n$ is always even. Then use the identity $(n+1)^5 = n^5 + 5n^4 + 10n^3 + 10n^2 + 5n + 1$ [from the binomial theorem]. More detail: The difference $n^5 - n$ is even since both n and n^5 are even if n is even and both are odd if n is odd. Use the First Principle of induction to show that $n^5 - n$ is always divisible by 5. If this is true for n, then this is true for $n+1$ because $(n+1)^5 - (n+1) = n^5 - n + 5(n^4 + 2n^3 + 2n^2 + n)$. This was done in detail in Example 1 on page 201.

4. (a) $b_6 = 2b_5 + b_4 = 2 \cdot 41 + 17 = 99$.

   (b) $a_9 = 9$. We omit the step-by-step computations of a_3, a_4, etc.

5. Yes. The oddness of a_n depends only on the oddness of a_{n-1}, since $2a_{n-2}$ is even whether a_{n-2} is odd or not.

6. (b) $a_n = 2^n$ for $n \in \mathbb{N}$.

   (c) Use the general Second Principle on page 246 with $m = 0$, $l = 1$. Let $p(n) = $ "$a_n = 2^n$." By definition $p(0)$ and $p(1)$ are true. Consider $n \geq 2$ and assume that $a_k = 2^k$ for all k satisfying $0 \leq k < n$. Then

$$a_n = \frac{a_{n-1}^2}{a_{n-2}} = \frac{(2^{n-1})^2}{2^{n-2}} = 2^{2n-2-n+2} = 2^n.$$

   By the Second Principle $a_n = 2^n$ for every $n \in \mathbb{N}$.

7. (b) $a_n = 1$ for all $n \in \mathbb{N}$.

   (c) The basis needs to be checked for $n = 0$ and $n = 1$. For the inductive step, consider $n \geq 2$ and assume $a_k = 1$ for $0 \leq k < n$. Then $a_n = \frac{a_{n-1}^2 + a_{n-2}}{a_{n-1} + a_{n-2}} = \frac{1^2 + 1}{1 + 1} = 1$. This completes the inductive step, so $a_n = 1$ for all $n \in \mathbb{N}$ by the Second Principle of Induction.

8. (b) $a_n = n + 1$ for $n \in \mathbb{N}$.

   (c) Use the general Second Principle with $m = 0$, $l = 1$. Check for $n = 0, 1$. For the inductive step

$$a_n = \frac{a_{n-1}^2 - 1}{a_{n-2}} = \frac{(n-1+1)^2 - 1}{(n-2+1)} = \frac{n^2 - 1}{n - 1} = n + 1.$$

9. (b) $a_n = n^2$ for all $n \in \mathbb{N}$.

   (c) The basis needs to be checked for $n = 0$ and $n = 1$. For the inductive step, consider $n \geq 2$ and assume that $a_k = k^2$ for $0 \leq k < n$. To complete the inductive step, note that

   $$a_n = \frac{1}{4}(a_{n-1} - a_{n-2} + 3)^2 = \frac{1}{4}[(n-1)^2 - (n-2)^2 + 3]^2 = \frac{1}{4}[2n]^2 = n^2.$$

10. (a) $a_3 = 4$, $a_4 = 7$, $a_5 = 10$, $a_6 = 15$, $a_7 = 24$.

    (b) Check for $n = 1, 2, 3$. For the inductive step for $n \geq 4$,
    $a_n = a_{n-2} + 2a_{n-3} > (\frac{3}{2})^{n-2} + 2(\frac{3}{2})^{n-3} = (\frac{3}{2})^n[(\frac{2}{3})^2 + 2(\frac{2}{3})^3]$
    $= (\frac{3}{2})^n \cdot \frac{28}{27} > (\frac{3}{2})^n$.

11. (b) The basis needs to be checked for $n = 0$, 1 and 2. For the inductive step, consider $n \geq 3$ and assume that a_k is odd for $0 \leq k < n$. Then a_{n-1}, a_{n-2}, a_{n-3} are all odd. Since the sum of three odd integers is odd [if not obvious, prove it], a_n is also odd.

    (c) Since the inequality is claimed for $n \geq 1$ and since you will want to use the identity $a_n = a_{n-1} + a_{n-2} + a_{n-3}$ in the inductive step, you will need $n - 3 \geq 1$ in the inductive step. So check the basis for $n = 1$, 2 and 3. For the inductive step, consider $n \geq 4$ and assume that $a_k \leq 2^{k-1}$ for $1 \leq k < n$. To complete the inductive step, note that

    $$a_n = a_{n-1} + a_{n-2} + a_{n-3} < 2^{n-2} + 2^{n-3} + 2^{n-4} = \frac{7}{8} \cdot 2^{n-1} < 2^{n-1}.$$

12. (a) $a_3 = 11$, $a_4 = 21$, $a_5 = 43$, $a_6 = 85$, $a_7 = 171$.

    (b) Check for $n = 1, 2, 3$. For the inductive step with $n \geq 4$,

    $$a_n = 3a_{n-2} + 2a_{n-3} > 3 \cdot 2^{n-2} + 2 \cdot 2^{n-3} = 2^n.$$

    (c) Check for $n = 1, 2, 3$. For $n \geq 4$, $a_n = 3a_{n-2} + 2a_{n-3} < 3 \cdot 2^{n-1} + 2 \cdot 2^{n-2} = 2^{n+1}$.

    (d) Check for $n = 1, 2, 3$. For $n \geq 4$,

    $$\begin{aligned} a_n &= 3a_{n-2} + 2a_{n-3} = 3 \cdot [2a_{n-3} + (-1)^{n-3}] + 2 \cdot [2a_{n-4} + (-1)^{n-4}] \\ &= 2 \cdot [3a_{n-3} + 2a_{n-4}] + (-1)^{n-3} \cdot [3 - 2] = 2a_{n-1} + (-1)^{n-1}. \end{aligned}$$

13. (a) 2, 3, 4, 6.

    (b) The inequality must be checked for $n = 3$, 4 and 5 before applying the Second Principle of Mathematical Induction on page 246 to $b_n = b_{n-1} + b_{n-3}$. For the inductive step, consider $n \geq 6$ and assume $b_k \geq 2b_{k-2}$ for $3 \leq k < n$. Then

    $$b_n = b_{n-1} + b_{n-3} \geq 2b_{n-3} + 2b_{n-5} = 2b_{n-2}.$$

(c) The inequality must be checked for $n = 2$, 3 and 4. Then use the Second Principle of Mathematical Induction and part (b). For the inductive step, consider $n \geq 5$ and assume $b_k \geq (\sqrt{2})^{k-2}$ for $2 \leq k < n$. Then

$$b_n = b_{n-1} + b_{n-3} \geq 2b_{n-3} + b_{n-3} = 3b_{n-3} \geq 3(\sqrt{2})^{n-5}$$

$$> (\sqrt{2})^3 (\sqrt{2})^{n-5} = (\sqrt{2})^{n-2}.$$

Note that $3 > (\sqrt{2})^3 \approx 2.828$. This can also be proved without using part (b):

$$b_n \geq (\sqrt{2})^{n-3} + (\sqrt{2})^{n-5} = (\sqrt{2})^{n-2} \cdot \left[\frac{1}{\sqrt{2}} + \frac{1}{2^{3/2}} \right] > (\sqrt{2})^{n-2}.$$

14. Check for $n = 1$, 2, 3. For the induction step, consider $n \geq 4$ and assume $b_k \leq (\frac{3}{2})^{k-1}$ for $1 \leq k < n$. Then $b_n = b_{n-1} + b_{n-3} \leq (\frac{3}{2})^{n-2} + (\frac{3}{2})^{n-4} = (\frac{3}{2})^{n-1} \cdot [(\frac{2}{3}) + (\frac{2}{3})^3] = (\frac{3}{2})^{n-1} \cdot \frac{26}{27} < (\frac{3}{2})^{n-1}$.

15. Check for $n = 0$ and 1 before applying induction. It may be simpler to prove "$\text{SEQ}(n) \leq 1$ for all n" separately from "$\text{SEQ}(n) \geq 0$ for all n". For example, assume that $n \geq 2$ and that $\text{SEQ}(k) \leq 1$ for $0 \leq k < n$. Then

$$\text{SEQ}(n) = (1/n) * \text{SEQ}(n-1) + ((n-l)/n) * \text{SEQ}(n-2) \leq (1/n) + ((n-l)/n) = 1.$$

The proof that $\text{SEQ}(n) \geq 0$ for $n \geq 0$ is almost the same.

16. First note that

$$\text{SEQ}(n+1) = \sum_{i=0}^{n} \text{SEQ}(i) = \text{SEQ}(n) + \sum_{i=0}^{n-1} \text{SEQ}(i) = \text{SEQ}(n) + \text{SEQ}(n) = 2 \cdot \text{SEQ}(n).$$

Now the First Principle on page 246 is sufficient to prove $\text{SEQ}(n) = 2^{n-1}$ for $n \geq 1$. For the inductive step, $\text{SEQ}(n+1) = 2 \cdot \text{SEQ}(n) = 2 \cdot 2^{n-1} = 2^n$.

17. The First Principle of Induction is enough. Use (R) to check for $n = 3$. For the inductive step from n to $n+1$,

$$\text{FIB}(n+1) = \text{FIB}(n) + \text{FIB}(n-1) = 1 + \sum_{k=1}^{n-2} \text{FIB}(k) + \text{FIB}(n-1) = 1 + \sum_{k=1}^{n-1} \text{FIB}(k).$$

18. (a) 1, 3, 4, 7, 11, 18, etc.

(b) First check for $n = 2$ and 3. Then apply the Second Principle of Induction:

$$
\begin{aligned}
\text{LUC}(n) &= \text{LUC}(n-1) + \text{LUC}(n-2) \\
&= [\text{FIB}(n) + \text{FIB}(n-2)] + [\text{FIB}(n-1) + \text{FIB}(n-3)] \\
&= [\text{FIB}(n) + \text{FIB}(n-1)] + [\text{FIB}(n-2) + \text{FIB}(n-3)] \\
&= \text{FIB}(n+1) + \text{FIB}(n-1).
\end{aligned}
$$

Explanations should be supplied.

19. For $n > 0$, let $L(n)$ be the largest integer 2^k with $2^k \leq n$. Show that $L(n) = T(n)$ for all n by showing first that $L(\lfloor n/2 \rfloor) = L(n/2)$ for $n \geq 2$ and then using the Second Principle of Induction.

20. (a) In fact, $T(n) \leq n$ for all n, by Exercise 19 or by a proof using the Second Principle of Induction.

(b) There are lots of proofs. To show that $Q(n) \leq n^2$ by the Second Principle of Induction, observe in the proof of the inductive step that $n \leq n^2/2$ for $n \geq 2$.

(c) Show that $Q(n) \leq 2n \log n$ for $n \geq 2$. The inductive step is

$$
\begin{aligned}
Q(n) &= 2 \cdot Q(\lfloor n/2 \rfloor) + n \leq 2 \cdot 2 \lfloor n/2 \rfloor \log \lfloor n/2 \rfloor + n \leq 2 \cdot \frac{2n}{2} \cdot \log(n/2) + n \\
&= 2n(\log n - 1) + n = 2n \log n - n < 2n \log n.
\end{aligned}
$$

21. Show that $S(n) \leq n$ for every n by the Second Principle of Induction.

4.7 Answers

1. (a) 20.   (b) 10.   (c) 1.   (d) 20.
   (e) 4.   (f) 20.   (g) 6.   (h) 1.

2. (a) 17.   (b) 1.   (c) 17.
   (d) 170.   (e) 17.   (f) 170.

3. (a) (20,14), (14,6), (6,2), (2,0); gcd = 2.
   (b) (20,7), (7,6), (6,1), (1,0); gcd = 1.
   (c) (20,30), (30,20), (20,10), (10,0); gcd = 10.
   (d) (2000,987), (987,26), (26,25), (25,1), (1,0); gcd = 1.

4. (a) (30,30), (30,0); gcd = 30.   (b) (30,10), (10,0); gcd = 10.
   (c) (30,60), (60,30), (30,0); gcd = 30.
   (d) (3000,999), (999,3), (3,0); gcd = 3.

5. (a) $\gcd(20, 14) = 2$, $s = -2$, $t = 3$.

a	q	s	t
20		1	0
14	1	0	1
6	2	1	−1
2	3	−2	3
0			

(b) $\gcd(72, 17) = 1$, $s = -4$, $t = 17$.

a	q	s	t
72		1	0
17	4	0	1
4	4	1	−4
1	4	−4	17
0			

(c) $\gcd(20, 30) = 10$, $s = -1$, $t = 1$.

a	q	s	t
20		1	0
30	0	0	1
20	1	1	0
10	2	−1	1
0			

(d) $\gcd(320, 30) = 10$, $s = -1$, $t = 11$.

a	q	s	t
320		1	0
30	10	0	1
20	1	1	−10
10	2	−1	11
0			

6. (a) $\gcd(14259, 3521) = 7$, $s = 161$, $t = -652$.

a	q	s	t
14259		1	0
3521	4	0	1
175	20	1	−4
21	8	−20	81
7	3	161	−652
0			

(b) $\gcd(8359, 9373) = 13$, $s = 342$, $t = -305$.

a	q	s	t
8359		1	0
9373	0	0	1
8359	1	1	0
1014	8	-1	1
247	4	9	-8
26	9	-37	33
13	2	342	-305
0			

7. (a) $x = 21$ $[\equiv -5 \pmod{26}]$.   (b) $x = 19$ $[\equiv -7 \pmod{26}]$.

   (c) No solution exists, because 4 and 26 are not relatively prime.

   (d) $x = 3$.   (e) $x = 23$ $[\equiv -3 \pmod{26}]$.

   (f) No solution exists, because 13 and 26 are not relatively prime.

8. (a) $x = 5$.   (b) $x = 11$.

   (c) No solution exists, because 4 and 24 are not relatively prime.

   (d) No solution exists, because 9 and 24 are not relatively prime.

   (e) $x = 17$.   (f) $x = 13$.

9. (a) $x \equiv 5 \pmod{13}$.   (b) $x \equiv 5 \cdot 4 \equiv 7 \pmod{13}$.

   (c) Same as (a), since $99 \equiv 8 \pmod{13}$.

   (d) $x \equiv 5 \cdot 5 \equiv 12 \pmod{13}$.

10. (a) $x \equiv -163 \equiv 480 \pmod{643}$.

    (b) $x \equiv 507 \pmod{2000}$.   (c) $x \equiv 111 \pmod{788}$.

    (d) $x \equiv 24 \cdot (-232) \equiv -5568 \equiv 1020 \pmod{1647}$.

11. Assume that $a = s \cdot m + t \cdot n$ and $a' = s' \cdot m + t' \cdot n$ at the start of the loop. The equation $a' = s' \cdot m + t' \cdot n$ becomes $a_{\text{next}} = s_{\text{next}} \cdot m + t_{\text{next}} \cdot n$ at the end, and $a'_{\text{next}} = a' - q \cdot a = s' \cdot m + t' \cdot n - q \cdot s \cdot m - q \cdot t \cdot n = (s' - q \cdot s) \cdot m + (t' - q \cdot t) \cdot n = s'_{\text{next}} \cdot m + t'_{\text{next}} \cdot n$ at the end.

12. By Theorem 3 on page 258, $\gcd(m, n) = s \cdot m + t \cdot n$ for some s and t, so $\gcd(m, n)$ is of this form. Suppose that $e = a \cdot m + b \cdot n$ with $0 < e \le \gcd(m, n)$. Since $\gcd(m, n)$ divides both m and n, it divides e, just as in the Corollary to Theorem 3 on page 258. Hence $\gcd(m, n) \le e$.

13. (a) $1 = s \cdot (m/d) + t \cdot (n/d)$ for some integers s and t. Apply Exercise 12 to m/d and n/d in place of m and n. A longer proof can be based on prime factorization.

    (b) $k = s't - st'$ works. Note that $d \cdot s = ss' \cdot m + st' \cdot n$ and $d \cdot s' = s's \cdot m + s't \cdot n$; subtract.

    (c) Let $x = s \cdot a/d$.

14. (a) $s' \cdot m + t' \cdot n = s \cdot m + k \cdot (n/d) \cdot m + t \cdot n - k \cdot (m/d) \cdot n = s \cdot m + t \cdot n = d$.

(b) Let $s' = s \operatorname{MOD} \frac{n}{d}$ and $t' = t + (s \operatorname{DIV} \frac{n}{d}) \cdot \frac{m}{d}$, so that

$$t' \cdot n = t \cdot n + m \cdot (s \operatorname{DIV} \frac{n}{d}) \cdot \frac{n}{d} = t \cdot n + m \cdot (s - s \operatorname{MOD} \frac{n}{d}).$$

15. (a) Check for $l = 1$. For the inductive step it suffices to show that if $a = m = $ FIB$(l + 3)$ and $b = n = $ FIB$(l + 2)$, $l \geq 1$, then after the first pass of the while loop, $a = $ FIB$(l + 2)$ and $b = $ FIB$(l + 1)$. For then, by the inductive hypothesis, exactly l more passes would be needed before terminating the algorithm. By the definition of (a, b) in the while loop, it suffices to show that FIB$(l+3) \operatorname{MOD}$ FIB$(l+2) = $ FIB$(l+1)$. But FIB$(l+3) \operatorname{MOD}$ FIB$(l+2) = $ $[\text{FIB}(l + 2) + \text{FIB}(l + 1)] \operatorname{MOD}$ FIB$(l + 2) = $ FIB$(l + 1) \operatorname{MOD}$ FIB$(l + 2) = $ FIB$(l + 1)$, since FIB$(l + 1) < $ FIB$(l + 2)$ for $l \geq 1$.

(b) Use induction on k. Check for $k = 2$. For the inductive step

$$\begin{aligned} \log_2 \text{FIB}(k + 1) &= \log_2(\text{FIB}(k) + \text{FIB}(k - 1)) \\ &\leq \log_2(2\text{FIB}(k)) = 1 + \log_2 \text{FIB}(k). \end{aligned}$$

[This estimate is far from best possible. The Fibonacci numbers are the worst case for the Euclidean algorithm on page 258.]

(c) By part (a), GCD makes l passes through the loop. By part (b) we see that $\log_2(m + n) = \log_2 \text{FIB}(l + 3) \leq l$ if $l \geq 2$.

16. Let $p(k)$ be the assertion for a product of k positive integers. $p(2)$ was established in Lemma 1 on page 260. Suppose that $p(k)$ holds and that a prime p divides a product $m_1 \cdot m_2 \cdots m_k \cdot m_{k+1}$. By the $p(2)$ case applied to $m_1 \cdot m_2 \cdots m_k$ and m_{k+1}, the prime p divides $m_1 \cdot m_2 \cdots m_k$ or it divides m_{k+1}. If p divides m_{k+1}, we are done. Otherwise, p divides $m_1 \cdot m_2 \cdots m_k$ and the induction hypothesis $p(k)$ shows that p divides one of its factors. It either case, p divides one of the factors $m_1, m_2, \ldots, m_k, m_{k+1}$. This shows that $p(k + 1)$ holds (if $p(k)$ holds). By the Principle of Induction, all the statements $p(k)$ are true.

Chapter 5

Most of this chapter is about formulas that count sets without actually listing their members. Sections on probability seem to fit naturally here, since lots of elementary probability questions can be answered by counting.

Section 5.1 lays out some basic terminology and simple techniques. You might want to draw a couple more examples of decision trees in the style of Figure 1 on page 268 and then ask students what the tree for choosing a 5-card poker hand would look like. Although the tree is a good conceptual tool, we don't want to list all its leaves; we just want to know how many there are. The tree helps bring Product Rule on page 267 to life.

The account of probability in § 5.2 is just meant to be an introduction. The first dozen exercises give a sense of what we really expect students to be able to do here, but it doesn't hurt to assign some of the more challenging ones as well. Though we expect our readers to be thinking of finite sample spaces, the main probability facts in this chapter are still true, suitably interpreted, in a more general setting.

Section 5.3 presents two new methods and proves the binomial theorem, which we'll view in § 5.4 as a special case of the multinomial theorem. The Inclusion-Exclusion Principle on page 287 is awkward to write out as a formula, but it is easy to illustrate and to understand. The formula for placing objects in boxes can be remembered more easily if its proof is understood. The examples in the text are more complicated than the exercises, on purpose. Students should be encouraged to follow arguments they would perhaps not arrive at themselves. They need practice reading with understanding, and the examples illustrate extensions of the basic techniques. Moreover, as we point out in Example 6(c) on page 293, it is very easy to ask very hard combinatorial questions, so we cannot expect the exercises to come close to covering all situations that arise naturally. We don't assign Exercise 16, but do call attention to it in class. This section has plenty of ideas for two class meetings.

Section 5.4 contains still more counting tools. It is not an accident that the formulas for the number of ordered partitions and for the number of permutations of a multiset are the same. Students need to see how the Counting Lemma relates these two, as illustrated in Example 6 on page 302. Exercise 5 should be assigned or done in class.

In a sense, the methods in §§ 5.3 and 5.4 are like techniques for integration in a calculus class. They don't handle everything, but they do provide practical tools. In a similar way, the Pigeon-Hole Principle in § 5.5 is like the Mean Value Theorem. It says that something must occur, but it doesn't help find the occurrence. Section 5.5 can be covered in one day, though here again the text is trickier than many of the exercises. Really weak students won't be able to do much with any of the problems. Do Example 4 on page 311 or Example 5 on page 312 in class—Ross likes 5 and Wright likes 4—and urge the students to read the other one.

Section 5.6 introduces conditional probability and independence. Our point of view is that $P(\ |S)$ is a probability on Ω determined by the probability $P(\ )$ and the choice of S. Independence is, of course, a fundamental concept. Give examples of events that are not independent as well as ones that are. Illustrate Bayes' Formula with a couple of examples. Exercise 19, drawn from actual facts, is a real surprise to most people.

5.1   Answers

1. (a) 56.   (b) 1.   (c) 56.

   (d) 1326.   (e) 1.   (f) 52.

2. (a) One example: How many words of length 10 are there in $\{a, b, \ldots, z\}$ with no repeated letter? Order should be important in any good example.

   (b) One example: How many 10-letter subsets of $\{a, b, \ldots, z\}$ are there? Order should not matter in this one.

3. (a) 10.   (b) 1.   (c) $0 + 0 = 0$.

   (d) $(100!/60!)/(99!/60!) = 100$.

   (e) $(1000!/650!)/(999!/649!) = 1000/650$.

   (f) 9900.

4. (a) 14, 4, 10.   (b) $2^{10} = 1024$.

   (c) $\binom{10}{4} = 210$.   (d) $\binom{5}{3} \cdot 5 = 50$.

5. (a) $\binom{20}{8} = 125{,}970$.

   (b) $P(20, 8) = \frac{20!}{12!} = 5{,}079{,}110{,}400$.

6. (a) $\binom{28}{7} = 1{,}184{,}040$.   (b) $\binom{12}{3} \cdot \binom{16}{4} = 400{,}400$.

   (c) $\binom{12}{7} + \binom{16}{7} = 792 + 11{,}440 = 12{,}232$.

7. (a) 126.   (b) 105.

8. $\binom{8}{4} \cdot \binom{6}{4} = 1050$.

9. (a) 0.   (b) 840.   (c) 2401.

10. (a) $\binom{9}{4} = 126$.   (b) $5! = 120$.   (c) $5^3 \cdot 9^2 = 10,125$.

11. (a) This is the same as the number of ways of drawing ten cards so that the *first* one is not a repetition. Hence $52 \cdot (51)^9$.

(b) $52^{10} - 52(51)^9$.

12. (a) 5^k.   (b) $5 \cdot 4 \cdot 3 = 60$.

(c) $4 \cdot 4^3 = 256$.   (d) $5^4 - 4^4 = 369$.

13. (a) $9 \cdot 10^6$.

(b) $5 \cdot 9 \cdot 10^5 = 9 \cdot 10^6/2 = 4,500,000$.

(c) $5 \cdot 9 \cdot 10^5 = 9 \cdot 10^6/2 =$ answer to (a) $-$ answer to (b). This is also $\lfloor (10^7 - 1)/2 \rfloor - \lfloor (10^6 - 1)/2 \rfloor$.

(d) $2 \cdot 9 \cdot 10^5 = 9 \cdot 10^6/5$. This is also $= \lfloor (10^7 - 1)/5 \rfloor - \lfloor (10^6 - 1)/5 \rfloor$.

(e) $9 \cdot 9 \cdot 8 \cdot 7 \cdot 6 \cdot 5 \cdot 4 = 9 \cdot P(9,6)$. Choose the digits from left to right.

(f) $5 \cdot 8 \cdot 8 \cdot 7 \cdot 6 \cdot 5 \cdot 4 = 5 \cdot 8 \cdot P(8,5)$. Choose the 1's digit, then the rest from left to right.

(g) $9 \cdot 9 \cdot 8 \cdot 7 \cdot 6 \cdot 5 \cdot 4 - 5 \cdot 8 \cdot 8 \cdot 7 \cdot 6 \cdot 5 \cdot 4 = 41 \cdot 8 \cdot 7 \cdot 6 \cdot 5 \cdot 4$.

14. (a) $\lfloor 10000/21 \rfloor = 476$.

(b) $\lfloor 10000/3 \rfloor + \lfloor 10000/7 \rfloor - \lfloor 10000/21 \rfloor = 4285$.

(c) $10000 - 4285 = 5715$.   (d) $4285 - 476 = 3809$.

15. (a) $13 \cdot \binom{4}{4} \cdot \binom{48}{1} = 624$.   (b) 5108.

(c) $13 \cdot \binom{4}{3} \cdot \binom{12}{2} \cdot 4 \cdot 4 = 54,912$.   (d) $1,098,240$.

16. (a) $2 \cdot 5! = 240$. Treat ab as a single letter and then do the same for ba.

(b) $6! - 2 \cdot 5! = 480$.

(c) $2 \cdot 5! - 2 \cdot 4! = 192$. The arrangements in part (a) with bac or cab do not qualify.

17. (a) It is the $n \times n$ matrix with 0's on the diagonal and 1's elsewhere.

(b) $(n^2 - n)/2$.

18. (a) $n!$ (b) $5 \cdot 4 \cdot 3 \cdot 2 \cdot 1 + 5 \cdot 4 \cdot 3 \cdot 2 + 5 \cdot 4 \cdot 3 + 5 \cdot 4 = 320$.

19. (a) $n \cdot (n-1)^3$. If the vertex sequence is written $v_1\, v_2\, v_3\, v_4$, there are n choices for v_1 and $n - 1$ choices for each of v_2, v_3 and v_4.

(b) $n(n-1)(n-2)(n-3)$.

(c) $n(n-1)(n-2)(n-2)$. v_1, v_2, v_3 must be distinct but v_4 can be v_1.

20. One possible process constructs an $(r+s)$-permutation of an n-element set by first constructing an r-permutation, in one of $P(n,r)$ ways, and then following it by an s-permutation of the remaining $n - r$ elements, chosen from among $P(n-r, s)$ possibilities. Thus, by the Product Rule $P(n,r) \cdot P(n-r, s) = P(n, r+s)$.

5.2 Answers

1. (a) $\frac{8}{25} = .32$. (b) .20. (c) $\frac{9}{25} = .36$.

2. $\frac{5}{26}$.

3. (a) $\frac{5 \cdot 4 \cdot 3 \cdot 2}{5^4} = .192$. (b) $\frac{3^4}{5^4} = .1296$. (c) $\frac{2}{5} = .40$.

4. (a) 0. (b) $\frac{2^5}{3^5} \approx .132$. (c) $\frac{1 \cdot 3^4}{3^5} = \frac{1}{3}$.

5. Note that $\binom{7}{3} = 35$ is the number of ways to select three balls from the urn.

   (a) $\frac{1}{35}$. (b) $\frac{4}{35}$. (c) $\frac{3 \cdot \binom{4}{2}}{35} = \frac{18}{35}$.

   (d) $\frac{\binom{3}{2} \cdot 4}{35} = \frac{12}{35}$. (e) 1.

6. (a) $\frac{3}{10}$. (b) $\frac{1}{10}$. (c) $\frac{6}{10}$.

7. (a) .2. (b) .9. (c) .6.

8. $P(A \cap B) = P(A) + P(B) - P(A \cup B) \geq P(A) + P(B) - 1 = .3$.

9. Here $N = 2,598,960$.

   (a) $624/N \approx .000240$. (b) $54,912/N \approx .0211$.
   (c) $10,200/N \approx .00392$. (d) $123,552/N \approx .0475$.
   (e) $1,098,240/N \approx .423$.

10. (a) The number of such hands is $4 + 36 + 624 + 3744 + 5108 + 10,200 + 54,912 + 123,552 = 198,180$, so probability is $198,180/N \approx .0763$ where $N = 2,598,960$.

    (b) 4/13 of the 1,098,240 pairs found in Exercise 15(d) on page 276 are pairs of Jacks, Queens, Kings or Aces. Adding this to the sum in part (a) yields 536,100. The answer is $\approx .206$.

11. (a) $\frac{1}{2}$. (b) $P(\{(k, l) : k < l\}) = \frac{15}{36}$. (c) $\frac{3}{36} = \frac{1}{12}$.

12. (a) $P(\{(k, l) : \max\{k, l\} = 4\}) = \frac{7}{36}$.
    (b) $P(\{(k, l) : \min\{k, l\} = 4\}) = \frac{5}{36}$.
    (c) $P(\{(k, l) : k \cdot l = 4\}) = \frac{3}{36}$.

13. We have $P(E_1 \cup E_2 \cup E_3) = P(E_1 \cup E_2) + P(E_3) - P((E_1 \cup E_2) \cap E_3)$. Now $P(E_1 \cup E_2) = P(E_1) + P(E_2) - P(E_1 \cap E_2)$ and $P((E_1 \cup E_2) \cap E_3) = P((E_1 \cap E_3) \cup (E_2 \cap E_3)) = P(E_1 \cap E_3) + P(E_2 \cap E_3) - P(E_1 \cap E_3 \cap E_2 \cap E_3)$. Substitute. Alternatively, use $E_1 \cup E_2 \cup E_3 = (E_1 \setminus E_2) \cup (E_2 \setminus E_3) \cup (E_3 \setminus E_1) \cup (E_1 \cap E_2 \cap E_3)$.

14. F is a disjoint union of E and $F \setminus E$ and so $P(F) = P(E) + P(F \setminus E) \geq P(E)$.

15. (a) $\frac{1}{64}$.   (b) $\frac{6}{64}$.   (c) $\frac{15}{64}$.   (d) $\frac{20}{64}$.   (e) $\frac{22}{64}$.

16. $1 - P(\text{tossed} \leq 3 \text{ times}) = 1 - \{\frac{1}{2} + \frac{1}{4} + \frac{1}{8}\} = \frac{1}{8}$.

17. Let Ω_n be all n-tuples of H's and T's and E_n all n-tuples in Ω_n with an even number of H's. It suffices to show that $|E_n| = 2^{n-1}$, which can be done by induction. Assume true for n. Every n-tuple in E_{n+1} has the form (ω, H) where $\omega \in \Omega_n \setminus E_n$ or (ω, T) where $\omega \in E_n$. There are 2^{n-1} n-tuples of each type, so E_{n+1} has 2^n elements. This problem is easier using conditional probabilities [§ 5.6].

18. With suggestive notation, $1 - P(W_1 \cup W_2) = 1 - [.5 + .4 - .3] = .4$.

19. (a) If Ω is the set of all 4-element subsets of S, the outcomes are equally likely. If E_2 is the event "exactly 2 are even," then $|E_2| = \binom{4}{2} \cdot \binom{4}{2} = 36$. Since $|\Omega| = \binom{8}{4} = 70$, $P(E_2) = \frac{36}{70} \approx .514$.

     (b) $\frac{1}{70}$.   (c) $\frac{16}{70}$.   (d) $\frac{16}{70}$.   (e) $\frac{1}{70}$.

20. (a) $\frac{1}{2^3}[3 + 1] = \frac{1}{2}$.   (b) $\frac{1}{2^6}[15 + 6 + 1] \approx .344$.

     (c) $\frac{1}{2^9}[84 + 36 + 9 + 1] \approx .254$.

21. (a) The sample space Ω is all triples (k, l, m) where k, l, $m \in \{1, 2, 3\}$, so $|\Omega| = 3^3$. The triples where $k, l, m \in \{2, 3\}$ correspond to no selection of 1. So $P(1 \text{ not selected}) = \frac{2^3}{3^3}$ and answer $= 1 - \frac{8}{27} \approx .704$.

     (b) $1 - \frac{3^4}{4^4} \approx .684$.   (c) $1 - (\frac{n-1}{n})^n$.

     (d) $1 - (.999999)^{1,000,000} \approx .632120$. This is essentially $1 - \frac{1}{e} \approx .632121$, since
$$\lim_{n \to \infty} \left(\frac{n}{n-1}\right)^n = e.$$

22. (a) $1/2$. For each permutation with A first there is another with B first.

     (b) $1/2$, as in (a).

     (c) $25!/26! = 1/26$. Consider AB as a single letter to get the $25!$ permutations in the event.

5.3   Answers

1. 125.

2. (a) $900 - 7 \cdot 8 \cdot 8 = 452$. Note that $7 \cdot 8 \cdot 8 =$ number of numbers in S that use neither 3 nor 7.

     (b) Note that $900 - 8 \cdot 9 \cdot 9 = 252$ numbers have at least one 3. Similarly, 252 numbers have at least one 7. So $252 + 252 - 452 = 52$ have a 3 *and* a 7.

         Alternatively, let S_3 be the numbers in S with no digit that is 3. Similarly for S_7. We seek $900 - |S_3 \cup S_7|$, but

$$|S_3 \cup S_7| = |S_3| + |S_7| - |S_3 \cap S_7| = 8 \cdot 9 \cdot 9 + 8 \cdot 9 \cdot 9 - 7 \cdot 8 \cdot 8 = 848.$$

3. (a) .142.   (b) .09.

(c) .78 since $1000 - |D_7 \cup D_{11}| = 1000 - (142 + 90 - 12) = 780$.

(d) .208 since $|D_7 \oplus D_{11}| = |D_7| + |D_{11}| - 2 \cdot |D_7 \cap D_{11}| = 142 + 90 - 2 \cdot 12 = 208$.

4. (a) $\binom{7+3-1}{3-1} = 36$.

(b) $\binom{4+3-1}{3-1} = 15$. Put \$1000 into each fund first, and then invest the remaining \$4000.

5. There are 466 such numbers in the set, so the probability is .466. Remember that $D_4 \cap D_6 = D_{12}$ not D_{24}. Hence

$$
\begin{aligned}
|D_4 \cup D_5 \cup D_6| &= |D_4| + |D_5| + |D_6| - |D_4 \cap D_5| - |D_4 \cap D_6| \\
&\quad - |D_5 \cap D_6| + |D_4 \cap D_5 \cap D_6| \\
&= 250 + 200 + 166 - 50 - 83 - 33 + 16 = 466.
\end{aligned}
$$

6. Let W_a be the set of words in Σ^5 that do not use the letter a, with similar meanings for W_e and W_i. We need the size of $W_a \cup W_e \cup W_i$. Since $|W_a| = |W_e| = |W_i| = 4^5 = 1024$, $|W_a \cap W_e| = |W_a \cap W_i| = |W_e \cap W_i| = 3^5 = 243$, and $|W_a \cap W_e \cap W_i| = 2^5 = 32$, the Inclusion-Exclusion Principle shows that

$$|W_a \cup W_e \cup W_i| = 3 \cdot 1024 - 3 \cdot 243 + 32 = 2375.$$

Since $|\Sigma^5| = 5^5 = 3125$, $3125 - 2375 = 750$ of the words use all three vowels, and the desired probability is $\frac{750}{3125} = 0.24$.

7. (a) $\binom{12+4-1}{4-1} = 455$.

(b) $\binom{4+4-1}{4-1} = 35$. Put two letters in each box first, and then distribute the remaining four letters.

8. 286, as in Example 8 on page 294.

9. (a) $x^4 + 8x^3y + 24x^2y^2 + 32xy^3 + 16y^4$.

(b) $x^6 - 6x^5y + 15x^4y^2 - 20x^3y^3 + 15x^2y^4 - 6xy^5 + y^6$.

(c) $81x^4 + 108x^3 + 54x^2 + 12x + 1$.

(d) $x^5 + 10x^4 + 40x^3 + 80x^2 + 80x + 32$.

10. (a) Basis: $(a+b)^0 = 1 = \binom{0}{0} \cdot 1 \cdot 1 = \sum_{r=0}^{0} \binom{0}{r} a^r b^{-r}$, since $\binom{0}{0} = \frac{0!}{0! \cdot 0!} = \frac{1}{1 \cdot 1}$.
Inductive step: $(a+b)^n (a+b)$

$$= \sum_{r=0}^{n} \binom{n}{r} a^r b^{n-r} (a+b)$$

$$= \sum_{r=0}^{n} \binom{n}{r} a^{r+1} b^{n-r} + \sum_{r=0}^{n} \binom{n}{r} a^r b^{n-r+1}$$

$$= \sum_{s=1}^{n+1} \binom{n}{s-1} a^s b^{n-(s-1)} + \sum_{r=0}^{n} \binom{n}{r} a^r b^{n-r+1} \quad [\text{ using } s = r+1 \text{ in the first sum}]$$

$$= \binom{n}{n+1-1} a^{n+1} b^{n-n} + \sum_{s=1}^{n} \binom{n}{s-1} a^s b^{n+1-s} + \sum_{r=0}^{n} \binom{n}{r} a^r b^{n+1-r} + \binom{n}{0} a^0 b^{n+1}$$

$$= a^{n+1} b^0 + \sum_{t=1}^{n} \left\{ \binom{n}{t-1} + \binom{n}{t} \right\} a^t b^{n+1-t} + a^0 b^{n+1}$$

$$= a^{n+1} b^0 + \sum_{t=1}^{n} \binom{n+1}{t} a^t b^{n+1-t} + a^0 b^{n+1}$$

[using the relation proved following the statement of the Binomial Theorem]

$$= \sum_{t=0}^{n+1} \binom{n+1}{t} a^t b^{n+1-t}.$$

(b) $\binom{n}{r-1} + \binom{n}{r}$

$$= \frac{n!}{(r-1)!(n-r+1)!} + \frac{n!}{r!(n-r)!}$$

$$= \frac{n!}{r!(n-r+1)!} \cdot [r + (n-r+1)] = \frac{(n+1)}{r!(n-r+1)!} = \binom{n+1}{r}.$$

11. (b) There are $\binom{n}{r}$ subsets of size r for each r, so there are $\sum_{r=0}^{n} \binom{n}{r}$ subsets in all.

(c) If true for n, then

$$\sum_{r=0}^{n+1} \binom{n+1}{r} = 1 + \sum_{r=1}^{n} \binom{n+1}{r} + 1 = 1 + \sum_{r=1}^{n} \binom{n}{r-1} + \sum_{r=1}^{n} \binom{n}{r} + 1$$

$$= \sum_{r=1}^{n+1} \binom{n}{r-1} + \sum_{r=0}^{n} \binom{n}{r} = 2 \sum_{r=0}^{n} \binom{n}{r} = 2 \cdot 2^n = 2^{n+1}.$$

12. Set $a = 2$ and $b = 1$ in the Binomial Theorem.

13. (a) $\sum_{k=3}^{5} \binom{k}{3} = \binom{3}{3} + \binom{4}{3} + \binom{5}{3} = 15 = \binom{6}{4}$.

(b) Let $p(n)$ be "$\displaystyle\sum_{k=m}^{n} \binom{k}{m} = \binom{n+1}{m+1}$" for $n \geq m$. Check that $p(m)$ is true. Assume that $p(n)$ is true for some $n \geq m$. Then

$$
\begin{aligned}
\sum_{k=m}^{n+1} \binom{k}{m} &= \left[\sum_{k=m}^{n} \binom{k}{m} \right] + \binom{n+1}{m} \\
&= \binom{n+1}{m+1} + \binom{n+1}{m} \qquad \text{[by the inductive assumption]} \\
&= \binom{n+2}{m+1} \qquad \text{[by Exercise 10(b)].}
\end{aligned}
$$

(c) The set $\mathcal{A}$ of $(m+1)$-element subsets of $\{1, 2, \ldots, n+1\}$ is the disjoint union $\displaystyle\bigcup_{k=m}^{n} \mathcal{A}_k$, where $\mathcal{A}_k$ is the collection of $(m+1)$-element subsets whose largest element is $k+1$. A set in $\mathcal{A}_k$ is an m-element subset of $\{1, 2, \ldots, k\}$ with $k+1$ added to it, so $\displaystyle |\mathcal{A}| = \sum_{k=m}^{n} \binom{k}{m}$.

14. (a)

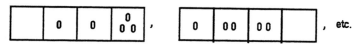

(b) 0 1 0 1 0 1 0 0, etc.

15. (a) Put 8 in one of the 3 boxes, then distribute the remaining 6 in three boxes. Answer is $3 \cdot \binom{8}{2} = 84$ ways.

(b) $\binom{16}{2} - 3 \cdot \binom{8}{2} = 36$.

(c) Since $1 + 9 + 9 < 20$, each digit is at least 2. Then we have $(d_1 - 2) + (d_2 - 2) + (d_3 - 2) = 20 - 6 = 14$ with $2 \leq d_i \leq 9$ for $i = 1, 2, 3$. By part (b) there are 36 numbers. Another way to get this number is to hunt for a pattern: 299; 398, 389; 497, 488, 479; 596, 587, 578, 569; .... Looks like $1 + 2 + 3 + \cdots + 8 = \binom{9}{2} = 36$.

16. The formula adds $\left| \bigcap_{i \in I} A_i \right|$ if $|I| + 1$ is even, i.e., if I has an odd number of elements, and subtracts $\left| \bigcap_{i \in I} A_i \right|$ if $|I|$ is even. Thus it produces the result of the Inclusion-Exclusion Principle on page 287.

The formula can be proved by induction on n, using the observation that

$$
\mathcal{P}_+(n+1) = \mathcal{P}_+(n) \cup \{I \cup \{n+1\} : I \in \mathcal{P}_+(n)\} \cup \{n+1\}.
$$

17. (a) Think of putting 9 objects in 4 boxes, starting with 1 object in the first box. $\binom{8+4-1}{4-1} = 165$.

(b) Now start with 1 object in each box; $\binom{5+4-1}{4-1} = 56$.

18. (a) $1/6!$.

   (b) 0. If five passengers return to their same seats, the sixth passenger must also.

   (c) This is very like Example 3. Let A_1 be the set of assignments for which the first passenger gets his or her own seat back, with similar meanings for $A_2, \ldots, A_6$. Then $|A_1| = 5!$, $|A_1 \cap A_2| = 4!$, etc., and by the Inclusion-Exclusion formula, $|A_1 \cup \cdots \cup A_6| = 6 \cdot 5! - \binom{6}{2} \cdot 4! + \binom{6}{3} \cdot 3! - \binom{6}{2} \cdot 2! + \binom{6}{1} \cdot 1! - 1 = 6![1 - \frac{1}{2!} + \frac{1}{3!} - \frac{1}{4!} + \frac{1}{5!} - \frac{1}{6!}]$. So the desired probability is $1 - \frac{1}{2!} + \frac{1}{3!} - \frac{1}{4!} + \frac{1}{5!} - \frac{1}{6!} \approx .632$.

19. Note that there are no such sets unless $2l \le p+1$. For each set make a sequence of length p with a 0 for each integer not in the set and a 1 for each integer in it. The 1's create $l+1$ boxes. To avoid consecutive integers, we need a 0 in each box except the two at the ends. To count such sequences, we put $l-1$ 0's in the middle boxes and count the number of ways of placing the remaining $p-l-(l-1)$ 0's in the $l+1$ boxes. The answer is $\binom{p-l-(l-1)+(l+1)-1}{(l+1)-1} = \binom{p-l+1}{l}$.

20. (a) This follows from the previous exercise.

   (b) $1 - \frac{\binom{39}{6}}{\binom{44}{6}} \approx .538$.

5.4 Answers

1. (a) $\dfrac{15!}{3!4!5!3!}$.

   (b) $\dbinom{15}{3}\dbinom{15}{4}\dbinom{15}{5}$.

2. Both numbers are the same in each case. Write the binomial and multinomial coefficients in terms of factorials and compare.

3. (a) As in Example 8, count ordered partitions $\{A, B, C, D\}$ where $|A| = 5$, $|B| = 3$, $|C| = 2$ and $|D| = 3$. Answer $= \frac{13!}{5! \cdot 3! \cdot 2! \cdot 3!} = 720,720$.

   (b) Count ordered partitions where $|A| = 4$ and $|B| = |C| = |D| = 3$, but note that partitions $\{A, B, C, D\}$ and $\{A, C, B, D\}$ are equivalent. Answer $= \frac{1}{2} \cdot \frac{13!}{4! \cdot 3! \cdot 3! \cdot 3!} = 600,600$.

   (c) Count ordered partitions where $|A| = |B| = |C| = 3$ and $|D| = 4$, but note that permutations of A, B and C give equivalent sets of committees. Answer $= \frac{1}{6} \cdot \frac{13!}{3! \cdot 3! \cdot 3! \cdot 4!} = 200,200$.

4. $9!/(3! \cdot 2! \cdot 4!) = 1260$.

5. (a) $3^{10} = 59,049$.   (b) $\binom{10}{5} = 252$.   (c) $\binom{10}{3} = 120$.

   (d) $\binom{10}{3} \cdot 2^7 = 15,360$.   (e) $\frac{10!}{3! \cdot 4! \cdot 3!} = 4200$.

   (f) $3^{10} - 3 \cdot 2^{10} + 3 \cdot 1 - 1 \cdot 0 = 55,980$, using the Inclusion-Exclusion Principle on page 287 on the sets of sequences with no 0's, no 1's and no 2's.

6. (a) $7! = 5040.$ (b) $\frac{10!}{2! \cdot 2!} = 907{,}200.$

   (c) $\frac{11!}{4! \cdot 4! \cdot 2!} = 34{,}650.$ (d) $\frac{4!}{2!} = 12.$

7. (a) $625.$ (b) $5^4 - 5 \cdot 4 \cdot 3 \cdot 2 = 505.$ (c) $5^3 \cdot 2 = 250.$

   (d) $(3/5) \cdot 505 = 303.$ Or $3 \cdot 5^3 - 3 \cdot 4 \cdot 3 \cdot 2 = 303.$

8. These are like Example 3(c). For instance, there are $3! \cdot 6!/(4! \cdot 2!) = 90$ words of type 4—2—0, because there are $3!$ ways to choose the letters with 4, 2 and 0 occurrences, but there are $3 \cdot 6!/(3! \cdot 3!) = 60$ words of type 3—3—0, because there are 3 ways to choose which letter does not occur.

9. There are $\frac{1}{2}\binom{2n}{n}$ unordered such partitions and $\binom{2n}{n}$ ordered partitions.

10. The function $\chi_A + \chi_B$ has value 2 on the set $A \cap B$ and value 1 on the set $A \oplus B$. Similarly for $\chi_C + \chi_D$, so $A \cap B = C \cap D$ and $A \oplus B = C \oplus D$. Hence $|A| + |B| = |A \oplus B| + 2|A \cap B| = |C \oplus D| + 2|C \cap D| = |C| + |D|.$

11. (a) $10 \cdot \binom{8}{2} \cdot \binom{5}{2} \cdot \binom{2}{2} = 2800.$ Just choose a third member of their team and then choose 3 teams from the remaining 9 contestants.

   (b) $10/\binom{11}{2} = 2/11 \approx .18.$

12. $\dfrac{16!}{2^8 \cdot 8!} = 15 \cdot 13 \cdot 11 \cdot 9 \cdot 7 \cdot 5 \cdot 3 \cdot 1 = 2{,}027{,}025.$

13. Fifteen. Just count. We know no clever trick, other than breaking them up into types 4, 3—1, 2—2, 2—1—1, and 1—1—1—1. There are 1, 4, 3, 6 and 1 partitions of these respective types.

   This solves the problem because there is a one-to-one correspondence between equivalence relations and partitions; see Theorem 1 on page 171.

14. $1/1680.$ This is N O N S E N S E revisited.

15. (a) $\left(\begin{smallmatrix} & 9 & \\ 3 & 2 & 4 \end{smallmatrix}\right) = \frac{9!}{3! \cdot 2! \cdot 4!} = 1260.$

   (b) Same as (a).

   (c) $\left(\begin{smallmatrix} & 9 & \\ 2 & 2 & 3 & 2 \end{smallmatrix}\right) = \frac{9!}{2! \cdot 2! \cdot 3! \cdot 2!} = 7560.$

   (d) Same as (a), or $\left(\begin{smallmatrix} & 9 & \\ 0 & 2 & 3 & 4 \end{smallmatrix}\right).$

   (e) $\left(\begin{smallmatrix} & 9 & \\ 0 & 2 & 3 & 4 \end{smallmatrix}\right) \cdot 2^2 \cdot 3^3 \cdot 4^4 = 34{,}836{,}480.$

5.5   Answers

1. As suggested in the book's answer: by Example 1(b) with $p = 10$ two of the integers, say m and n, are congruent mod 10. Thus $m \bmod 10 = n \bmod 10$, and this common value is the 1's digit of m and n.

   Alternatively, apply the Pigeon-Hole Principle to the partition $\{A_0, \ldots, A_9\}$ of the set S of eleven integers, where $A_i = \{n \in S : n\text{'s last digit is } i\}.$

2. (a) By the Pigeon-Hole Principle, there are at least $50/4 = 12.5$ marbles of some color, so there are at least 13 of that color.

(b) Use the Pigeon-Hole Principle with the remaining 42 marbles and 3 colors.

3. Here $|S| = 73$ and $73/8 > 9$, so some box has more than 9 marbles.

4. (a) For each ordered pair (a, b) in B let $f(a, b) = a + b$. There are only 11 possible values of $f(a, b)$, namely $2, 3, \ldots, 12$. Apply the second version of the Pigeon-Hole Principle on page 310.

(b) At most 11 times; see part (a).

5. For each 4-element subset B of A, let $f(B)$ be the sum of the numbers in B. Then $f(B) \geq 1 + 2 + 3 + 4 = 10$, and $f(B) \leq 50 + 49 + 48 + 47 = 194$. There are thus only 185 possible values of $f(B)$. Since A has $\binom{10}{4} = 210$ subsets B, at least two of them must have the same sum $f(B)$ by the second version of the Pigeon-Hole Principle on page 310.

6. For each nonempty subset B of S let $f(B)$ be the element of $\mathbb{Z}(6)$ that is congruent to the sum of the numbers in B. Since S has $2^3 - 1 = 7$ nonempty subsets and $f(B)$ takes at most six values, at least two nonempty subsets B of S have the same sum modulo 6, by the second version of the Pigeon-Hole Principle.

7. For each 2-element subset T of A, let $f(T)$ be the sum of the two elements. Then f maps the 300 2-element subsets of A into $\{3, 4, 5, \ldots, 299\}$.

8. (a) There is no such sequence. This shows that the number $n^2 + 1$ in Example 5 cannot be replaced by n^2; here $n = 4$.

(b) Example 5 guarantees that there is at least one example. One such is 17, 13, 9, 5, 1. All contain 17.

(c) 2, 3, 7, 9, 15 is one example. 17, 16, 13, 11, 9, 4, 1 is an example of length 7.

9. The repeating blocks are various permutations of 142857.

10. If $1 \leq k \leq n$ and if n nonnegative numbers have sum m, then there must be k of them with sum at least km/n. One way to show this is the first approach in Example 6(b).

An alternative is a proof by induction on k, as in the third approach to that example. Assume that $a_1 \geq a_2 \geq \cdots \geq a_n$ and let $s = a_1 + \cdots + a_k$ for the inductive step. Then

$$m - s = a_{k+1} + \cdots + a_n \leq (n - k)a_{k+1}$$

and hence $a_{k+1} \geq (m-s)/(n-k)$. The inductive assumption is that $s \geq km/n$. Thus $a_1 + \cdots + a_k + a_{k+1}$

$$
\begin{aligned}
&= \; s + a_{k+1} \geq s + \frac{m-s}{n-k} = s\left[1 - \frac{1}{n-k}\right] + \frac{m}{n-k} \\
&\geq \; \frac{km}{n}\left[1 - \frac{1}{n-k}\right] + \frac{m}{n-k} \qquad \left[\text{ since } 1 > \frac{1}{n-k} \text{ for } k < n\right] \\
&= \; \frac{km}{n} + \frac{m - km/n}{n-k} = \frac{km}{n} + \frac{m}{n} = (k+1)\frac{m}{n}.
\end{aligned}
$$

11. (a) Look at the six blocks

$$(n_1, n_2, n_3, n_4), \;\; (n_5, n_6, n_7, n_8), \; \ldots, \; (n_{21}, n_{22}, n_{23}, n_{24}).$$

    (b) Use Example 2(b) on page 204.

    (c) Look at the 8 blocks $(n_1, n_2, n_3), (n_4, n_5, n_6), \ldots, (n_{22}, n_{23}, n_{24})$. By part (b), at least one block has sum at least $300/8 = 37.5$.

    (d) Look at the five blocks

$$(n_1, \ldots, n_5), \;\; (n_6, \ldots, n_{10}), \;\; (n_{11}, \ldots, n_{15}), \;\; (n_{16}, \ldots, n_{20}), \;\; (n_{21}, \ldots, n_{24}).$$

    Note that the last block has only 4 members. If some block has sum greater than $300/5$ we are done. Otherwise, all have sum exactly 60, and adjoining an element to the last block gives sum at least 61.

12. (a) The average of all such sums is $18.5 \cdot 4 = 74$.

    (b) As in Example 7(b) on page 315, group the 36 sectors into 9 disjoint consecutive blocks of 4. If all blocks sum to exactly 74, shift clockwise one sector and get new sums.

    (c) The average of all such sums is $18.5 \cdot 5 = 92.5$.

    (d) Ignore the sector numbered 1 and group the other 35 sectors into 7 disjoint consecutive blocks of 5. Since $\frac{666-1}{7} = 95$, some block has sum at least 95.

13. If $0 \in \text{Im}(f)$, then n_1, $n_1 + n_2$ or $n_1 + n_2 + n_3$ is divisible by 3. Otherwise f is not one-to-one and there are three cases:
    If $n_1 \equiv n_1 + n_2 \pmod 3$, then $n_2 \equiv 0 \pmod 3$ and n_2 is divisible by 3.
    Similarly, if $n_1 \equiv n_1 + n_2 + n_3 \pmod 3$, then $n_2 + n_3$ is divisible by 3.
    And if $n_1 + n_2 \equiv n_1 + n_2 + n_3 \pmod 3$, then n_3 is divisible by 3.

14. There are $\binom{15}{5} = 3003$ such committees in all.

    (a) Since $\binom{6}{2} \cdot \binom{9}{3} = 1260$, the probability is $\frac{1260}{3003} \approx .420$.

    (b) Since $\binom{15}{5} - \binom{9}{5} - \binom{6}{5} = 2871$, the probability is $\frac{2871}{3003} \approx .956$.

    (c) Since $\binom{9}{5} + \binom{6}{5} = 132$, the probability is $\frac{132}{3003} \approx .044$.

15. (a) $8^6 = 262,144$.

(b) Let A be the set of numbers with no 3's and B be the set with no 5's. We want $|A^c \cap B^c| = |(A \cup B)^c|$. Since $|A| = |B| = 7^6$ and $|A \cap B| = 6^6$, $|A \cup B| = 2 \cdot 7^6 - 6^6$ and the answer is $8^6 - (2 \cdot 7^6 - 6^6) = 73,502$.

(c) $8!/2! = 20,160$. 　　　　(d) $6!/(1! \cdot 2! \cdot 3!) = 60$.

16. $(4+1) \cdot (1+1) \cdot (3+1) = 40$.

17. (a) We show that S must contain both members of some pair $(2k - 1, 2k)$. Partition $\{1, 2, \ldots, 2n\}$ into the n subsets $\{1,2\}, \{3,4\}, \ldots, \{2n-1, 2n\}$. Since $|S| = n + 1$, some subset $\{2k - 1, 2k\}$ contains 2 members of S by the Pigeon-Hole Principle. The numbers $2k - 1$ and $2k$ are relatively prime.

(b) For each $m \in S$, write $m = 2^k \cdot l$ where l is odd and let $f(m) = l$. See Exercise 21 on page 200. Then $f: S \to \{1, 3, 5, \ldots, 2n-1\}$. By the second version of the Pigeon-Hole Principle on page 310, there are distinct m and m' in S with $m = 2^k \cdot n$ and $m' = 2^{k'} \cdot n$ for some odd n. Say $k > k'$. Then $m = 2^{k-k'} \cdot m'$, so m' divides m.

(c) Let $S = \{2, 4, 6, \ldots, 2n\}$.

(d) Let $S = \{n + 1, n + 2, \ldots, 2n\}$.

18. (a) Let $B = \{p - n : n \in A\}$. Then $|A \cap B| = |A| + |B| - |A \cup B| \geq |A| + |B| - (p + 1) > 2[(p/2) + 1] - (p + 1) = 1$. Hence $|A \cap B| \geq 2$ and there are distinct $m, n \in A$ such that $p - m, p - n \in A$. If $m \neq p - m$, use m and $p - m$. If $m = p - m$, use n and $p - n$.

(b) and (c) One example is $\{0, 1, 2, 3\}$.

19. (a) By the remark at the end of the proof of the Generalized Pigeon-Hole Principle on page 315, the average size is $2 \cdot 21/7 = 6$.

(b) One way is to number the students 0 to 20 and group them as follows: $\{0, 1, 2, 3, 4, 5\}$, $\{6, 7, 8, 9, 10, 11\}$, $\{12, 13, 14, 15, 16, 17\}$, $\{18, 19, 20, 0, 1, 2\}$, $\{3, 4, 5, 6, 7, 8\}$, $\{9, 10, 11, 12, 13, 14\}$, $\{15, 16, 17, 18, 19, 20\}$.

20. (a) The five vowels partition the set of consonants into six strings of consecutive consonants. Since there are 21 consonants, at least one string must have 4 or more consonants.

(b) One such list is $b\,c\,d\,f\,a\,g\,h\,j\,k\,e\,l\,m\,n\,p\,i\,q\,r\,s\,t\,o\,v\,w\,x\,y\,u\,z$.

(c) Now the five vowels partition the set of consonants into *five* strings of consecutive consonants and so at least one string must have 5 or more consonants.

5.6   Answers

1. (a) $\dfrac{\binom{3}{2}}{\binom{11}{2}} = \dfrac{3}{55}$.   (b) $\dfrac{\binom{8}{2}}{\binom{11}{2}} = \dfrac{28}{55}$.   (c) $\dfrac{3 \cdot 8}{\binom{11}{2}} = \dfrac{24}{55}$.

2. (a) $\dfrac{9}{121}$.   (b) $\dfrac{64}{121}$.   (c) $\dfrac{48}{121}$.

   With replacement, it's easier to get two marbles of the same color.

3. (a) $P(S_o) = P(L_o) = P(E) = \frac{1}{2}$ and $P(S_o \cap L_o) = P(S_o \cap E) = P(L_o \cap E) = \frac{1}{4}$.

   (b) $P(S_o | E \cap L_o) = 1 \neq P(S_o)$.

4. See answer to Exercise 5.

5. $\{S, L\}$ are dependent since $P(S \cap L) = \frac{6}{36}$ while $P(S) \cdot P(L) = \frac{15}{36} \cdot \frac{15}{36}$.

   $\{S, E\}$ are dependent since $P(S \cap E) = \frac{3}{36}$ while $P(S) \cdot P(E) = \frac{15}{36} \cdot \frac{6}{36}$.

   $\{L, E\}$ are dependent since $P(L|E) = 0 \neq P(L)$. Similarly for $\{L, G\}$.

6. (a) $\dfrac{P(\text{red} \geq 5 \text{ and sum } \geq 9)}{P(\text{sum } = 9)} = \dfrac{1}{2}$.

   (b) $\dfrac{P(\text{red} \geq 5 \text{ and sum } \geq 9)}{P(\text{sum } \geq 9)} = \dfrac{7}{10}$.

7. No. $P(B|A) = \frac{1}{2}$ while $P(B) = \dfrac{\binom{4}{2}}{2^4} = \dfrac{3}{8}$.

8. (a) $\frac{1}{2}$.   (b) $\frac{8}{11}$.

9. (a) .25.   (b) .7.

   (c) No, $P(A|B) = .25 \neq P(A)$.

   (d) No, $P(A^c \cap B) = .3 \neq P(A^c) \cdot P(B) = .28$.

10. (a) $P(A|B) = P(A) = .4$.

    (b) $P(A \cup B) = P(A) + P(B) - P(A \cap B) = .4 + .6 - .24 = .76$.

    (c) $P(B) - P(A \cap B) = .6 - .24 = .36$.

11. (a) $\frac{4}{52} \cdot \frac{3}{51} \cdot \frac{2}{50} \approx .00018$.   (b) $\frac{4}{52} \cdot \frac{4}{51} \cdot \frac{4}{50} \approx .00048$.

    (c) $1 - \frac{48}{52} \cdot \frac{47}{51} \cdot \frac{46}{50} \approx .217$.

12. Half of the 5108 flushes involve red cards only. There are $\binom{26}{5} = 65,780$ five card hands with all cards red. So the answer is $\frac{2554}{65,780} \approx .0388$.

13. (a) $P(B) = \frac{1}{3} \cdot \frac{2}{3} + \frac{1}{3} \cdot \frac{2}{5} + \frac{1}{3} \cdot \frac{1}{2} = \frac{47}{90}$.

    (b) $P(U_1|B) = \dfrac{\frac{1}{3} \cdot \frac{2}{3}}{P(B)} = \frac{20}{47}$. $P(U_2|B) = \dfrac{\frac{1}{3} \cdot \frac{2}{5}}{P(B)} = \frac{12}{47}$. $P(U_3|B) = \dfrac{\frac{1}{3} \cdot \frac{1}{2}}{P(B)} = \frac{15}{47}$.

    (c) $P(B \cap U_1) = \frac{1}{3} \cdot \frac{2}{3} = \frac{2}{9}$.

14. (a) $0 + \frac{1}{3} \cdot \frac{\binom{3}{2}}{\binom{5}{2}} + \frac{1}{3} \cdot \frac{1}{\binom{4}{2}} = \frac{7}{45}$. (b) $\frac{1}{3} \cdot \frac{1}{\binom{3}{2}} + \frac{1}{3} \cdot \frac{1}{\binom{5}{2}} + \frac{1}{3} \cdot \frac{1}{\binom{4}{2}} = \frac{1}{5}$.

15. (a) $\frac{5}{9}$. (b) 0.

16. (a) $P(\text{all white}) = \frac{1}{3} \cdot \frac{3}{5} \cdot \frac{2}{4} = \frac{1}{10}$; $P(\text{all black}) = \frac{2}{3} \cdot \frac{2}{5} \cdot \frac{2}{4} = \frac{2}{15}$.

17. (a) $P(C) = P(E) \cdot P(C|E) + P(F) \cdot P(C|F) + P(G) \cdot P(C|G) = .043$.
  (b) $P(E|C) = \frac{10}{43} \approx .23$, $P(F|C) = \frac{21}{43} \approx .49$, $P(G|C) = \frac{12}{43} \approx .28$.

18. (a) $\frac{3}{4}$. (b) $\frac{2}{3}$. (c) $\frac{5}{8}$.

19. (a) $P(D) = P(N^c \cap D) + P(N \cap D) = .0041$, so $P(N^c|D) = \frac{P(N^c \cap D)}{P(D)} = \frac{.004}{.0041} \approx .9756$.

  (b) Since $P(N^c) = .044$, $P(N) = .956$, so $P(N \cap D^c) = P(N) - P(N \cap D) = .9559$. Hence $P((N^c \cap D) \cup (N \cap D^c)) = .004 + .9559 = .9599$. This is the probability that the test confirms the subject's condition.

  (c) $P(D|N^c) = \frac{P(D \cap N^c)}{P(N^c)} = \frac{.004}{.044} \approx .091$. Thus the probability of having the disease, given a positive test, is less than .10. The following table may help clarify the situation.

	D [diseased]	D^c [not diseased]
N^c [tests positive]	.004	.04
N [tests negative]	.0001	.9559

20. $P(A \cap B^c) = P(A) - P(A \cap B) = P(A) - P(A) \cdot P(B) = P(A) \cdot [1 - P(B)] = P(A) \cdot P(B^c)$. Similarly $P(A^c \cap B) = P(A^c) \cdot P(B)$ and $P(A^c \cap B^c) = P(A^c) \cdot P(B^c)$.

21. (a) $1 - (1 - q)^n$. We are assuming that the failures of the components are independent.
  (b) $1 - (.99)^{100} \approx .634$. This is close to $1 - \frac{1}{e} \approx .632$ because $\lim_n (1 - \frac{1}{n})^n = \frac{1}{e}$.
  (c) $1 - (.999)^{100} \approx .0952$. (d) $1 - (.9)^{100} \approx .99997$.

22. $P(A|B) > P(A) \Longleftrightarrow P(A \cap B) > P(A) \cdot P(B) \Longleftrightarrow P(B|A) > P(B)$.

23. (a) $\frac{\binom{18}{5}}{\binom{20}{5}} = \frac{15 \cdot 14}{20 \cdot 19} = \frac{21}{38} \approx .55$. (b) $\frac{\binom{18}{10}}{\binom{20}{10}} = \frac{9}{38} \approx .24$.

24. Since $P(A \cap B) = P(A) + P(B) - P(A \cup B) = \frac{4}{3} - P(A \cup B) \geq \frac{4}{3} - 1 = \frac{1}{3}$, we have $P(A|B) = \frac{P(A \cap B)}{P(B)} = \frac{3}{2} \cdot P(A \cap B) \geq \frac{3}{2} \cdot \frac{1}{3} = \frac{1}{2}$.

25. No. For example, toss a fair coin three times and let A_k = "kth toss is a head." Then A_1, A_2, A_3 are independent, but $A_1 \cap A_2$ and $A_1 \cap A_3$ are not. Indeed

$$P(A_1 \cap A_3 | A_1 \cap A_2) = \frac{1}{2} \neq \frac{1}{4} = P(A_1 \cap A_3).$$

26. Use induction on n. Given events A_1, $A_2, \ldots, A_{n+1}$, apply the induction hypothesis to $B_1 = A_1 \cap A_2$, $B_2 = A_3, \ldots, B_n = A_{n+1}$. Then
$$P(A_1 \cap A_2 \cap \cdots \cap A_n \cap A_{n+1})$$
$$= P(A_1 \cap A_2) \cdot P(A_3|A_1 \cap A_2) \cdots P(A_{n+1}|A_1 \cap A_2 \cap \cdots \cap A_n)$$
$$= P(A_1) \cdot P(A_2|A_1)P(A_3|A_1 \cap A_2) \cdots P(A_{n+1}|A_1 \cap A_2 \cap \cdots \cap A_n).$$

For $n = 3$, we have

$$P(A_1 \cap A_2 \cap A_3) = P(A_1 \cap A_2) \cdot P(A_3|A_1 \cap A_2) = P(A_1) \cdot P(A_2|A_1) \cdot P(A_3|A_1 \cap A_2).$$

Then for $n = 4$, we get

$$
\begin{aligned}
P(A_1 \cap A_2 \cap A_3 \cap A_4) &= P(A_1 \cap A_2) \cdot P(A_3|A_1 \cap A_2) \cdot P(A_4|A_1 \cap A_2 \cap A_3) \\
&= P(A_1) \cdot P(A_2|A_1) \cdot P(A_3|A_1 \cap A_2) \cdot P(A_4|A_1 \cap A_2 \cap A_3).
\end{aligned}
$$

27. (a) No. If true, then A and B independent and B and A independent would imply that A and A are independent, which generally fails by part (b).

    (b) No. Only if $P(A) = 0$ or $P(A) = 1$, since $P(A \cap A) = P(A) \cdot P(A)$ implies $P(A)^2 = P(A)$.

    (c) Absolutely not, unless $P(A) = 0$ or $P(B) = 0$.

28. (a) $P(B|A) = \frac{P(B \cap A)}{P(A)} > P(A \cap B) = P(B) \cdot \frac{P(A \cap B)}{P(B)} = P(B) \cdot P(A|B) = P(B)$.

    (b) If $P(A) = 1$, then $P(A \cup B) = 1$, so $P(A \cap B) = P(A) + P(B) - P(A \cup B) = P(B)$. Hence $P(A|B) = 1$ automatically and also $P(B|A) = P(B)$.

29. (a) $\dfrac{P^*(E)}{P^*(F)} = \dfrac{P(E|S)}{P(F|S)} = \dfrac{\frac{P(E \cap S)}{P(S)}}{\frac{P(F \cap S)}{P(S)}} = \dfrac{P(E \cap S)}{P(F \cap S)}.$

    (b) Set $F = \Omega$ in part (a).

Chapter 6

This chapter gives the core material on graphs and trees. Chapters 7 and 8 go into more detail and present the algorithms. Some of the terminology has already been introduced in § 3.2.

Section 6.1 treats undirected graphs. Cycles and acyclicity are key ideas. One way to illustrate the truth of Theorem 1 on is to draw a snarly path and cut off side trips with an eraser. It's hard to illustrate the proof of Theorem 2, but a picture can make its contrapositive seem plausible. In earlier editions we made some fuss over graph isomorphism. Our approach now is that isomorphism is merely a precise way of saying "look just alike". The idea of the degree of a vertex is of course basic, independent of any discussion of isomorphism.

Section 6.2 contains a plausible but phony proof of Euler's theorem just after Example 2. It's a good idea to go slowly through a counterexample to the "proof". We get out of trouble by producing an algorithm that constructs an Euler circuit by pasting together simple closed paths. Our version is iterative; although a recursive algorithm seems conceptually simpler, its verification seems to be more complicated. This section also introduces connectedness.

Trees have come up earlier, but § 6.3 gives the first careful discussion of them. Draw a picture to illustrate the ideas in Theorem 1. Emphasize: (1) the theorem is natural and (2) it gives a link between cycles and connectedness, so a test for connectedness gives a test for cycles. Theorems 3 and 4 will be needed later. Most of the trees in computer science are rooted, and hence directed in a coherent way. Section 6.4 introduces basic terminology. Other terms that we do not use but that students may have heard in this connection are **fan-in** for indegree and **fan-out** for out-degree. Essentially every rooted tree that we see is ordered in some natural way, so we can think of order as a way of organizing a typical rooted tree.

Section 6.5 is less intuitive than § 6.2. Contrast the statements of Theorems 1 and 2. Ask students how hard it would be to verify the hypotheses of Theorem 3. [It takes $O(n^2)$ time.] Point out that its proof is nonconstructive.

Gray codes are an important application and our account just scratches the surface. Try to get class members who are familiar with Gray codes from computer science to say a few words about them. [For instance, Gray code hardware is readily available.] Theorem 4 need not be stressed.

Section 6.6 gives three algorithms for finding spanning trees and forests. The first one, which builds one tree at a time, takes no account of weights for edges. It's actually a stripped-down version of PRIM'S algorithm. We have included it because when weights don't matter it's faster than PRIM'S and it shows the idea of PRIM'S algorithm free of distractions. The other two algorithms we give, KRUSKAL'S and PRIM'S, construct minimum weight spanning forests. Exercise 11 provides good motivation for considering them. KRUSKAL'S algorithm requires an initial sorting of the edges by weight. It builds a graph that is always acyclic and light in weight and eventually is as connected as possible. We recommend going through the proof of Theorem 2 with an example. PRIM'S algorithm is easy to follow, since it works like the unweighted algorithm TREE, but its verification is tricky. As with KRUSKAL'S algorithm, a loop invariant is the key. A classroom example can illustrate the invariant.

This section contains detailed time-complexity analyses of all three algorithms. Now is the time to decide how much emphasis you want to place on such analyses. The ones in this section are easy, but if you omit discussing them now, students will find it hard to get interested in or to understand the analyses later on in Chapters 7 and 8.

6.1   Answers

1. (a) stv or suv; length 2.

   (b) $stvwxz$ and 3 others; length 5.

   (c) $uvwy$; length 3.   (d) vw; length 1.

2. (a) stv is one.   (b) $stuvwxyz$ is one.

   (c) $ustuvwyxzy$.   (d) $vustvw$ is one.

   There are no longest paths connecting vertices. For example, one can go from s to v as follows: $suvuvuv\cdots uv$.

3. (a) is true and (b) is false. To see the failure of (b), consider the graph in Figure 6(a).

4. (a) and (b) are both true.

5. (a) and (b) are now both true.

6. (a) 12, 6; 14, 7; 16, 8; 20, 10. In each case, the sum of the degrees is twice the number of edges.

   (b) No. By Theorem 3 the degree sum is even, whereas the sum would be odd if there were an odd number of vertices of odd degree.

7. See Figure 1(c). u and w are vertices of a cycle, and so are w and x. But no cycle uses both u and x.

8. If a cycle contains a loop at v, its entire vertex sequence must be vv, since otherwise v would be repeated in the middle of the cycle. Hence a cycle cannot contain two loops.

9. (a)

e	a	b	c	d	e	f	g	h	k
$\gamma(e)$	$\{w,x\}$	$\{x,u\}$	$\{t,u\}$	$\{t,v\}$	$\{u,v\}$	$\{u,y\}$	$\{v,z\}$	$\{x,y\}$	$\{y,z\}$

(b) $a = \{w,x\}$, $b = \{x,u\}$, $c = \{u,t\}$, $d = \{t,v\}$, $e = \{u,v\}$, $f = \{u,y\}$, $g = \{v,z\}$, $h = \{x,y\}$, $k = \{y,z\}$.

10.

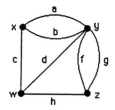

11. (a) $e\,b\,h\,k\,g$ and its reversal $g\,k\,h\,b\,e$.

(b) $b\,c\,d\,g\,k\,h$ and its reversal.

(c) $e\,c\,d$, $b\,h\,f$ and their reversals.

12. (a) 1   (b) (0,1,2,3,1).

(c) There is just the identity isomorphism. The vertices w and u must correspond to themselves, since they are the only vertices of degrees 1 and 4. Then x is the only vertex joined to both w and u, t is the only vertex of degree 2 joined to u, z is the only other vertex of degree 2, etc.

(d) There is just one isomorphism. [Otherwise, going over to H with one and back to G with the inverse of another would give a non-identity isomorphism of G onto itself, contrary to part (c).]

13. (a)

(b) The only such graph is K_4; see Figure 5.

(c) There are none by Theorem 3, since $5 \cdot 3$ is not even.

14. (a)

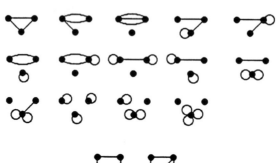

(b)

(c)

15. (a), (c) and (d) are regular, but (b) is not. (a) and (c) have cycles of length 3, but (d) does not. Or count edges. (a) and (c) are isomorphic; the labels show an isomorphism between (a) and (c).

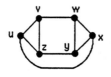 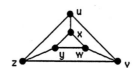

16. The labels show one isomorphism.

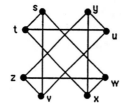 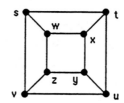

17. (a) $\binom{8}{5} = 56$.

(b) 1 with 1 edge, 6 with 2 edges and $6 \cdot 5 = 30$ with 3 edges, so 37 altogether.

(c) $8 \cdot 7 + 8 \cdot 7 \cdot 6 + 8 \cdot 7 \cdot 6 \cdot 6 = 2{,}408$.

18. (a) By Theorem 3, $42 = 1 \cdot 7 + 2 \cdot 3 + 3 \cdot 7 + 4 \cdot D_4(G)$, so $4 \cdot D_4(G) = 8$, $D_4(G) = 2$ and the total number of vertices is $7 + 3 + 7 + 2 = 19$.

(b) The graph would have $19 + 6 = 25$ vertices.

19. (a)   (b)

(c) No such graph. Use Theorem 3 [consider Exercise 6(b)].

(d)   (e)

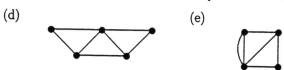

(f) No such graph. Use Theorem 3.

(g) K_4.   (h) K_5.

20. (a) The identity mappings on $V(G)$ and $E(G)$ define an isomorphism, so $G \simeq G$ and $\simeq$ is reflexive. If α and β define an isomorphism of G onto H, then $\alpha^{\leftarrow}$ and $\beta^{\leftarrow}$ define an isomorphism of H onto G. Thus $\simeq$ is symmetric.

Finally $\simeq$ is transitive as follows. The inverses of $\alpha_2 \circ \alpha_1$ and $\beta_2 \circ \beta_1$ are $\alpha_1^{\leftarrow} \circ \alpha_2^{\leftarrow}$ and $\beta_1^{\leftarrow} \circ \beta_2^{\leftarrow}$, respectively, so both $\alpha_2 \circ \alpha_1$ and $\beta_2 \circ \beta_1$ are one-to-one correspondences. Say G, H and K are described by γ_1, γ_2 and γ_3. Suppose $e \in E(G)$ and $\gamma_1(e) = \{u, v\}$. Then, since α_1 and β_1 describe an isomorphism, $\gamma_2(\beta_1(e)) = \{\alpha_1(u), \alpha_1(v)\}$. Since α_2 and β_2 describe an isomorphism, whenever $f \in E(H)$ and $\gamma_2(f) = \{w, x\}$ then $\gamma_3(\beta_2(f)) = \{\alpha_2(w), \alpha_2(x)\}$. In particular, $\gamma_3(\beta_2(\beta_1(e))) = \{\alpha_2(\alpha_1(u)), \alpha_2(\alpha_1(v))\}$. This shows that $\gamma_3((\beta_2 \circ \beta_1)(e)) = \{(\alpha_2 \circ \alpha_1)(u), (\alpha_2 \circ \alpha_1)(v)\}$ whenever $\gamma_1(e) = \{u, v\}$, i.e., $\alpha_2 \circ \alpha_1$ and $\beta_2 \circ \beta_1$ describe an isomorphism.

(b) There are 2 classes; see Example 4.

21. Assume no loops or parallel edges. Consider a longest path $v_1 \cdots v_m$ with distinct vertices. There is another edge at v_m. Adjoin it to the path to get a closed path and use Proposition 1.

22. If $n = 1$ the graph has at least one loop, so it contains a cycle. Suppose inductively that the assertion is true for some $n \in \mathbb{P}$ and consider a graph G with $n + 1$ vertices and at least $n + 1$ edges. If every vertex has degree at least 2 the graph contains a cycle by Exercise 21. Otherwise, G has a vertex v of degree 0 or degree 1. In that case, delete v and the edge to it if there is one. What's left has n vertices and at least n edges, so it contains a cycle by the inductive assumption. Hence G itself contains a cycle. The claim follows by induction.

23. Use $|V(G)| = D_0(G) + D_1(G) + D_2(G) + \cdots$ and Theorem 3.

6.2   Answers

1. Only Figure 7(b) has an Euler circuit. To find one, do Exercise 3.

2. (a) One answer is $s\,t\,v\,u\,x\,y\,z\,w\,y\,v\,s$.   (b) No.

3. One solution starts with vertex r and simple closed path $C = r\,s\,v\,u\,r$. Then successive while loops might proceed as follows.

   1. Choose v, construct $v\,y\,z\,w\,v$, obtain new $C = r\,s\,v\,y\,z\,w\,v\,u\,r$.

   2. Choose s, construct $s\,t\,v\,x\,y\,u\,s$, obtain final $C = r\,s\,t\,v\,x\,y\,u\,s\,v\,y\,z\,w\,v\,u\,r$.

   You should find your own solutions, starting perhaps at other vertices.

4. Label the vertices v_1, v_2, v_3, v_4, v_5, say. One solution starts with vertex v_1 and simple closed path $C = v_1\,v_2\,v_3\,v_4\,v_5\,v_1$. Then select any vertex and the construction of the remaining path in $V(G) \setminus C$ is forced [except for direction]. Using vertex v_2, for example, might give $v_2\,v_4\,v_1\,v_3\,v_5\,v_2$ and hence final $C = v_1\,v_2\,v_4\,v_1\,v_3\,v_5\,v_2\,v_3\,v_4\,v_5\,v_1$. Alternatively, one might start with some vertex and a simple closed path of length 3, 4, 6 or 7.

5. You will find that the closed paths all have length 4. After you remove any one of them the remaining edge set will contain no closed paths.

6. No. The edges and corners form a graph with eight vertices, each of degree 3. It has no Euler path. See Figure 5(c) on page 375.

7. (a) $v_3\,v_1\,v_2\,v_3\,v_6\,v_2\,v_4\,v_6\,v_5\,v_1\,v_4\,v_5\,v_3\,v_4$ is one.

   (b) There is no Euler circuit since v_3 and v_4 have odd degree.

8. There is no Euler path or circuit since four vertices have odd degree.

9. (a) Add an edge e to G to get G^* with all vertices of even degree. Run EulerCircuit(G^*) to get C^*, then remove e from C^*.

   Alternatively, choose v initially to have odd degree, and use Closed-Path [with a modified input] to yield a starting path C from v that cannot be extended. The while loop remains the same.

   (b) It returns an Euler circuit for one of the connected components of G.

10. Here is one possible solution. Put in a new edge h joining u and v. Start with $C = e\,c\,b$, leaving a graph whose edges form the closed path $a\,f\,g\,d\,h$. Attach these paths at v to get $e\,c\,b\,a\,f\,g\,d\,h$ and leave off h.

   Here's another. Start with the path $b\,c\,f\,d$ from v that cannot be extended. Attach to it the closed paths $a\,e$ and g, to get $a\,e\,b\,c\,f\,g\,d$.

11. $\{0,1\}^3$ consists of 3-tuples of 0's and 1's, which we may view as binary strings of length 3. The graph is then

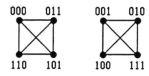

(a) 2.

(b) All eight vertices have degree 3.

(c) No.

12. View $\{0,1\}^3$ as binary strings of length 3. The graph is then:

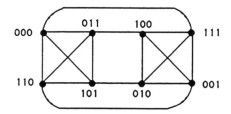

(a) There is one component.

(b) All eight vertices have degree 4.

(c) Yes, by Euler's theorem.

13. (a) Join the odd-degree vertices in pairs, with k new edges. The new graph has an Euler circuit, by Theorem 2. The new edges do not appear next to each other in the circuit and they partition the circuit into k simple paths of G.

(b) One solution is:

(c) Imitate the proof. That is, add edges $\{v_2, v_3\}$ and $\{v_5, v_6\}$, say, create an Euler circuit, and then remove the two new edges. Then you will obtain $v_3\,v_1\,v_2\,v_7\,v_3\,v_4\,v_5\,v_7\,v_6\,v_1\,v_5$ and $v_6\,v_4\,v_2$, say.

14. The ones with n odd.

15. (a) No such walk is possible. Create a graph as follows. Put a vertex in each room and one vertex outside the house. For each door draw an edge joining the vertices for the regions on its two sides. The resulting graph has two vertices of degree 4, three of degree 5 and one of degree 9. Apply the corollary to Theorem 1.

(b) An Euler path starting outside is possible. In this case the graph has four vertices of degree 4, one of degree 5 and one of degree 9.

6.3   Answers

1.

2. (a) T_4.   (b) T_4.   (c) T_5.   (d) T_9.   (e) T_9.
   (f) T_5.   (g) T_4.   (h) T_8.   (i) T_3.   (j) T_7.

3. (a) 4.   (b) $4 \cdot 4 = 16$.

   (c) $4 + 2 \cdot 2 = 8$. Here are their pictures.

   For (d) and (e) the answer is $8 \cdot 8 = 64$. Any spanning tree in (d) or (e) can be viewed as a pair of spanning trees, one for the upper half and one for the lower half of the graph. Each half of the spanning tree is a spanning tree for the graph in (c). Hence there are $8 \cdot 8 = 64$ such pairs.

4. $3 \cdot 8 = 24$. There are 3 ways to delete one of e_2, e_3, e_4. There are 10 ways to delete two of $e_6, e_7, e_8, e_9, e_{10}$, but we can't delete both e_6 and e_7, or both e_9 and e_{10}.

5. All but edges e_1 and e_5.

6. The pictures

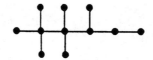

   illustrate the three possible isomorphism types.

7. (a) Since $2n - 2$ is the sum of the degrees of the vertices, we must have $2n - 2 = 4 + 4 + 3 + 2 + 1 \cdot (n - 4)$. Solve for n to get $n = 11$.

   (b) Here is one example:

8. (a) If the tree has n vertices, then it must have $n - 7$ of degree 1. So we must have

$$5 + 5 + 3 + 3 + 3 + 2 + 2 + 1 \cdot (n - 7) = 2n - 2$$

as noted in Exercise 7. Solve for n to get $n = 18$.

(b) Here is an example:

9. (a)

(b) Prove by induction on n. The cases $n = 1, 2, 3$ are easy. Assume that the result is true for some $n \geq 4$. Suppose that $d_1 + \cdots + d_{n+1} = 2(n+1) - 2$. At least one d_k is 1, say $d_{n+1} = 1$. At least one d_k exceeds 1, say d_1. Define $d_1^* = d_1 - 1$ and $d_k^* = d_k$ for $2 \leq k \leq n$. Then $d_1^* + \cdots + d_n^* = 2n - 2$ and by the inductive hypothesis there is a tree with n vertices whose vertices have degrees $d_1^*, \ldots, d_n^*$. Attach a leaf to the vertex of degree d_1^* to obtain a tree with $n + 1$ vertices. The new vertex has degree $1 = d_{n+1}$ and the vertex of degree d_1^* now has degree $d_1^* + 1 = d_1$.

(c) $d_1 = 5$, $d_2 = 3$, $d_3 = 2$, $d_4 = \cdots = d_9 = 1$ and their sum is $16 = 2 \cdot 9 - 2$.

11. (a) Suppose the components have $n_1, n_2, \ldots, n_m$ vertices, so that altogether $n_1 + n_2 + \cdots + n_m = n$. The ith component is a tree, so it has $n_i - 1$ edges, by Theorem 4. The total number of edges is $(n_1 - 1) + (n_2 - 1) + \cdots + (n_m - 1) = n - m$.

(b) A spanning forest for the graph has m components, so it has $n - m$ edges, by part (a). Thus the spanning forest is the whole graph.

12. Use Theorem 2 and note that a spanning tree of the graph will have $n - 1$ edges by Theorem 4.

13. By Lemma 1 to Theorem 4 it must be infinite. Use $\mathbb{Z}$ for the set of vertices; see Figure 3(a) on page 609.

6.4 Answers

---

1. (a) (b) 1. (c) 3.

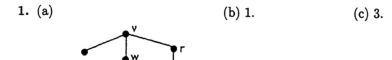

2. Here is one.

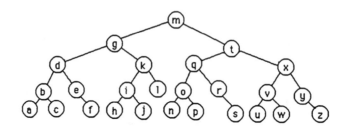

3. (a) Rooted trees in Figures 5(b) and 5(c) have height 2; the one in 5(d) has height 3.

(b) Only the rooted tree in Figure 5(c) is a regular 3-ary tree.

4. People have two parents, whereas vertices in a rooted tree have at most one parent.

5. (a)

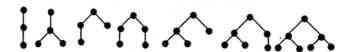

(b) The fifth and seventh.   (c) The seventh.

(d) 21. There are 4 corresponding to the first type of tree in (a), namely

Similarly, there are 2, 4, 4, 2, 4 and 1 of each of the other types of trees in (a).

6. (a)

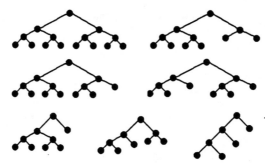

(b) 21; 1, 2, 4, 4, 2, 4 and 4 of each of the types of trees in (a).

7. (a)

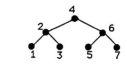

(b)

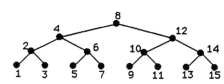

(c) The possibilities are

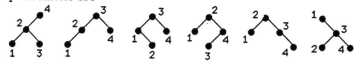

(d) The possible trees are

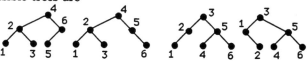

8.

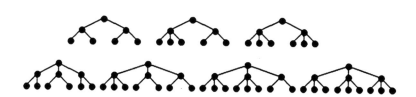

9. (a)

(b) All do. See Example 5.

10. (a) 2^h. (b) $2^{h+1} - 1$.

11. From Example 5, we have $(m-1)p = m^h - 1$, so $(m-1)p + 1 = m^h = t$.

12. Examples can be found by looking at federal laws, handbooks of tables, parts catalogs, etc.

13. There are 2^k words of length k.

14. Use the last tree in our answer to Exercise 9(a) and label the vertices λ, a, b, c, aa, ab, ac, ba, etc.

15. (a) Move either Lyon's or Ross's records to the Rose node and delete the empty leaf created.

(b) There are three possible good choices, leading to:

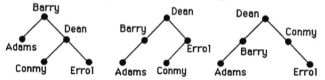

16. (a) The two revisions that only affect the right branch yield:

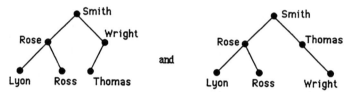

and

(b) The only possibility is a major rearrangement, resulting in:

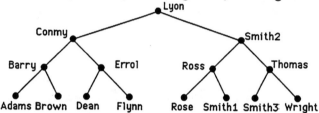

(c) If four clients were added, there would be sixteen clients in all, so the height of the binary search tree would have to be increased.

6.5 Answers

1. (a) In the vertex sequence for a Hamilton circuit [if one existed], the vertex w would have to both precede and follow the vertex v. I.e., the vertex w would have to be visited twice.

(b) In the vertex sequence for a Hamilton path [if one existed], the vertices of degree 1 would have to be at the beginning or end, since otherwise the adjacent vertex would be repeated. But there are three vertices of degree 1 in Figure 1(d).

2. (a) Any path that used every vertex would have to use the central vertex more than once. So no Hamilton circuit exists.

(b) Note that each edge connects an upper vertex to a lower vertex. If there were a Hamilton circuit, its vertex sequence would alternate between upper and lower vertices and would consist of exactly 8 vertices. The first and eighth vertices would have to be different [one would be an upper one and one would be lower] and yet they would have to be the same to complete the circuit. So no such circuit exists.

(c) If there were a Hamilton circuit, consider its vertex sequence and the vertices just before and after the central vertex v. If these three vertices and the edges connected to them were removed from the graph, the remaining graph would have two components. No vertex in one component could be connected to a vertex in the other component without visiting one of the three removed vertices. So no Hamilton circuit exists.

3. (a) Yes. Try $v_1 v_2 v_6 v_5 v_4 v_3 v_1$, for example.

   (b) No.

   (c) No. If v_1 is in V_1 then $\{v_2, v_3, v_4, v_5\} \subseteq V_2$, but v_2 and v_3 are joined by an edge.

   (d) No.

4. (a) No. See part (c) and Theorem 4.

   (b) No.

   (c) Yes, with partition $\{\{v_1, v_4, v_7\}, \{v_2, v_3, v_5, v_6\}\}$.

   (d) Yes.

5. (a) Since there are $n!$ choices for the order in which the vertices in V_1 and in V_2 are visited and the initial vertex can be in either V_1 or V_2, there are $2(n!)^2$ possible Hamilton circuits.

   (b) $n! \cdot (n-1)!$.

   (c) m and n even, or m odd and $n = 2$, or $m = n = 1$.

6.   (a)   (b)   (c)

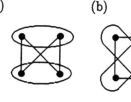 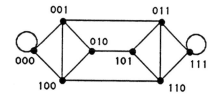

7. Here is the graph:

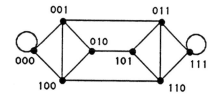

One possible Hamilton circuit has vertex sequence 000, 001, 011, 111, 110, 101, 010, 100, 000 corresponding to the circular arrangement 0 0 0 1 1 1 0 1. Although there are four essentially different Hamilton circuits in $\{0, 1\}^3$, there are only two different circular arrangements, 0 0 0 1 1 1 0 1 and 0 0 0 1 0 1 1 1, which are just the reverses of each other.

8. The twelve Gray codes of length 3 are the circular lists
      (000, 001, 011, 111, 101, 100, 110, 010),
      (000, 001, 101, 100, 110, 111, 011, 010),
      (000, 100, 101, 001, 011, 111, 110, 010),
      (000, 100, 110, 111, 101, 001, 011, 010),
      (000, 001, 101, 111, 011, 010, 110, 100),
      (000, 001, 011, 010, 110, 111, 101, 100),
      and their reverses.

9. There is no Hamilton path because the graph is not connected. The graph is drawn in the answer on page 101 to Exercise 11 on page 352.

10. Yes to both questions. One Hamilton circuit is 000, 011, 100, 111, 001, 010, 101, 110, 000. The graph is drawn in the answer on page 101 to Exercise 12 on page 352.

11. (a) K_n^+ has n vertices and just one more edge than K_{n-1} has, so it has exactly $\frac{1}{2}(n-1)(n-2)+1$ edges.

    (b) Consider vertices v and w in K_n^+ which are not connected by an edge. One of them is in K_{n-1}, so it has degree $n-2$ and the other is the new vertex of degree 2. Hence $\deg(v) + \deg(w) = n$, so K_n^+ is Hamiltonian by Theorem 3.

12. Since any circuit through the new vertex must traverse the new edge at least twice, K_n^{++} is not Hamiltonian.

13. (a)    (b) 2.

    (c) Choose two vertices u and v in G. If they are *not* joined by an edge in G, then they are joined by an edge in the complement. If they *are* joined by an edge in G, then they are in the same component of G. Choose w in some other component. Then $u\,w\,v$ is a path in the complement. In either case, u and v are joined by a path in the complement.

    (d) One example is drawn in the answer to part (e).

    (e) No. Consider

14. Suppose $|V(G)| = n$. Each vertex of the complement of G has degree $n-1-k$. Since $n \geq 2k+2$, $k+1 \leq n/2$. Thus $n-1-k \geq n-n/2 = n/2$. By Theorem 1, G is Hamiltonian.

15. Given G_{n+1}, consider the subgraph H_0 where $V(H_0)$ consists of all binary $(n+1)$-tuples with 0 in the $(n+1)$-st digit and $E(H_0)$ is the set of all edges of G_{n+1} connecting vertices in $V(H_0)$. Define H_1 similarly. Show H_0, H_1 are

isomorphic to G_n, and so have Hamilton circuits. Use these to construct a Hamilton circuit for G_{n+1}. For $n = 2$, see how this works in Figure 5.

Here are the details. Let $V(H_1)$ consist of $(n+1)$-tuples with 1 in the $(n+1)$-st digit and let $E(H_1)$ consist of the edges in G_{n+1} connecting vertices in $V(H_1)$. The function from G_{n+1} to G_n which simply leaves off the last coordinate determines isomorphisms from H_0 and H_1 onto G_n. Suppose e is an edge from v to w in a Hamilton circuit for G_n and that v_0, w_0 in H_0 and v_1, w_1 in H_1 correspond to v, w. I.e., v_0 is the n-tuple v with a 0 attached to the end, etc. Form a Hamilton circuit for G_{n+1} as follows. Starting with w_0 in H_0 follow the copy in H_0 of the Hamilton circuit for G_n until you reach v_0. Then take the edge from v_0 to v_1, which exists since v_0 and v_1 only differ in the $(n+1)$-st coordinate. Then go backwards along the copy of the G_n-circuit in H_1 until you reach w_1. Then take the edge from w_1 to w_0, the starting point. Every vertex in H_0 and H_1 will have been visited exactly once. Since $V(G_{n+1}) = V(H_0) \cup V(H_1)$, the path is a Hamilton circuit of G_{n+1}.

16. The graph G_m has 2^m vertices, each of degree m. For $m \geq 3$, $2^m > m + m$ so G_m does not satisfy the hypothesis $\deg(v) + \deg(w) \geq 2^m$ of Theorem 3 for any pairs of vertices v and w. It follows, as in the proofs of Theorems 1 and 2, that G_m does not satisfy the hypothesis of either of those theorems. So none of the theorems apply to G_m.

6.6   Answers

1. (a) and (b)   (c)   (d)

2.

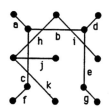

3. (a)   (b)

Both trees have weight 1330.

4.

5. (a) and (c)

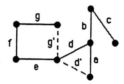

Either d or d' can be chosen, and either g or g', so there are 4 possible answers to (a).

(b) 1330.

6. (a) e_{10}, e_9, e_7, e_5, e_4, e_3, e_1.

(b) Same as (a).

7. (a) e_1, e_2, e_3, e_5, e_6, e_7, e_9.

(b) e_7, e_5, e_2, e_1, e_3, e_6, e_9.

8. (a)

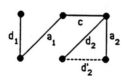

Edges a_1 and a_2 can be chosen in either order. So can d_1 and d_2. Edge d'_2 can be chosen instead of d_2. The weight is 10.

(b)

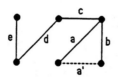

Either a or a' can be chosen. The weight is still 10.

9. (a)

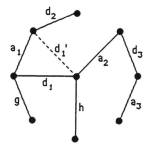

Edges a_1, a_2, a_3 can be chosen in any order. So can d_1, d_2, d_3. Edge d_1' can be chosen instead of d_1. The weight is 16.

(b)

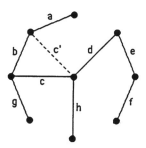

Either c or c' can be chosen. The weight is 16.

10. (a) $\{e_1, e_2, e_3, e_4, e_5\}$, $\{e_1, e_2, e_3, e_4, e_6\}$, $\{e_1, e_2, e_3, e_5, e_6\}$.

(b) e_1, e_2, e_3.

(c) An edge e belongs to every spanning tree of a finite connected graph G if and only if its removal will disconnect the graph. *Proof:* $\impliedby$ This is clear since spanning trees must be connected. $\implies$ We prove the contrapositive, so suppose $G \setminus \{e\}$ is connected. By Theorem 2 on page 355, $G \setminus \{e\}$ has a spanning tree, which will be a spanning tree for G that does not use e.

11. 1687 miles.

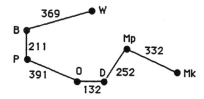

12. Yes. Given an edge, order the edges of the graph so that the given edge is e_1. Then Kruskal's algorithm will pick e_1 at the start, so e_1 will be part of the spanning tree produced by that algorithm.

13. Here is one possible algorithm.

> *PrimForest(weighted graph)*
>
> Set $E := \emptyset$.
> Choose w in $V(G)$ and set $V := \{w\}$.
> while $V \neq V(G)$ do
>   if there is an edge $\{u,v\}$ in $E(G)$
>   with $u \in V$ and $v \in V(G) \setminus V$ then
>   Choose such an edge of smallest weight.
>   Put $\{u,v\}$ in E and put v in V.
>   else
>   Choose $v \in V(G) \setminus V$ and put v in V.
> return E ∎

14. (a) Consider a minimum spanning tree S of G contained in H. Since $S \subseteq H$, $V(H) = V(S) = V(G)$. Since S is a minimum spanning tree of G, S is a minimum spanning tree of H. Now if T is any minimum spanning tree of H, then $W(T) = W(S)$, so T is a minimum spanning tree of G.

(b) Here are the details of the outline given. The Kruskal tree K for E is a minimum spanning tree for G by part (a), since E contains some minimum spanning tree for G by assumption. It suffices to show that $K \subseteq E \setminus \{e\}$. Since e is to be deleted, e is in a cycle C of E. Since K is a tree, $C \not\subseteq K$. Consider any edge f of $C \setminus K$ with $f \neq e$. Since f is in a cycle of E and f has not been discarded, f precedes e on the list of edges of G. Since $f \in E \setminus K$, Kruskal's algorithm rejected f; hence f is part of a cycle made from edges in K that precede f, and hence that precede e. That is, the endpoints of f are joined by a path in K of edges preceding e. Replacing each f in $C \setminus K$ by such a path gives a path in $K \setminus \{e\}$ joining the endpoints of e. Since K is a tree, this means that $e \notin K$, and so $K \subseteq E \setminus \{e\}$.

15. Assume that G has more than one minimum spanning tree. Consider the edge e of smallest weight that belongs to some but not all minimum spanning trees. Let S, T be minimum spanning trees with $e \in T \setminus S$. By Theorem 3(d) on page 356, $S \cup \{e\}$ has a cycle C that must contain e since S is acyclic. Since T is acyclic there must be some other edge, call it f, in C that is not in T. Then f is an edge of S. Now $U = (S \cup \{e\}) \setminus \{f\}$ is connected, by Theorem 1 on page 354, and has the same number of edges as S. So U is a spanning tree by Theorem 4 on page 357. Since S is a *minimum* spanning tree,

$$\text{weight}(S) \leq \text{weight}(U) = \text{weight}(S) + W(e) - W(f),$$

so $W(e) \geq W(f)$. Since $e \neq f$, $W(e) > W(f)$. Since $f \in S \setminus T$, this contradicts our choice of e.

Chapter 7

Recursion is a fundamental idea in computer science. Our students who have had some experience with recursive programs seem simply to have been told that a recursive algorithm is one that calls itself. Even though it's not hard to put recursion on a respectable mathematical footing, students often appear just to have been shown a few examples and told to go and do likewise. In this chapter we describe and relate the various ways in which recursion arises, and we point out what it takes to verify a recursive algorithm. Whether one thinks of such an algorithm as working its way downward or upward, there's generally a tree lurking in the background. We've chosen to discuss algorithms in which the tree is in more or less plain sight, not only to encourage thinking of recursion and trees together but also because the algorithms themselves have important applications.

Section 7.1 presents three views of recursion: recursive definition of sets, a recursive inductive framework, and recursive definition of functions. Recursive algorithms can be thought of as computing values of recursively defined functions; their correctness is guaranteed by the inductive framework. At the root of it all are the recursively defined sets on which the algorithms act. We have tried in this introductory section to give a coherent and convincing discussion of the basic abstract ideas without getting overly technical. What we say is enough for our purposes and should be useful even for those students who go on to study computability questions.

Section 7.2 begins to deal with the algorithms themselves. Testing membership in a recursively defined set is an obvious kind of motivating example. Parsing algorithms for compilers are of this sort. The main theme of this section is the connection between recursive algorithms and the abstract ideas of § 7.1. If you didn't do § 4.7 you can skip over the recursive versions of the Euclidean algorithm in Example 6.

The first part of § 7.3 deals with traversal algorithms whose inputs are trees with labels on their nodes. We'll apply this material to Polish notation in the next section. Go through a couple of examples to illustrate how the algorithms work and to show a format for describing the stages of their operation. Students seem to find all three of these algorithms easy and fun. Their complexity analysis brings in a new and powerful trick, the method of "charges."

113

The idea of depth-first search is useful even when we don't start with a tree. We illustrate with an algorithm, whose output is interesting in its own right, for producing a topologically sorted labeling of an acyclic digraph. Students find tree traversal pretty easy but LABEL and TREESORT somewhat less intuitive. Work some examples in class for each of these. The idea of keeping track of where we've been with the set L is a new wrinkle that we will see again in Chapter 8. Exercise 14 shows that there are some subtleties in our design of TREESORT. This section is fundamental enough to warrant two class days.

Section 7.4 builds on § 7.3 to discuss an important application. The theorem gives the theoretical justification for the use of Polish and reverse Polish notation. Its proof is slippery. Go through it with an example to see what the notation really means.

Weighted trees have numerous applications. In § 7.5 we discuss two: list-merging and prefix codes. Though we don't explicitly talk about **pruning**, that's in fact what we do in HUFFMAN'S algorithm. Huffman codes are sometimes used for file compression.

7.1   Answers

1. (a) Use induction on m. Clearly 2^0 is in S by (B). If 2^m is in S, then $2 \cdot 2^m = 2^{m+1}$ is in S by (R).

   (b) Use the Generalized Principle of Induction on page 396, where $p(n) =$ "n has the form 2^m for some $m \in \mathbb{N}$." Statement $p(1)$ is true since $1 = 2^0$. We show that $p(n)$ implies $p(2n)$. If $p(n)$ holds, then $n = 2^m$ for some $m \in \mathbb{N}$. Since $2n = 2^{m+1}$ and $m + 1 \in \mathbb{N}$, statement $p(2n)$ also holds.

2. (a) λ is in Σ^* by (B). $c \in \Sigma$, so $\lambda c = c \in \Sigma^*$ by (R). $a \in \Sigma$, so $ca \in \Sigma^*$ by (R). $t \in \Sigma$, so $cat \in \Sigma^*$ by (R).

   (b), (c), (d) are similar.

3. (a) $S = \{(m, n) : m \leq n\}$.

   (b) By (B), $(0, 0) \in S$. So by (R), $(0, 1) \in S$. Again by (R), $(1, 1) \in S$ so by (R) $(0, 2) \in S$. Finally, by (R), $(1, 2) \in S$.

   (c) Yes. A pair $(0, n)$ is in S only by (B) or because $(n - 1, n - 1) \in S$, and a pair (m, n) with $0 < m \leq n$ can only come from $(m - 1, n)$.

4. (a) $T = \{(m, n) : m \leq n\}$.

   (b) $(0, 0) \in T$ by (B), so $(1,1)$, $(2,2)$, $(3,3)$, $(3,4)$, $(3,5)$ are in T, by repeated use of (R). [Other sequences are possible; for example $(0,0)$, $(0,1)$, $(1,2)$, $(1,3)$, $(2,4)$, $(3,5)$.]

   (c) No, as noted in the answer to part (b). Compare with the answer to Exercise 3(c).

5. (a) (B) λ is in S,   (R) if $w \in S$, then $aw \in S$ and $wb \in S$.

   (b) $\lambda \in S$ by (B). Now repeated use of (R) yields $a\lambda \in S$, i.e., $a \in S$, so $ab \in S$, so $abb \in S$, so $abbb \in S$.

   (c) $\lambda \in S$ by (B), so a, aa and aab are in S by (R).

   (d) Our definition is not uniquely determined. For example, aab can also be built using the sequence λ, b, ab, aab.

6. (a) (B) $a \in T$,   (R) if $w \in T$, then $bw \in T$ and $wb \in T$.

   (b) $a \in T$ by (B), so ba, bba and $bbab$ are in T by (R).

   (c) Our definition is not uniquely determined. For example, $bbab$ can also be built from the sequence a, ab, bab, $bbab$.

7. (a) Two possible constructions are

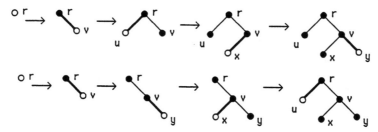

   (b) First obtain the subtree with root v by hanging the trivial trees with vertices x and y. Then obtain the tree with root r by hanging the subtree with root v and the trivial tree with vertex u.

8. S_0 consists of the trivial one-vertex tree. Assume that S_{n-1} contains all trees with at most n vertices, and consider a tree T with $n + 1$ vertices. Then T has at least two leaves by Lemma 1 on page 357. Prune a leaf of T to get a new tree T''. Then T'' belongs to S_{n-1}. Since T can be obtained from T'' by reattaching the leaf, (R) shows that T belongs to the set S_n.

9. Use the Generalized Principle of Induction on $p(n) = $ "$n \equiv 0 \pmod 3$ or $n \equiv 1 \pmod 3$." Certainly $p(1)$ is true. It suffices to show that $p(n) \Longrightarrow p(3n)$ and $p(2n + 1) \Longrightarrow p(n)$. The first implication is trivial because $3n \equiv 0 \pmod 3$ for all n. For the second implication, show the contrapositive, i.e., $n \equiv 2 \pmod 3$ implies $(2n + 1) \equiv 2 \pmod 3$. The contrapositive implication is easy to show directly, since $n = 3k + 2$ implies $2n + 1 = 3(2k + 1) + 2$.

10. The chain in Example 6(a) shows that 9, 13 and 7 are in A. Since $9 = 2 \cdot 4 + 1$ and $13 = 2 \cdot 6 + 1$ are in A, (R) shows that 4 and 6 are in A. Since $4 \in A$, we have $12 \in A$. Finally, since $7 \in A$ we have $21 \in A$ and hence $10 \in A$.

11. (a) Use (B) and (R) to show that the sequence 1, 2, 4, 8, 16, 5, 10, 3, 6 lies in S.

   (b) From part (a), 10 is in S. Now use the sequence 10, 20, 40, 13, 26, 52, 17, 34, 11, 22, 7.

12. (a) Imitate the definition in Example 11(b); in (R) change "at most" to "exactly".

    (b) The class of full m-ary trees is defined by:
    (B) A trivial one-vertex rooted tree is a full m-ary tree of height 0.
    (R) If (T, r) is obtained by hanging exactly m full m-ary rooted trees of height $h - 1$ from r, then (T, r) is a full m-ary tree of height h.

    Note that full m-ary trees are essentially completely determined by giving m and the height h.

13. We follow the hint. Let $p(w) = $ "$l'(w)$ is the number of letters in w." By (1) of Example 10(b), $p(w)$ is true if $w \in X = \{\lambda\} \cup \Sigma$. Suppose that $w = uv$ with $p(u)$ and $p(v)$ true. By (2) of Example 10(b), $l'(w) = l'(u) + l'(v) = $ (number of letters in u) + (number of letters in v) = number of letters in w, so $p(w)$ is true. [This argument is valid no matter how w is produced from members of Σ^* by (2).] Thus $p(w)$ is true for every w in Σ^* by the Generalized Principle of Induction.

14. (a) If $x \in \Sigma$, then $x = x\lambda = x\overset{\leftarrow}{\lambda}$ [by (B)] $= \overset{\leftarrow}{\lambda x}$ [by (R)] $= \overset{\leftarrow}{x}$.

    (b) $\overset{\leftarrow}{cab} = b\overset{\leftarrow}{ca} = ba\overset{\leftarrow}{c} = bac$, by two applications of (R) and one application of the result of part (a).

    (c) $\overset{\leftarrow}{abbaa} = a\overset{\leftarrow}{abba} = aa\overset{\leftarrow}{abb} = aaba\overset{\leftarrow}{b} = aabb\overset{\leftarrow}{a} = aabba$, by repeated use of (R) and part (a).

    (d) $\overset{\leftarrow}{w_1 w_2} = \overset{\leftarrow}{w_2}\overset{\leftarrow}{w_1}$; $\overset{\Leftarrow}{w_1} = w_1$.

15. (a) (2,3), (4,6), etc.

    (b) (B) is clear since 5 divides $0 + 0$. For (R) you need to check

    "if 5 divides $m + n$, then 5 divides $(m + 2) + (n + 3)$."

    Alternatively, prove that every member of S is of the form $(2k, 3k)$ for $k \in \mathbb{N}$.

    (c) No. For example, (3,2) does not belong to S.

16. (a) T consists of all pairs (m, n) with $n \leq 2m$.

    (b) Use the Generalized Principle of Induction with $p(m, n) = $ "$2m \geq n$." Check that $p(0, 0)$ is true. Assuming that $2m \geq n$ for some member (m, n) of T, then $2(m + 1) = 2m + 2 \geq n + 2$; also $2(m + 1) \geq n + 1$ and $2(m + 1) \geq n$. So $2x \geq y$ for $(x, y) = (m + 1, n), (m + 1, n + 1)$ and $(m + 1, n + 2)$, i.e., $2x \geq y$ for every pair (x, y) in T specified from (m, n) by (R).

    (c) No. Some pairs in T can be defined in terms of more than one pair. For example, (3,2) arises from (2,2), (2,1) and (2,0) under (R).

17. (a) Obviously $A \subseteq \mathbb{N} \times \mathbb{N}$. To show $\mathbb{N} \times \mathbb{N} \subseteq A$, apply the ordinary First Principle of Mathematical Induction to the propositions

$$p(k) = \text{``if } (m,n) \in \mathbb{N} \times \mathbb{N} \text{ and } m + n = k, \text{ then } (m,n) \in A.\text{''}$$

(b) Let $p(m,n)$ be a proposition-valued function defined on $\mathbb{N} \times \mathbb{N}$. To show that $p(m,n)$ is true for all (m,n) in $\mathbb{N} \times \mathbb{N}$ it is enough to show:
(B) $p(0,0)$ is true, and
(I) if $p(m,n)$ is true, then $p(m+1,n)$ and $p(m,n+1)$ are true.

18. (a) Some examples are a, aba, bab, $ababb$, $babab$.

(b) Use the result of Example 9(c) and the Generalized Principle of Induction with $p(w) = \text{``length}(w)$ is odd.'' It is enough to show:
(B) $p(w)$ is true for all $w \in \{a, b\}$;
(I) if $p(w)$ is true for $w \in B$, so are $p(abw)$ and $p(baw)$.
Both of these assertions are clear. (B) holds because $\text{length}(a) = \text{length}(b) = 1$. (I) holds because $\text{length}(abw) = \text{length}(baw) = 2 + \text{length}(w)$ for all w.

(c) No. $w = aaa$ has odd length, but $w \notin B$.

(d) Yes. Each word in B of length at least 3 is of just one form abw or baw, and in either case the word w is unique.

19. (a) For w in Σ^*, let $p(w) = \text{``length}(\overleftarrow{w}) = \text{length}(w)\text{''}$. Apply the Generalized Principle of Induction. Since $\overleftarrow{\lambda} = \lambda$, $p(\lambda)$ is clearly true. You need to show that if $p(w)$ is true, then so is $p(wx)$:

$$\text{length}(\overleftarrow{w}) = \text{length}(w) \quad \text{implies} \quad \text{length}(\overleftarrow{wx}) = \text{length}(wx).$$

In detail, suppose $\text{length}(\overleftarrow{w}) = \text{length}(w)$. Then
$$
\begin{aligned}
\text{length}(\overleftarrow{wx}) &= \text{length}(x\overleftarrow{w}) \\
&= \text{length}(x) + \text{length}(\overleftarrow{w}) \\
&= \text{length}(x) + \text{length}(w) \quad \text{[by assumption]} \\
&= \text{length}(wx).
\end{aligned}
$$

(b) Fix w_1, say, and work with $p(w) = \text{``}\overleftarrow{w_1 w} = \overleftarrow{w}\,\overleftarrow{w_1}.\text{''}$ To show $p(w)$ true for every $w \in \Sigma^*$ it is enough to show:
(B) $p(\lambda)$ is true;
(I) if $p(w)$ is true, then $p(wx)$ is true [for $w \in \Sigma^*$ and $x \in \Sigma$].
Since $\overleftarrow{\lambda} = \lambda$, $\overleftarrow{w_1 \lambda} = \overleftarrow{w_1} = \overleftarrow{\lambda}\,\overleftarrow{w_1}$ and so (B) holds. If $p(w)$ is true and $x \in \Sigma$ then

$$
\begin{aligned}
\overleftarrow{w_1 wx} &= x\overleftarrow{w_1 w} && \text{[by definition of reversal]} \\
&= x\overleftarrow{w}\,\overleftarrow{w_1} && \text{[by } p(w)] \\
&= \overleftarrow{wx}\,\overleftarrow{w_1} && \text{[by definition of reversal]}.
\end{aligned}
$$

Thus $p(wx)$ holds. This establishes (I).

7.2   Answers

1.   (a)   Test(20)
                          Test(10)
                              Test(5)= (false, $-\infty$)
                          = (false, $-\infty$)
                      = (false, $-\infty$).

                (b)   Test(8)
                          Test(4)
                              Test(2)
                                  Test(1) = (true, 0)
                              = (true, $0 + 1 = 1$)
                          = (true, $1 + 1 = 2$)
                      = (true, $2 + 1 = 3$).

2. (a) This is essentially the graph in Figure 1. Prune leaves until a single vertex is reached. The output is "true," i.e., the graph is a tree.

   (b) This is essentially the graph H' in Figure 2. Prune leaves until the graph H''' is obtained. Then the output is "false," so the graph is not a tree.

   (c) Prune leaves until a single vertex is left; then the output is "true" and the graph is a tree.

3. (a) $((x + y) + z)$ or $(x + (y + z))$.

   (b) $(x + (y/z))$ or $((x + y)/z)$, or $x + (y/z)$ or $(x + y)/z$ if we omit outside parentheses.

   (c) $((xy)z)$ or $(x(yz))$.

   (d) $((x + y)^{(x+y)})$ or $(x + y)^{(x+y)}$.

4. (a) $(X + Y) + Z$ or $X + (Y + Z)$.   (b) $X * (Y + Z)$.

   (c) $(X \wedge 2) + ((2 * X) + 1)$ or $((X \wedge 2) + (2 * X)) + 1$ or $((X \wedge 2) + 2) * (X + 1)$ or $(X \wedge (2+2)) * (X + 1)$ or $(X \wedge 2) + (2 * (X + 1))$ or $X \wedge ((2 + (2 * X)) + 1)$ or $X \wedge (((2+2) * X) + 1)$ or $X \wedge ((2+2) * (X + 1))$ or $X \wedge (2 + (2 * (X+1)))$ or $X \wedge (2 + ((2*X) + 1))$ or $(X \wedge (2 + (2*X))) + 1$ or $(X \wedge ((2+2) * X)) + 1$ or $(((X \wedge 2) + 2) * X) + 1$ or $((X \wedge (2 + 2)) * X) + 1$.

   (d) $(X + (Y/Z)) - (Z * X)$ or one of 13 others.

   [For simplicity, we have omitted outside parentheses in these answers.]

5. (a) By (B), x, y and 2 are wff's. By the (f^g) part of (R), we conclude that (x^2) and (y^2) are wff's. So by the $(f + g)$ part of (R), $((x^2) + (y^2))$ is a wff.

   (b) $X, 2$ and Y are wff's by (B). $(X \wedge 2)$ and $(Y \wedge 2)$ are wff's by the (f^g) part of (R). $((X \wedge 2) + (Y \wedge 2))$ is a wff by the $(f + g)$ part of (R). Finally, $(((X \wedge 2) + (Y \wedge 2)) \wedge 2)$ is a wff by the (f^g) part of (R).

(c) By (B), X and Y are wff's. By the $(f + g)$ part of (R), $(X + Y)$ is a wff. By the $(f - g)$ part of (R), $(X - Y)$ is a wff. Finally, by the $(f * g)$ part of (R), $((X + Y) * (X - Y))$ is a wff.

6. (a) The algorithm terminates, but the output is always 0.

   (b) If the input is n the output is $(n - 1)!$ [recall that $0! = 1$ by definition].

   (c) If the input n is odd, the output is $n \cdot (n - 2) \cdots 1$; for example, with input $n = 7$, the output is $7 \cdot 5 \cdot 3 \cdot 1 = 105$. However, if the input is even, the algorithm eventually calls GOO(0), GOO(-2), etc. It does not terminate, since the chain $0, -2, -4, -6, \ldots$ goes on forever.

7. Blank entries below signify that the algorithm doesn't terminate with the indicated input n.

n	FOO	GOO	BOO	MOO	TOO	ZOO
8	8	40,320		4	4	8
9	9	362,880			4	8

8. This is similar to Exercise 9. Let $p(k)$ be the statement "TOO(n) $= k + 1$ whenever $2^k \leq n < 2^{k+1}$." Then $p(0)$ asserts that "TOO(n) $= 1$ whenever $1 \leq n < 2$," which is clear. Assume that $p(k)$ is true for some $k \in \mathbb{N}$ and consider n such that $2^{k+1} \leq n < 2^{k+2}$. Then $2^k \leq \lfloor n/2 \rfloor < 2^{k+1}$, so TOO($\lfloor n/2 \rfloor$) $= k + 1$. Since $n \neq 1$, the else branch of TOO applies and gives TOO(n) $= (k + 1) + 1$, so $p(k + 1)$ is true. Hence all statements $p(k)$ are true by induction.

9. Let $p(k)$ be the statement "ZOO(n) $= 2^k$ whenever $2^k \leq n < 2^{k+1}$." Then $p(0)$ asserts that "ZOO(n) $= 2^0 = 1$ whenever $1 \leq n < 2$," which is clear. Assume that $p(k)$ is true for some $k \in \mathbb{N}$ and consider n such that $2^{k+1} \leq n < 2^{k+2}$. Then $2^k \leq \lfloor n/2 \rfloor < 2^{k+1}$, so ZOO($\lfloor n/2 \rfloor$) $= 2^k$. Since $n \neq 1$, the else branch of ZOO applies and gives ZOO(n) $= 2^k * 2 = 2^{k+1}$, so $p(k + 1)$ is true. Hence all statements $p(k)$ are true by induction.

10.   Euclid$^+$(80,35)
             Euclid$^+$(35,10)
                 Euclid$^+$(10,5)
                     Euclid$^+$(5,0) $= (5, 1, 0)$
                 $= (5, 0, 1 - 0 \cdot (10 \, \mathrm{DIV} \, 5)) = (5, 0, 1)$
             $= (5, 1, 0 - 1 \cdot (35 \, \mathrm{DIV} \, 10)) = (5, 1, -3)$
         $= (5, -3, 1 - (-3) \cdot (80 \, \mathrm{DIV} \, 35)) = (5, -3, 7)$.
     Check: $80 \cdot (-3) + 35 \cdot 7 = 5$.

11.   Euclid$^+$(108,30)

Euclid$^+$(30,18)

Euclid$^+$(18,12)

Euclid$^+$(12,6)

Euclid$^+$(6,0) = $(6, 1, 0)$

= $(6, 0, 1 - 0 \cdot (12 \operatorname{DIV} 6)) = (6, 0, 1)$

= $(6, 1, 0 - 1 \cdot (18 \operatorname{DIV} 12)) = (6, 1, -1)$

= $(6, -1, 1 - (-1) \cdot (30 \operatorname{DIV} 18)) = (6, -1, 2)$

= $(6, 2, -1 - 2 \cdot (108 \operatorname{DIV} 30)) = (6, 2, -7)$.

Sure enough, $108 \cdot 2 + 30 \cdot (-7) = 6$.

12.   Euclid$^+$(56,21)

Euclid$^+$(21,14)

Euclid$^+$(14,7)

Euclid$^+$(7,0) = $(7, 1, 0)$

= $(7, 0, 1 - 0 \cdot (14 \operatorname{DIV} 7)) = (7, 0, 1)$

= $(7, 1, 0 - 1 \cdot (21 \operatorname{DIV} 14)) = (7, 1, -1)$

= $(7, -1, 1 - (-1) \cdot (56 \operatorname{DIV} 21)) = (7, -1, 3)$.

Check: $56 \cdot (-1) + 21 \cdot 3 = 7$.

13. (a) Since $\gcd(m, n) = m$ when $n = 0$, we may assume that $n \neq 0$. We need to check that the algorithm terminates and that if $\text{Euclid}(n, m \operatorname{MOD} n) = \gcd(n, m \operatorname{MOD} n)$, then $\text{Euclid}(m, n) = \gcd(m, n)$. The latter observation follows from the equality $\gcd(n, m \operatorname{MOD} n) = \gcd(m, n)$, which was verified in the Proposition on page 253.

To check that the algorithm terminates, we need to be sure that the second input variable n in $\text{Euclid}(, n)$ is eventually 0. This is clear, since at each step the new $n' = m \operatorname{MOD} n$ is less than n and greater than or equal to 0, so the values must decrease to 0.

(b) The algorithm terminates because it's the same algorithm as in part (a), but with extra outputs. We need to verify that $sm + tn = d$ at each stage of the algorithm. Since this equation holds when $n = 0$, $d = m$, $s = 1$ and $t = 0$, we may assume that $n \neq 0$. As in (a), we need to check that if $\text{Euclid}^+(n, m \operatorname{MOD} n)$ is correct, then so is $\text{Euclid}^+(m, n)$. That is, that if $d' = s' \cdot n + t' \cdot (m \operatorname{MOD} n)$, then $d' = t' \cdot m + (s' - t' \cdot m \operatorname{DIV} n) \cdot n$. This follows from the identity $m \operatorname{MOD} n = m - m \operatorname{DIV} n \cdot n$:

$$
\begin{aligned}
s' \cdot n + t' \cdot m \operatorname{MOD} n &= s' \cdot n + t' \cdot m - t' \cdot m \operatorname{DIV} n \cdot n \\
&= t' \cdot m + (s' - t' \cdot m \operatorname{DIV} n) \cdot n.
\end{aligned}
$$

14. (a) 2.   (b) 3.   (c) 2.

(d) 5.   (e) 4.   (f) 3.

15. (a) p and q are wff's by (B). $p \vee q$ is a wff by (R). $\neg (p \vee q)$ is a wff by (R).

(b) p and q are wff's by (B). $\neg p$ and $\neg q$ are wff's by (R). So the expression $(\neg p \wedge \neg q)$ is a wff by (R).

(c) p, q and r are wff's by (B). $(p \leftrightarrow q)$ and $(r \rightarrow p)$ are wff's by (R). $((r \rightarrow p) \vee q)$ is a wff by (R), so $((p \leftrightarrow q) \rightarrow ((r \rightarrow p) \vee q))$ is a wff by (R).

16. Simply add "$(P \oplus Q)$," to the recursive clause (R).

17. (a) $p, q \in \mathcal{F}$ by (B). $(p \vee q) \in \mathcal{F}$ by (R) with $P = p, Q = q$. Hence $(p \wedge (p \vee q))$ is in $\mathcal{F}$ by (R) with $P = p, Q = (p \vee q)$.

(b) As stated in the hint, we need to prove all $r(P)$ are true where

$$r(P) = \text{``if } p \text{ and } q \text{ are false, then } P \text{ is false."}$$

To prove $r(P)$ for all $P \in \mathcal{F}$ it is enough to show:

(B) $r(p)$ and $r(q)$ are true;
(I) if $r(P)$ and $r(Q)$ are true, then so are $r((P \wedge Q))$ and $r((P \vee Q))$.

(B) obviously holds. Suppose $r(P)$ and $r(Q)$ are true for some $P, Q \in \mathcal{F}$, and suppose p and q are false. Then P is false, by $r(P)$, and Q is false, by $r(Q)$. Hence $P \wedge Q$ and $P \vee Q$ are false by definition of $\wedge$ and $\vee$, so $r((P \wedge Q))$ and $r((P \vee Q))$ are true. Thus (I) holds.

(c) If p and q are false then $(p \rightarrow q)$ is true, so $r((p \rightarrow q))$ is false. Thus $(p \rightarrow q)$ cannot be logically equivalent to a proposition in $\mathcal{F}$, by part (b). This provides a negative answer to the question in Exercise 17(c) on page 119: $p \rightarrow q$ cannot be written in some way using just p, q, $\wedge$ and $\vee$.

18. (a) SmallestEntry(1 2 3 4 5 6)
      SmallestEntry(1 2 3)
        SmallestEntry(1 2)
          SmallestEntry(1) = 1
          SmallestEntry(2) = 2
        $= \min\{1, 2\} = 1$
        SmallestEntry(3) = 3
      $= \min\{1, 3\} = 1$
      SmallestEntry(4 5 6)
        SmallestEntry(4 5)
          SmallestEntry(4) = 4
          SmallestEntry(5) = 5
        $= \min\{4, 5\} = 4$
        SmallestEntry(6) = 6
      $= \min\{4, 6\} = 4$
    $= \min\{1, 4\} = 1$

(b)   SmallestEntry(5 2 8 4 2)
     SmallestEntry(5 2 8)
       SmallestEntry(5 2)
           SmallestEntry(5) = 5
           SmallestEntry(2) = 2
       $= \min\{5, 2\} = 2$
       SmallestEntry(8) = 8
     $= \min\{2, 8\} = 2$
     SmallestEntry(4 2)
       SmallestEntry(4) = 4
       SmallestEntry(2) = 2
     $= \min\{4, 2\} = 2$
   $= \min\{2, 2\} = 2$

(c)   SmallestEntry(5 2 8 4 2 5 3)
     SmallestEntry(5 2 8 4)
       SmallestEntry(5 2)
           SmallestEntry(5) = 5
           SmallestEntry(2) = 2
       $= \min\{5, 2\} = 2$
       SmallestEntry(8 4)
           SmallestEntry(8) = 8
           SmallestEntry(4) = 4
       $= \min\{8, 4\} = 4$
     $= \min\{2, 4\} = 2$
     SmallestEntry(2 5 3)
       SmallestEntry(2 5)
           SmallestEntry(2) = 2
           SmallestEntry(5) = 5
       $= \min\{2, 5\} = 2$
       SmallestEntry(3) = 3
     $= \min\{2, 3\} = 2$
   $= \min\{2, 2\} = 2$

19.   (a)   ConvertToBinary(25); $25 \bmod 2 = 1$
               ConvertToBinary(12); $12 \bmod 2 = 0$
                 ConvertToBinary(6); $6 \bmod 2 = 0$
                   ConvertToBinary(3); $3 \bmod 2 = 1$
                     ConvertToBinary(1) = 1
                   = 11
                 = 110
               = 1100
             = 11001

(b)   ConvertToBinary(16); $16 \, \text{MOD} \, 2 = 0$
  ConvertToBinary(8); $8 \, \text{MOD} \, 2 = 0$
   ConvertToBinary(4); $4 \, \text{MOD} \, 2 = 0$
    ConvertToBinary(2); $2 \, \text{MOD} \, 2 = 0$
     ConvertToBinary(1) $= 1$
     $= 10$
    $= 100$
   $= 1000$
  $= 10000$

(c) Replace $n \, \text{DIV} \, 2$ and $n \, \text{MOD} \, 2$ by $n \, \text{DIV} \, 16$ and $n \, \text{MOD} \, 16$, respectively. You would need new digits for 10, 11, 12, 13, 14 and 15; the standard ones are A, B, C, D, E, F.

7.3   Answers

1. Preorder: $r\,x\,w\,v\,y\,z\,s\,u\,t\,p\,q$.   Postorder: $v\,y\,w\,z\,x\,t\,p\,u\,q\,s\,r$.

2. Preorder: $r\,w\,v\,x\,y\,z\,u\,t\,s\,p\,q$.   Postorder: $x\,y\,v\,u\,t\,z\,w\,p\,q\,s\,r$.

3. Preorder: $r\,t\,x\,v\,y\,z\,w\,u\,p\,q\,s$.   Postorder: $v\,y\,z\,x\,w\,t\,p\,q\,s\,u\,r$.

4. 000, 00, 001, 0, 01, root, 10, 1, 1100, 110, 1101, 11, 111.

5. The order of traversing the tree is

$$r, w, v, w, x, y, x, z, x, w, r, u, t, u, s, p, s, q, s, u, r.$$

(a) Preorder: $r\,w\,v\,x\,y\,z\,u\,t\,s\,p\,q$. $L(w) = w\,v\,x\,y\,z$. $L(u) = u\,t\,s\,p\,q$.

(b) Postorder: $v\,y\,z\,x\,w\,t\,p\,q\,s\,u\,r$. $L(w) = v\,y\,z\,x\,w$. $L(u) = t\,p\,q\,s\,u$.

6.

vertex	1	2	3	4	5	6	7	8
SUCC( )	$\varnothing$	$\{1\}$	$\varnothing$	$\{1,3\}$	$\{1,2,4\}$	$\{5\}$	$\{2\}$	$\{5,7\}$
ACC( )	$\{1\}$	$\{1,2\}$	$\{3\}$	$\{1,3,4\}$	$\{1,2,3,4,5\}$	$\{1,2,3,4,5,6\}$	$\{1,2,7\}$	$\{1,2,3,4,5,7,8\}$

7. The order of traversing the tree is

$$u, x, w, v, w, y, w, x, r, z, r, t, r, x, u, s, p, s, q, s, u.$$

(a) Postorder: $v\,y\,w\,z\,t\,r\,x\,p\,q\,s\,u$.   (b) Preorder: $u\,x\,w\,v\,y\,r\,z\,t\,s\,p\,q$.

(c) Inorder: $v\,w\,y\,x\,z\,r\,t\,u\,p\,s\,q$.

8. The tree in Figure 3 and the ones in Figure 4 all have inorder listing $v\,w\,y\,x\,z\,r\,t\,u\,p\,s\,q$. The trees in Figure 3 and Figure 5(a) both have preorder listing $r\,w\,v\,x\,y\,z\,u\,t\,s\,p\,q$. The trees in Figure 3 and Figure 5(b) both have postorder listing $v\,y\,z\,x\,w\,t\,p\,q\,s\,u\,r$.

9. (a)   (c)

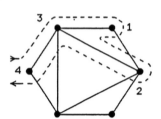   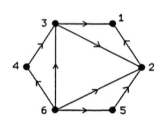

(b) Start with a, choose its successor b, choose its successor c, label c with 1.
Return to b, choose its successor d and label d with 2.
Return to b and label b with 3.
Return to a and label a with 4.

10. (a)   (b)

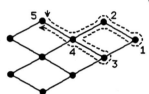   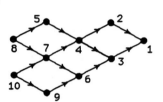

11. (a)   (b)

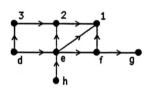   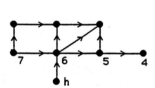

(c)

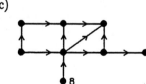

12.

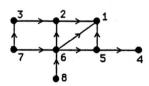

13. (a) 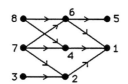   (b)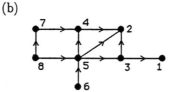

14. (a) The labeling is

(b) Neither the labeling nor its reverse is sorted. Note that $2 < 3 < 4$ but that d is a successor of both b and c.

15. The number of descendants of v is a good measure. Each child w of v has fewer descendants than v has. The measure of a base case is 0.

16. (b) There are exactly $n(n-1)/2$ pairs of distinct vertices, so for each pair (u,v) there is either an edge from u to v or one from v to u [but not both, by acyclicity]. If every vertex has an edge leading from it, then by following edges we construct a closed path, and hence a cycle. Thus some vertex s has no edge pointing away from it. But then every other vertex has an edge to s, so s must be labeled 1. Remove s and the $n-1$ edges leading to it and apply induction.

17. Since the digraph is acyclic there can be at most one edge joining each of the $n(n-1)/2$ pairs of distinct vertices.

18. (a)

> **LeafList(rooted tree)**
>
> {Input: A finite ordered rooted tree with root v}
> {Output: A list of the leaves of the tree, ordered from left to right}
> if v has no children then
>   return v
> else
>   Set $L(v) := \lambda$.
>   for each child w of v, taken from left to right, do
>   Attach LeafList(w) to the end of $L(v)$.
>   return $L(v)$ ∎

(b)

$$
\begin{aligned}
&\text{LeafList}(T_r); \quad L(r) = \lambda \\
&\quad \text{LeafList}(T_v); \quad L(v) = \lambda \\
&\qquad \text{LeafList}(T_u) = u; \; L(v) = u \\
&\qquad \text{LeafList}(T_w); \quad L(w) = \lambda \\
&\qquad\quad \text{LeafList}(T_x) = x; \; L(w) = x \\
&\qquad\quad \text{LeafList}(T_y) = y; \; L(w) = x\,y \\
&\qquad\quad \text{LeafList}(T_z) = z; \; L(w) = x\,y\,z \\
&\qquad = x\,y\,z; \; L(v) = u\,x\,y\,z \\
&\quad = u\,x\,y\,z; \; L(r) = u\,x\,y\,z \\
&\quad \text{LeafList}(T_s); \quad L(s) = \lambda \\
&\qquad \text{LeafList}(T_p) = p; \; L(s) = p \\
&\qquad \text{LeafList}(T_q) = q; \; L(s) = p\,q \\
&\quad = p\,q; \; L(r) = u\,x\,y\,z\,p\,q \\
&= u\,x\,y\,z\,p\,q
\end{aligned}
$$

7.4 Answers

1. Reverse Polish: $x\,4\,2 \,\widehat{}\, - y * 2\,3\,/\,+$.   Polish: $+ * - x \,\widehat{}\, 4\,2\,y\,/\,2\,3$.

2. Reverse Polish: $2\,a \,\widehat{}\, 2\,b \,\widehat{}\, +$.   Infix: $(2 \,\widehat{}\, a) + (2 \,\widehat{}\, b)$, i.e., $2^a + 2^b$.

3. (a) Polish: $- * + a\,b - a\,b - \,\widehat{}\, a\,2 \,\widehat{}\, b\,2$;
      Infix: $(a + b) * (a - b) - ((a \,\widehat{}\, 2) - (b \,\widehat{}\, 2))$.

   (b) $(a + b)(a - b) - (a^2 - b^2) = 0$. The tree is trivial.

4. (a) 22.   (b) 49.   (c) 37.

5. (a) 20.   (b) 10.

6. (a) 73.   (b) 1.   (c) 223.

   (d) $14/49 = 2/7$.   (e) 20.

7. (a) $3\,x * 4 - 2 \,\widehat{}\,$.   (b) $a\,2\,b * + a\,2\,b * - /$.

   (c) The answer depends on how the terms are associated. For the choice
      $(x - x^2) + (x^3 - x^4)$, the answer is $x\,x\,2 \,\widehat{}\, - x\,3 \,\widehat{}\, x\,4 \,\widehat{}\, - +$.

8. (a) $\widehat{}\, - * 3\,x\,4\,2$.   (b) $/ + a * 2\,b - a * 2\,b$.

   (c) As in 7(c), the answer depends on how the terms are associated. For the
      grouping $((x - x^2) + x^3) - x^4$, the answer is $- + - x \,\widehat{}\, x\,2 \,\widehat{}\, x\,3 \,\widehat{}\, x\,4$.

9. (a) $a\,b\,c * *$ and $a\,b * c *$.

   (b) $a\,b\,c + *$ and $a\,b * a\,c * +$.

   (c) The associative law is $a\,b\,c * * = a\,b * c *$. The distributive law is $a\,b\,c + * = a\,b * a\,c * +$.

10. $[(x+y)^2 - (x-y)^2]/(xy) = 4$.

11. (a) $p \to (q \vee (\neg p))$.

(b) Reverse Polish: $p\,q\,p\,\neg\,\vee\,\to$;   Polish: $\to\,p\,\vee\,q\,\neg\,p$.

12. (a) Infix: $\neg((\neg p) \wedge (\neg q)) \leftrightarrow (p \vee q)$.

(b) Infix: $(p \wedge q) \leftrightarrow \neg(p \to \neg q)$.

13. (a) Infix: $(p \wedge (p \to q)) \to q$.

(b) Infix: $\{[(p \to q) \wedge (r \to s)] \wedge (p \vee r)\} \to (q \vee s)$.

14. (a) $p\,q \to q\,r \to \wedge p\,r \to \to$.   (b) $p\,q \vee p\,\neg \wedge q \to$.

15. (a) Both give $a\,/\,b+c$.   (b) Both give $a+b \wedge 3+c$.

16. (a) By (B), each of 3, x and 2 is a wff. So by (R), $x\,2\,\wedge$ is a wff. So by (R), $3\,x\,2\,\wedge\,*$ is.

(b) By (B), each of x, y and 1 is a wff. So by (R), $x\,y+$, $1\,x\,/$ and $1\,y\,/$ are wff's. So $1\,x\,/\,1\,y\,/+$ is a wff. Finally $x\,y+1\,x\,/\,1\,y\,/+*$ is a wff.

(c) By (B), each of 4, x, 2, y and z is a wff. By (R), $x\,2\,\wedge$ and $y\,z+$ are wff's. So $y\,z+2\,\wedge$ is a wff. So $x\,2\,\wedge\,y\,z+2\,\wedge\,/$ is a wff. Finally, $4\,x\,2\,\wedge\,y\,z+2\,\wedge\,/-$ is a wff.

17. (a) (B) Numerical constants and variables are wff's.
   (R) If f and g are wff's, so are $+f\,g$, $-f\,g$, $*f\,g$, $/f\,g$ and $\wedge f\,g$.

(b) By (B), each of x, 4 and 2 is a wff. By (R), $/4\,x$ is a wff. So by (R), $+x\,/4\,x$ is a wff and then $\wedge +x\,/4\,x\,2$ is a wff.

18. (a) By (B), the variables $x_1, x_2, \ldots$ and the constant 2 are wff's. By (R), $S_1 = x_1\,2\,\wedge$ is a wff. If S_n is a wff, then by (R) so are $x_{n+1}\,2\,\wedge$ and $S_{n+1} = S_n\,x_{n+1}\,2\,\wedge\,+$. So all S_n's are wff's by induction.

(b) $S_n = x_1^2 + \cdots + x_n^2$ or $\displaystyle\sum_{k=1}^{n} x_k^2$.

19. (a) (B) Variables, such as p, q, r, are wff's.
   (R) If P and Q are wff's, so are $P\,Q\,\vee$, $P\,Q\,\wedge$, $P\,Q \to$, $P\,Q \leftrightarrow$ and $P\,\neg$.

(b) Argue, in turn, that $q\,\neg$, $p\,q\,\neg \wedge$ and $p\,q\,\neg \wedge \neg$ are wff's. Likewise, $p\,q\,\neg \to$ is a wff. Thus $p\,q\,\neg \wedge \neg p\,q\,\neg \to \vee$ is a wff.

(c) (B) Variables, such as p, q, r, are wff's.
   (R) If P and Q are wff's, so are $\vee P\,Q$, $\wedge P\,Q$, $\to P\,Q$, $\leftrightarrow P\,Q$ and $\neg P$.

(d) By (B), p and q are wff's. By (R), $\neg q$ is a wff. So by (R), $\wedge p\,\neg q$ and $\to p\,\neg q$ are wff's. Also $\neg \wedge p\,\neg q$ is a wff. Finally, $\vee \neg \wedge p\,\neg q \to p\,\neg q$ is a wff.

20. (a)

vertex	s	t	v	y	r	z	w	u	x	q
available children	$\emptyset$	$\{s\}$	$\{s,t\}$	$\{s,t,v\}$	$\{s,y\}$	$\{r\}$	$\{r,z\}$	$\{r,z,w\}$	$\{r,z,w,u\}$	$\{r,z,x\}$
assigned children				$\{t,v\}$	$\{s,y\}$				$\{w,u\}$	$\{r,z,x\}$

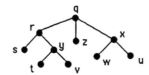

(b) No. s would have to be the root and have no children. Also, the last vertex q would have to be a leaf; it couldn't have 3 children.

21. The first operation is a unary operation and the second one is a binary operation. In a reverse Polish calculator, the first key pops just one entry off the stack, while the second key pops two entries off.

22. (a) $\ominus((4-(x+y))*(\ominus z))$, i.e., $-((4-(x+y))*(-z))$.

(b) Each $\ominus$ node has one child, which is a right child. One node $\ominus$ has child z and one has child $*$.

7.5 Answers

1. (a) 35, 56, 70, 82.   (b) 59, 95, 118, 135, 145, 150.

2. Both have weight 150.

3. We recommend the procedure in Examples 4 and 5.

(a) $1, 3, 4, 6, 9, 13 \rightarrow 4, 4, 6, 9, 13 \rightarrow 6, 8, 9, 13 \rightarrow 9, 13, 14 \rightarrow 14, 22$. Weight $= 84$.

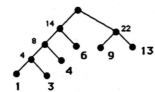

(b) Weight $= 136$.   (c) Weight $= 244$.

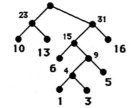
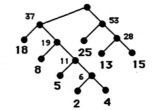

(d) Weight = 220.

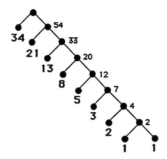

4. You will get essentially the tree in Figure 9(a) or the shorter tree

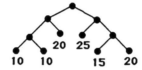

5. All but (b) are prefix codes. In (b), 01 consists of the first two digits of 0111.

6. (a)

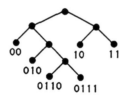

(b) ADAMHAD'EM or Adam had 'em.

(c) HE MADE ME MAD.

(d) DAD HAD MADAM. HE MADE MA MAD. MA MADE DAD DEAD.

7. (a)

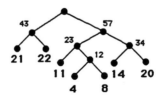

The corresponding optimal code is

letter	a	b	c	d	e	f	g
frequency	11	20	4	22	14	8	21
code	100	111	1010	01	110	1011	00

(b) 269.

8. (a)

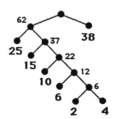

Optimal code

letter	a	b	c	d	e	f	g
frequency	25	2	15	10	38	4	6
code	00	011110	010	0110	1	011111	01110

(b) Average length per 100 letters: 239.

9. (a) The vertex labeled 0 has only one child, 00. See figure below.

(b) Consider any string beginning with 01.

(a)   (c)

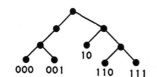   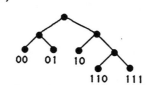

In both (a) and (c), no labeled vertex lies below another such vertex. The binary tree in (c) is regular.

10. (a)

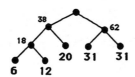

Optimal code

letter	a	d	e	h	m
frequency	31	31	12	6	20
code	10	11	001	000	01

(b) Average length per 100 letters: 218.

11. (a) $(61 + 73 - 1) + (31 + 61 + 73 - 1) + (23 + 31 + 61 + 73 - 1)$
$= 133 + 164 + 187 = 484.$

(b) $(23 + 73 - 1) + (23 + 61 + 73 - 1) + 187 = 95 + 156 + 187 = 438.$

(c) $(23 + 31 - 1) + (61 + 73 - 1) + 187 = 53 + 133 + 187 = 373.$

(d) $(23 + 73 - 1) + (31 + 61 - 1) + 187 = 95 + 91 + 187 = 373.$

(e)

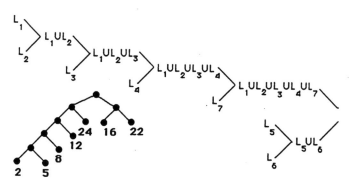

This merging involves at most $(23 + 31 - 1) + (23 + 31 + 61 - 1) + 187 = 53 + 114 + 187 = 354$ comparisons.

12. (a)

(b) $10 + 19 + 41 + 62 + 104 = 236$.

13. (a)

(b) 221.

14. This follows immediately from the lemma on page 450.

15. For example, in Exercise 1(a), the first tree has weight 35. The leaf of weight **21** $= 12 + 9$ was replaced by the subtree with weights 12 and 9, and the weight of the whole tree increased to 56, i.e., to $35 + 21$. Then the leaf of weight **14** $= 7 + 7$ was replaced by the subtree with weights 7 and 7, and the weight of the whole tree increased to 70, i.e., to $56 + 14$. Etc.

Chapter 8

Some of the material in this chapter is just digraph versions of results about graphs in Chapter 6, but most of it has a flavor that comes from the fact that edges are directed. Acyclic graphs are just forests of trees, but acyclic digraphs can have all kinds of complicated cross-connections.

Section 8.1 introduces sources, sinks and the reachability relation. The algorithm for numbering vertices based on sinks is easy to understand but not as fast as TREESORT in Chapter 7.

In § 8.2 we put weights on the edges, much as we did for graphs in § 6.6. The tables of edge weights W and min-weights W^* lead naturally to the use of matrices in algorithms to find W^* and do a variety of other chores. Here we explicitly consider paths of length 0. Later we'll see a way to ignore them selectively. The discussion of scheduling networks can be deemphasized, if desired. The basic ideas are just perversions of the min-weight ideas, but the application itself is of considerable practical importance. Critical path software is now available for microcomputers. The material prior to Example 4 in § 8.2 is background for § 8.3.

Section 8.3 presents several algorithms for computing min-weights and max-weights. Allow at least two class meetings for it, and ask the students to read Office Hours 8.2 to supplement your discussion. DIJKSTRA's algorithm spreads out from an initial vertex v_0, and when it labels a new vertex v it also computes the min-weight $W^*(v_0, v)$. WARSHALL's algorithm, on the other hand, only guarantees the right answer at the last iteration. Go through examples of both algorithms in class.

We have tried to motivate the final version of Dijkstra's algorithm by looking slowly at how one might try to build an algorithm that has the general plan of spreading from a single vertex and that is comparatively easy to verify. It would have been quicker simply to verify the resulting algorithm directly, but experience tells us that students have a hard time with that, and our hope is that the present treatment will remove some of the mystery. The format we have used to illustrate the progress of DIJKSTRA's algorithm in Figure 2 should be supplemented in class by marking the graph itself as the labeling proceeds and by keeping track of the pointers. WARSHALL's algorithm is harder to draw pictures of, though easier to understand: it looks first for paths with just v_1 as intermediate vertex, then for

132

those with v_1 or v_2 as intermediate vertices, then for those with v_1, v_2 or v_3, etc.

One suggestion for WARSHALL'S algorithm is to distribute sheets on which the algorithm is completely carried out, and discuss a few sample calculations. Or you can just display an intermediate matrix and discuss how to compute entries for the next matrix. Examples are essential.

The easiest way to understand how MAX-WEIGHT works is to walk through a simple example. Exercises 1- 9 are chosen to provide easy illustrations, with no tricks.

8.1 Answers

1. Sinks are t and z. Only source is u.

2. (a) SUCC$(t) = \emptyset$, SUCC$(u) = \{t, w, x\}$, SUCC$(v) = \{t, y\}$, SUCC$(w) = \{y\}$, etc.

   (b) z.   (c) t and z.

3. (a) $R(s) = \{s, t, u, w, x, y, z\} = R(t)$, $R(u) = \{w, x, y, z\}$, $R(w) = \{z\}$, $R(x) = \emptyset$, $R(y) = \{x, z\}$, $R(z) = \emptyset$.

   (b) x and z are the sinks.

   (c) $s\,t\,s$ is a cycle, so G is not acyclic.

4. No. It could go around a cycle forever and never stop.

5. (a)

   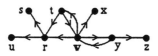

   (b) No, though the immediate successor sets do determine a digraph if multiple edges are not allowed.

   (c) s, u, x, z.

   (d) $w\,x$, $w\,r\,s$, $w\,r\,u$, $w\,y\,z$ are some.

6. Use NumberingVertices. One example labels $v = 1$, $u = 2$, $y = 3$, $x = 4$, $w = 5$, $t = 6$, $z = 7$.

7. Use NumberingVertices. One example labels $t = 1$, $z = 2$, $y = 3$, $w = 4$, $v = 5$, $x = 6$, $u = 7$.

8. (a) Here is one. The arrows can be given any directions.

(b) If x and y are two vertices there is either an edge from x to y, so that x is not a sink, or an edge from y to x, so that y is not a sink.

(c) Yes. See the answer to part (a).

(d) Not very much.

9. (a) One example is $r\,s\,w\,t\,v\,w\,v\,u\,x\,y\,z\,v\,r\,u\,y\,v\,s\,r$.

(b) One example is $w\,w\,x\,y\,x\,z\,z\,y\,w$.

10. One might use the sequence e_2, e_7, e_{13}, e_{12}, e_{11}, e_{14}, e_{16}, e_{15}, e_{10}, e_4, e_5, e_8, e_9, e_6, e_3, e_1 to get $1\,1\,0\,1\,1\,1\,1\,0\,0\,1\,0\,1\,0\,0\,0\,0$ in a circle. Another might use e_2, e_5, e_6, e_4, e_7, e_{13}, e_{12}, e_9, e_8, e_{11}, e_{14}, e_{16}, e_{15}, e_{10}, e_3, e_1 to get $1\,0\,0\,1\,1\,0\,1\,0\,1\,1\,1\,1\,0\,0\,0\,0$ in a circle.

11. (a) One such digraph is drawn in Figure 3(b) where $w = 0\,0$, $x = 0\,1$, $z = 1\,1$, and $y = 1\,0$.

(b) One possible sequence is $1\,1\,1\,0\,1\,0\,0\,0$ placed in a circle.

12. (a) The set of 2^{n-1} vertices consists of all strings of 0's and 1's of length $n-1$. A directed edge connects two such strings if the last $n-2$ digits of the initial vertex agree with the first $n-2$ digits of the terminal vertex. Label each edge with the last digit of the terminal vertex. An easy induction shows that for $k = 1, \dots, n-1$, the labels of the edges of a path of length k give the last k digits of the terminal vertex.

Now consider any sequence $d_1\,d_2 \cdots d_n$ of 0's and 1's. Then $d_1\,d_2 \cdots d_{n-1}$ is the initial vertex for an edge labeled d_n. Since the $n-1$ edges preceding it are labeled $d_1, \dots, d_{n-1}$, the n consecutive edges are labeled $d_1, \dots, d_n$, as desired.

(b) Put $0\,0\,1\,1$ in a circle.

13. Show that $\overline{G}$ is also acyclic. Apply Theorem 2 to $\overline{G}$. A sink for $\overline{G}$ is a source for G.

14. (a) Any algorithm that returns $\text{Sink}(\overline{G})$ will do this.

(b) Here is one possible algorithm.

> {Input: A finite acyclic digraph G with n vertices}
> {Gives $V(G)$ a sorted labeling in reverse order}
> Let $V := V(G)$ and $E := E(G)$.
> while $V \neq \emptyset$ do
>   Let H be the digraph with vertex set V and edge set E.
>   Apply Source to H {to get a source for H}.
>   Label Source(H) with $|V|$.
>   Remove Source(H) from V and all edges attached to it from E.
> return ∎

(c) Two possible answers are

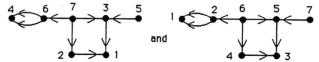

and

15. (a) See the second proof of Theorem 2.

(b) If a finite acyclic digraph has just one source, then there is a path to each vertex from the source.

16. (a) The reflexive and symmetric properties are built into the definition. Transitivity is a general property of reachability: string together a path from u to v and a path from v to w to get a path from u to w.

(b) $\{s,t\}, \{u\}, \{w\}, \{x\}, \{y\}, \{z\}$.

(c) It is the equality relation: $x \sim y$ if and only if $x = y$. To see this, suppose $x \sim y$ and $x \neq y$. Then there is a path from x to y and a path from y to x; together they give a closed path and Corollary 1 on page 457 shows that G has a cycle.

17. (a) In the proof of Theorem 1 on page 457 [given in the proof of Theorem 1 on page 335], choose a shortest path consisting of edges of the given path.

(b) If $u \neq v$, then Theorem 1 guarantees an acyclic path from u to v and Corollary 2 says such a path has no repeated vertices, so it surely has no repeated edges. If $u = v$, then Corollary 1 says there is a cycle from u to u. Again, all vertices are different, so all edges are too.

18. (a) Consider $w \in R(u)$. Then there is a path from u to w. Since there is a path from v to u there is one from v to w; i.e., $w \in R(v)$. Thus $R(u) \subseteq R(v)$.

(b) Consider a finite acyclic digraph G, and choose v in $V(G)$ with $|R(v)|$ as small as possible. We claim that $R(v) = \emptyset$, so that v is a sink. Suppose $w \in R(v)$. By part (a), $R(w) \subseteq R(v)$. Since $|R(v)|$ is minimal, $R(w) = R(v)$. Thus $w \in R(w)$. By Corollary 1 of Theorem 1, G contains a cycle, contrary to hypothesis.

(c) Yes. Given a list of the sets $R(v)$, one could examine them one at a time to see which has smallest size. In fact, the smallest ones will be empty.

19. Consider a cycle in a graph G, with vertex sequence $x_1 x_2 \cdots x_n x_1$. Then $x_1, \ldots, x_n$ are distinct and no edge appears twice. Assign directions to the edges in the cycle so they go from x_1 to x_2 to x_3 to ... to x_n to x_1. Since no edge appears twice, this assignment cannot contradict itself. Assign directions arbitrarily to the other edges of G. Then the edges in the cycle form a directed cycle in the resulting digraph.

Conversely, suppose it is possible to assign directions to edges in G so that a path with vertex sequence $x_1 x_2 \cdots x_m x_1$ is a directed cycle. Then $m \geq 1$ and $x_1, \ldots, x_m$ are all different. If $m \geq 3$ then the path is an undirected cycle by Proposition 1. If $m = 2$ the vertex sequence is $x_1 x_2 x_1$, but the edges from x_1 to x_2 and from x_2 to x_1 must be different because their directions are different. In this case the undirected path is simple, so it is a cycle. Finally, if $m = 1$ the path is a loop, so it's a cycle. In all cases the directed cycle is an undirected cycle.

8.2 Answers

1.

W	A	B	C	D
A	1.4	1.0	∞	∞
B	0.4	7	∞	0.2
C	0.7	0.3	7	∞
D	0.8	∞	0.2	7

W^*	A	B	C	D
A	∞	1.0	1.4	1.2
B	0.4	∞	0.4	0.2
C	0.7	0.3	∞	0.5
D	0.8	0.5	0.2	∞

2.

W^*	s	u	v	w	x	y	f
s	0	2	7	4	5	8	9
u	∞	0	∞	2	3	6	7
v	∞	∞	0	∞	∞	2	5
w	∞	∞	∞	0	∞	4	8
x	∞	∞	∞	∞	0	6	4
y	∞	∞	∞	∞	∞	0	4
f	∞	∞	∞	∞	∞	∞	0

3.

W	m	q	r	s	w	x	y	z
m	∞	6	∞	2	∞	4	∞	∞
q	∞	∞	4	∞	4	∞	∞	∞
r	∞	∞	∞	∞	∞	∞	∞	3
s	∞	3	∞	∞	5	1	∞	∞
w	∞	∞	2	∞	∞	∞	2	5
x	∞	∞	∞	∞	3	∞	6	∞
y	∞	∞	∞	∞	∞	∞	∞	1
z	∞	∞	∞	∞	∞	∞	∞	∞

W^*	m	q	r	s	w	x	y	z
m	∞	5	8	2	6	3	8	9
q	∞	∞	4	∞	4	∞	6	7
r	∞	∞	∞	∞	∞	∞	∞	3
s	∞	3	6	∞	4	1	6	7
w	∞	∞	2	∞	∞	∞	2	3
x	∞	∞	5	∞	3	∞	5	6
y	∞	∞	∞	∞	∞	∞	∞	1
z	∞	∞	∞	∞ ·	∞	∞	∞	∞

4. $s\,w\,v\,y\,x\,f$ is the other min-path.

5. (a) If the digraph is acyclic the weights must be as shown

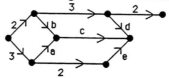

with $\min\{a+1,b\} = 4$ and $\min\{c+1,d,e\} = 3$.

(b) They might. For example, consider $b = 8$, $a = 3$ in part (a), and then consider $b = 4$, $a = 7$.

6. String together a min-path from u to v and one from v to w. The weight of the combined path is $W^*(u,v) + W^*(v,w) = W^*(u,w)$, so the path has minimum weight for paths from u to w.

7. (a) The critical paths are $s\,v\,x\,f$ and $s\,v\,x\,z\,f$.

(b) If the edges all have positive weights, then going around a cycle again and again would give arbitrarily large path weights.

8. $F(s,z) = L(z) - A(s) - W(s,z) = 104 - 0 - 20 = 84$. Also $F(z,f) = 84$.

9. (a)

	s	u	v	w	x	y	f
A	0	2	7	5	5	11	15
L	0	2	9	7	5	11	15

(b) $S(v) = S(w) = 2$. $S(t) = 0$ for all other vertices t.

(c) $s\,u\,x\,y\,f$ is the only critical path.

(d) Edges on the critical path have float time 0. Also $F(x,f) = 6$, $F(u,w) = F(v,f) = 3$ and $F(s,w) = F(w,y) = F(s,v) = F(v,y) = 2$.

10. (a)

	s	u	v	w	x	y	f
A	0	1	1	2	2	3	4
L	0	1	2	2	2	3	4

(b) $S(v) = 1$. $S(t) = 0$ for all other vertices t.

(c) The critical paths are $s\,u\,w\,y\,f$ and $s\,u\,x\,y\,f$.

(d) Edges on the critical paths have float time 0. Also $F(s,w) = F(s,v) = F(v,y) = F(x,f) = 1$ and $F(v,f) = 2$.

11. (a)

	m	s	q	x	w	r	y	z
A	0	2	6	4	10	12	12	15
L	0	3	6	7	10	12	14	15

(b) $S(s) = 1$, $S(x) = 3$, $S(y) = 2$ and $S(t) = 0$ for all other vertices t.

(c) There are two critical paths: $m\,q\,w\,z$ and $m\,q\,w\,r\,z$.

(d) Edges on the critical paths have float time 0. Also $F(s,x) = F(x,y) = 4$, $F(s,w) = F(x,w) = F(m,x) = 3$, $F(q,r) = F(w,y) = F(y,z) = 2$ and $F(s,q) = F(m,s) = 1$.

12. (a) $F(s,f) = 0$ and $F(s,u) = F(u,v) = F(v,f) = 6$.

(b) No. If each noncritical task in part (a) were delayed by its float time 6, the total time would be $1 + 2 + 1 + 3 \cdot 6 = 22$.

13. (a) The two critical paths are $s\,u\,w\,x\,y\,f$ and $s\,t\,w\,x\,y\,f$. The critical edges are (s,u), (u,w), (s,t), (t,w), (w,x), (x,y) and (y,f).

(b) 2.

(c) The edges are (u,v) and (x,z).

14.

	s	r	t	u	v	w	x	y	z	f
A	0	1	2	3	5	4	9	11	11	14
L	0	2	2	3	6	4	9	11	12	14
S	0	1	0	0	1	0	0	0	1	0

15. (a) Shrink the 0-edges to make their two endpoints the same.

(b)

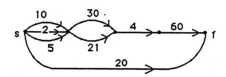

16. (a)

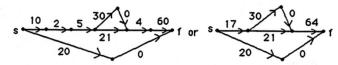

(b) The critical path is

s •———————→• /\ •———————→• f

(c) Only frying and rice cooking are not critical.

17. (a)

W	u	v	w	x	y
u	∞	1	∞	∞	∞
v	∞	∞	3	-2	∞
w	∞	∞	∞	∞	∞
x	4	∞	∞	5	∞
y	∞	∞	∞	5	∞

W^*	u	v	w	x	y
u	3	1	4	-1	∞
v	2	3	3	-2	∞
w	∞	∞	∞	∞	∞
x	4	5	8	3	∞
y	9	10	13	5	∞

(b) The diagonal entries of W^* are not all ∞'s, so the digraph contains a cycle. [It is, of course, $u\,v\,x\,u$.]

(c) There would be no min-weights at all for paths involving u, v or x, because going around the cycle $u\,v\,x\,u$ repeatedly would keep reducing the weight by 1.

(d) The sources are vertices whose columns are all ∞'s, and the sinks have rows all ∞'s. The only source is y; the only sink is w.

18. (a) The following are equivalent to $S(v) \le F(u,v)$:
$L(v) - A(v) \le L(v) - A(u) - W(u,v); \quad A(u) + W(u,v) \le A(v);$
$M(s,u) + W(u,v) \le M(s,v)$. The last inequality is clear.

(b) If (u,v) is a critical edge, then $F(u,v) = 0$ by (a) of the theorem. Then (b) of the same theorem shows that $S(u) = S(v) = 0$.

(c) (u,v) might not be critical. Here is an example.

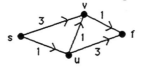

19. (a) $FF(u,v) = A(v) - A(u) - W(u,v)$.

(b) $FF(s,u) = FF(u,x) = FF(x,y) = FF(s,w) = FF(y,f) = FF(s,v) = 0$, $FF(u,w) = 1$, $FF(w,y) = FF(v,y) = 2$, $FF(v,f) = 3$, $FF(x,f) = 6$.

(c) The slack time at v.

20. (a) Consider a critical edge (u,v). There is a max-path from s to f that contains this edge and has weight $M(s,f)$. The same path with the added weight on (u,v) has total weight greater than $M(s,f)$.

(b) If there is a critical path that does not involve the step, no reduction occurs. For example, see the network in the answer to Exercise 18(c); reducing the weight of edge (s,v) will not reduce the total time needed.

21. (a) $A(u) = M(s,u) =$ weight of a max-path from s to u. If there is an edge (w,u), a max-path from s to w followed by that edge has total weight at most $M(s,u)$. That is, $A(w) + W(w,u) \le A(u)$. If (w,u) is an edge in a max-path from s to u, then $A(w) + W(w,u) = A(u)$.

(b) Consider a vertex u. If (u,v) is an edge, then (u,v) followed by a max-path from v to f has total weight at most $M(u,f)$. That is, $W(u,v)+M(v,f) \le M(u,f)$. Hence

$$L(v) - W(u,v) = M(s,f) - M(v,f) - W(u,v) \ge M(s,f) - M(u,f) = L(u)$$

for every edge (u,v), and so $\min\{L(v) - W(u,v) : (u,v) \in E(G)\} \ge L(u)$. Choosing an edge (u,v) in a max-path from u to f gives $L(v) - W(u,v) = L(u)$, so $L(u)$ is the minimum value.

8.3 Answers

1.   (a)   (b)

$$\mathbf{W}^* = \begin{bmatrix} \infty & 1 & 2 & 3 & 4 & 5 & 7 \\ \infty & \infty & \infty & 4 & 3 & 4 & 6 \\ \infty & \infty & \infty & 1 & 4 & 5 & 7 \\ \infty & \infty & \infty & \infty & 3 & 4 & 6 \\ \infty & \infty & \infty & \infty & \infty & 1 & 3 \\ \infty & \infty & \infty & \infty & \infty & \infty & 3 \\ \infty & \infty & \infty & \infty & \infty & \infty & \infty \end{bmatrix}, \quad \mathbf{W}^* = \begin{bmatrix} \infty & 6 & 8 & \infty & \infty & 1 & 12 \\ \infty & 14 & 2 & \infty & \infty & \infty & 6 \\ \infty & 12 & 14 & \infty & \infty & \infty & 4 \\ 3 & 9 & 11 & \infty & 9 & 4 & 15 \\ 2 & 7 & 9 & \infty & \infty & 3 & 13 \\ \infty & 5 & 7 & \infty & \infty & \infty & 11 \\ \infty & 8 & 10 & \infty & \infty & \infty & 14 \end{bmatrix}.$$

(c)

$$\mathbf{P}_0 = \begin{bmatrix} 0 & 2 & 3 & 0 & 0 & 0 & 0 \\ 0 & 0 & 0 & 4 & 5 & 0 & 0 \\ 0 & 0 & 0 & 4 & 5 & 6 & 0 \\ 0 & 0 & 0 & 0 & 5 & 6 & 0 \\ 0 & 0 & 0 & 0 & 0 & 6 & 7 \\ 0 & 0 & 0 & 0 & 0 & 0 & 7 \\ 0 & 0 & 0 & 0 & 0 & 0 & 0 \end{bmatrix}, \quad \mathbf{P}_{\text{final}} = \begin{bmatrix} 0 & 2 & 3 & 3 & 2 & 2 & 2 \\ 0 & 0 & 0 & 4 & 5 & 5 & 5 \\ 0 & 0 & 0 & 4 & 4 & 4 & 4 \\ 0 & 0 & 0 & 0 & 5 & 5 & 5 \\ 0 & 0 & 0 & 0 & 0 & 6 & 7 \\ 0 & 0 & 0 & 0 & 0 & 0 & 7 \\ 0 & 0 & 0 & 0 & 0 & 0 & 0 \end{bmatrix}.$$

(d)

$$\mathbf{P}_0 = \begin{bmatrix} 0 & 2 & 0 & 0 & 0 & 6 & 0 \\ 0 & 0 & 3 & 0 & 0 & 0 & 0 \\ 0 & 0 & 0 & 0 & 0 & 0 & 7 \\ 1 & 0 & 0 & 0 & 5 & 0 & 0 \\ 1 & 2 & 0 & 0 & 0 & 6 & 0 \\ 0 & 2 & 3 & 0 & 0 & 0 & 0 \\ 0 & 2 & 0 & 0 & 0 & 0 & 0 \end{bmatrix}, \quad \mathbf{P}_{\text{final}} = \begin{bmatrix} 0 & 6 & 6 & 0 & 0 & 6 & 6 \\ 0 & 3 & 3 & 0 & 0 & 0 & 3 \\ 0 & 7 & 7 & 0 & 0 & 0 & 7 \\ 1 & 1 & 1 & 0 & 5 & 1 & 1 \\ 1 & 2 & 2 & 0 & 0 & 1 & 2 \\ 0 & 2 & 2 & 0 & 0 & 0 & 2 \\ 0 & 2 & 2 & 0 & 0 & 0 & 2 \end{bmatrix}.$$

2.

$$\mathbf{M} = \begin{bmatrix} -\infty & 1 & 2 & 5 & 8 & 13 & 16 \\ -\infty & -\infty & -\infty & 4 & 7 & 12 & 15 \\ -\infty & -\infty & -\infty & 1 & 5 & 9 & 12 \\ -\infty & -\infty & -\infty & -\infty & 3 & 8 & 11 \\ -\infty & -\infty & -\infty & -\infty & -\infty & 1 & 4 \\ -\infty & -\infty & -\infty & -\infty & -\infty & -\infty & 3 \\ -\infty & -\infty & -\infty & -\infty & -\infty & -\infty & -\infty \end{bmatrix}.$$

3. (a)

M	$D(v_j)$						$P(v_j)$					
	v_2	v_3	v_4	v_5	v_6	v_7	v_2	v_3	v_4	v_5	v_6	v_7
$\{v_1\}$	1	2	∞	∞	∞	∞	v_1	v_1				
$\{v_1,v_2\}$	1	**2**	5	4	∞	∞	v_1	v_1	v_2	v_2		
$\{v_1,v_2,v_3\}$	1	2	3	4	9	∞	v_1	v_1	v_3	v_2	v_3	
$\{v_1,v_2,v_3,v_4\}$	1	2	3	4	9	∞	v_1	v_1	v_3	v_2	v_3	
$\{v_1,v_2,v_3,v_4,v_5\}$	1	2	3	4	5	7	v_1	v_1	v_3	v_2	v_5	v_5

no change now

(b)

M	$D(v_j)$						$P(v_j)$					
	v_2	v_3	v_4	v_5	v_6	v_7	v_2	v_3	v_4	v_5	v_6	v_7
$\{v_1\}$	7	∞	∞	∞	1	∞	v_1				v_1	
$\{v_1,v_6\}$	**6**	10	∞	∞	1	∞	v_6	v_6			v_1	
$\{v_1,v_6,v_2\}$	6	8	∞	∞	1	14	v_6	v_2			v_1	v_2
$\{v_1,v_6,v_2,v_3\}$	6	8	∞	∞	1	**12**	v_6	v_2			v_1	v_3

no change now

(c)

M	$D(v_j)$				$P(v_j)$			
	v_2	v_3	v_4	v_5	v_2	v_3	v_4	v_5
$\{v_1\}$	2	**1**	7	∞	v_1	v_1	v_1	
$\{v_1,v_3\}$	**2**	1	7	4	v_1	v_1	v_1	v_3
$\{v_1,v_3,v_2\}$	2	1	6	**4**	v_1	v_1	v_2	v_3
$\{v_1,v_3,v_2,v_5\}$	2	1	**5**	4	v_1	v_1	v_5	v_3

no change now

(d)

M	$D(v_j)$				$P(v_j)$			
	v_2	v_3	v_4	v_5	v_2	v_3	v_4	v_5
$\{v_1\}$	∞	**4**	∞	∞		v_1		
$\{v_1,v_3\}$	∞	4	**6**	∞		v_1	v_3	
$\{v_1,v_3,v_4\}$	∞	4	6	9		v_1	v_3	v_4

no change now

M	$D(v_j)$					$P(v_j)$				
	v_2	v_3	v_4	v_5	v_6	v_2	v_3	v_4	v_5	v_6
$\{v_1\}$	7	∞	**2**	∞	∞	v_1		v_1		
$\{v_1,v_4\}$	**6**	∞	2	∞	∞	v_4		v_1		
$\{v_1,v_4,v_2\}$	6	10	2	**7**	∞	v_4	v_2	v_1	v_2	
$\{v_1,v_4,v_2,v_5\}$	6	**9**	2	7	∞	v_4	v_5	v_1	v_2	
$\{v_1,v_4,v_2,v_5,v_3\}$	6	9	2	7	12	v_4	v_5	v_1	v_2	v_3

4.

no change now

The final values of $D(v_2),\dots,D(v_6)$ agree with the values $\mathbf{W}^*[1,2],\dots,\mathbf{W}^*[1,6]$ in Example 3.

5. (a)

$$\mathbf{W}_2 = \begin{bmatrix} \infty & \infty & \infty & \infty & 1 & \infty & \infty \\ \infty & \infty & \infty & \infty & \infty & \infty & 1 \\ \infty & \infty & \infty & 1 & \infty & 1 & \infty \\ \infty & \infty & 1 & \infty & 1 & \infty & \infty \\ 1 & \infty & \infty & 1 & 2 & \infty & \infty \\ \infty & \infty & 1 & \infty & \infty & \infty & 1 \\ \infty & 1 & \infty & \infty & \infty & 1 & 2 \end{bmatrix}, \quad \mathbf{W}_4 = \begin{bmatrix} \infty & \infty & \infty & \infty & 1 & \infty & \infty \\ \infty & \infty & \infty & \infty & \infty & \infty & 1 \\ \infty & \infty & 2 & 1 & 2 & 1 & \infty \\ \infty & \infty & 1 & 2 & 1 & 2 & \infty \\ 1 & \infty & 2 & 1 & 2 & 3 & \infty \\ \infty & \infty & 1 & 2 & 3 & 2 & 1 \\ \infty & 1 & \infty & \infty & \infty & 1 & 2 \end{bmatrix},$$

$$\mathbf{W}_7 = \begin{bmatrix} 2 & 6 & 3 & 2 & 1 & 4 & 5 \\ 6 & 2 & 3 & 4 & 5 & 2 & 1 \\ 3 & 3 & 2 & 1 & 2 & 1 & 2 \\ 2 & 4 & 1 & 2 & 1 & 2 & 3 \\ 1 & 5 & 2 & 1 & 2 & 3 & 4 \\ 4 & 2 & 1 & 2 & 3 & 2 & 1 \\ 5 & 1 & 2 & 3 & 4 & 1 & 2 \end{bmatrix}.$$

(b)

M	$D(v_j)$						$P(v_j)$					
	v_2	v_3	v_4	v_5	v_6	v_7	v_2	v_3	v_4	v_5	v_6	v_7
$\{v_1\}$	∞	∞	∞	1	∞	∞				v_1		
$\{v_1, v_5\}$	∞	∞	2	1	∞	∞			v_5	v_1		
$\{v_1, v_5, v_4\}$	∞	3	2	1	∞	∞		v_4	v_5	v_1		
$\{v_1, v_5, v_4, v_3\}$	∞	3	2	1	4	∞		v_4	v_5	v_1	v_3	
$\{v_1, v_5, v_4, v_3, v_6\}$	∞	3	2	1	4	5		v_4	v_5	v_1	v_3	v_6
$\{v_1, v_5, v_4, v_3, v_6, v_7\}$	6	3	2	1	4	5	v_7	v_4	v_5	v_1	v_3	v_6

6. (a) $\mathbf{W}_0 = \mathbf{W}_1 = \begin{bmatrix} \infty & 1 & 2 & \infty & \infty & \infty \\ \infty & \infty & \infty & 2 & 3 & \infty \\ \infty & \infty & \infty & 5 & \infty & \infty \\ \infty & \infty & \infty & \infty & \infty & 2 \\ \infty & \infty & \infty & \infty & \infty & 4 \\ \infty & \infty & \infty & \infty & \infty & \infty \end{bmatrix}, \quad \mathbf{W}_2 = \mathbf{W}_3 = \begin{bmatrix} \infty & 1 & 2 & 3 & 4 & \infty \\ \infty & \infty & \infty & 2 & 3 & \infty \\ \infty & \infty & \infty & 5 & \infty & \infty \\ \infty & \infty & \infty & \infty & \infty & 2 \\ \infty & \infty & \infty & \infty & \infty & 4 \\ \infty & \infty & \infty & \infty & \infty & \infty \end{bmatrix},$

$$\mathbf{W}_4 = \mathbf{W}_5 = \mathbf{W}_6 = \begin{bmatrix} \infty & 1 & 2 & 3 & 4 & 5 \\ \infty & \infty & \infty & 2 & 3 & 4 \\ \infty & \infty & \infty & 5 & \infty & 7 \\ \infty & \infty & \infty & \infty & \infty & 2 \\ \infty & \infty & \infty & \infty & \infty & 4 \\ \infty & \infty & \infty & \infty & \infty & \infty \end{bmatrix}.$$

(b)

$$\mathbf{W}_0 = \mathbf{W}_1 = \begin{bmatrix} -\infty & 1 & 2 & -\infty & -\infty & -\infty \\ -\infty & -\infty & -\infty & 2 & 3 & -\infty \\ -\infty & -\infty & -\infty & 5 & -\infty & -\infty \\ -\infty & -\infty & -\infty & -\infty & -\infty & 2 \\ -\infty & -\infty & -\infty & -\infty & -\infty & 4 \\ -\infty & -\infty & -\infty & -\infty & -\infty & -\infty \end{bmatrix},$$

$$\mathbf{W}_2 = \begin{bmatrix} -\infty & 1 & 2 & 3 & 4 & -\infty \\ -\infty & -\infty & -\infty & 2 & 3 & -\infty \\ -\infty & -\infty & -\infty & 5 & -\infty & -\infty \\ -\infty & -\infty & -\infty & -\infty & -\infty & 2 \\ -\infty & -\infty & -\infty & -\infty & -\infty & 4 \\ -\infty & -\infty & -\infty & -\infty & -\infty & -\infty \end{bmatrix},$$

$$\mathbf{W}_3 = \begin{bmatrix} -\infty & 1 & 2 & 7 & 4 & -\infty \\ -\infty & -\infty & -\infty & 2 & 3 & -\infty \\ -\infty & -\infty & -\infty & 5 & -\infty & -\infty \\ -\infty & -\infty & -\infty & -\infty & -\infty & 2 \\ -\infty & -\infty & -\infty & -\infty & -\infty & 4 \\ -\infty & -\infty & -\infty & -\infty & -\infty & -\infty \end{bmatrix},$$

$$\mathbf{W}_4 = \begin{bmatrix} -\infty & 1 & 2 & 7 & 4 & 9 \\ -\infty & -\infty & -\infty & 2 & 3 & 4 \\ -\infty & -\infty & -\infty & 5 & -\infty & 7 \\ -\infty & -\infty & -\infty & -\infty & -\infty & 2 \\ -\infty & -\infty & -\infty & -\infty & -\infty & 4 \\ -\infty & -\infty & -\infty & -\infty & -\infty & -\infty \end{bmatrix},$$

$$\mathbf{W}_5 = \mathbf{W}_6 = \begin{bmatrix} -\infty & 1 & 2 & 7 & 4 & 9 \\ -\infty & -\infty & -\infty & 2 & 3 & 7 \\ -\infty & -\infty & -\infty & 5 & -\infty & 7 \\ -\infty & -\infty & -\infty & -\infty & -\infty & 2 \\ -\infty & -\infty & -\infty & -\infty & -\infty & 4 \\ -\infty & -\infty & -\infty & -\infty & -\infty & -\infty \end{bmatrix}.$$

7. (a)

$$\mathbf{W}_0 = \mathbf{W}_1 = \begin{bmatrix} \infty & 1 & \infty & 7 & \infty \\ \infty & \infty & 4 & 2 & \infty \\ \infty & \infty & \infty & \infty & 3 \\ \infty & \infty & 1 & \infty & 5 \\ \infty & \infty & \infty & \infty & \infty \end{bmatrix}, \quad \mathbf{P}_0 = \mathbf{P}_1 = \begin{bmatrix} 0 & 2 & 0 & 4 & 0 \\ 0 & 0 & 3 & 4 & 0 \\ 0 & 0 & 0 & 0 & 5 \\ 0 & 0 & 3 & 0 & 5 \\ 0 & 0 & 0 & 0 & 0 \end{bmatrix},$$

$$\mathbf{W}_2 = \begin{bmatrix} \infty & 1 & 5 & 3 & \infty \\ \infty & \infty & 4 & 2 & \infty \\ \infty & \infty & \infty & \infty & 3 \\ \infty & \infty & 1 & \infty & 5 \\ \infty & \infty & \infty & \infty & \infty \end{bmatrix}, \quad \mathbf{P}_2 = \begin{bmatrix} 0 & 2 & 2 & 2 & 0 \\ 0 & 0 & 3 & 4 & 0 \\ 0 & 0 & 0 & 0 & 5 \\ 0 & 0 & 3 & 0 & 5 \\ 0 & 0 & 0 & 0 & 0 \end{bmatrix},$$

$$\mathbf{W}_3 = \begin{bmatrix} \infty & 1 & 5 & 3 & 8 \\ \infty & \infty & 4 & 2 & 7 \\ \infty & \infty & \infty & \infty & 3 \\ \infty & \infty & 1 & \infty & 4 \\ \infty & \infty & \infty & \infty & \infty \end{bmatrix}, \quad \mathbf{P}_3 = \begin{bmatrix} 0 & 2 & 2 & 2 & 2 \\ 0 & 0 & 3 & 4 & 3 \\ 0 & 0 & 0 & 0 & 5 \\ 0 & 0 & 3 & 0 & 3 \\ 0 & 0 & 0 & 0 & 0 \end{bmatrix},$$

$$\mathbf{W}_4 = \begin{bmatrix} \infty & 1 & 4 & 3 & 7 \\ \infty & \infty & 3 & 2 & 6 \\ \infty & \infty & \infty & \infty & 3 \\ \infty & \infty & 1 & \infty & 4 \\ \infty & \infty & \infty & \infty & \infty \end{bmatrix}, \quad \mathbf{P}_4 = \begin{bmatrix} 0 & 2 & 2 & 2 & 2 \\ 0 & 0 & 4 & 4 & 4 \\ 0 & 0 & 0 & 0 & 5 \\ 0 & 0 & 3 & 0 & 3 \\ 0 & 0 & 0 & 0 & 0 \end{bmatrix}.$$

Also, $\mathbf{W}_5 = \mathbf{W}^* = \mathbf{W}_4$ and $\mathbf{P}_5 = \mathbf{P}^* = \mathbf{P}_4$.

(b)

$$\mathbf{W}_0 = \mathbf{W}_1 = \begin{bmatrix} -\infty & 1 & -\infty & 7 & -\infty \\ -\infty & -\infty & 4 & 2 & -\infty \\ -\infty & -\infty & -\infty & -\infty & 3 \\ -\infty & -\infty & 1 & -\infty & 5 \\ -\infty & -\infty & -\infty & -\infty & -\infty \end{bmatrix}, \quad \mathbf{P}_0 = \mathbf{P}_1 = \begin{bmatrix} 0 & 2 & 0 & 4 & 0 \\ 0 & 0 & 3 & 4 & 0 \\ 0 & 0 & 0 & 0 & 5 \\ 0 & 0 & 3 & 0 & 5 \\ 0 & 0 & 0 & 0 & 0 \end{bmatrix},$$

$$\mathbf{W}_2 = \begin{bmatrix} -\infty & 1 & 5 & 7 & -\infty \\ -\infty & -\infty & 4 & 2 & 7 \\ -\infty & -\infty & -\infty & -\infty & 3 \\ -\infty & -\infty & 1 & -\infty & 5 \\ -\infty & -\infty & -\infty & -\infty & -\infty \end{bmatrix}, \quad \mathbf{P}_2 = \begin{bmatrix} 0 & 2 & 2 & 4 & 0 \\ 0 & 0 & 3 & 4 & 0 \\ 0 & 0 & 0 & 0 & 5 \\ 0 & 0 & 3 & 0 & 5 \\ 0 & 0 & 0 & 0 & 0 \end{bmatrix},$$

$$\mathbf{W}_3 = \begin{bmatrix} -\infty & 1 & 5 & 7 & 8 \\ -\infty & -\infty & 4 & 2 & 7 \\ -\infty & -\infty & -\infty & -\infty & 3 \\ -\infty & -\infty & 1 & -\infty & 5 \\ -\infty & -\infty & -\infty & -\infty & -\infty \end{bmatrix}, \quad \mathbf{P}_3 = \begin{bmatrix} 0 & 2 & 2 & 4 & 2 \\ 0 & 0 & 3 & 4 & 3 \\ 0 & 0 & 0 & 0 & 5 \\ 0 & 0 & 3 & 0 & 5 \\ 0 & 0 & 0 & 0 & 0 \end{bmatrix},$$

$$\mathbf{W}_4 = \mathbf{W}_5 = \mathbf{M} = \begin{bmatrix} -\infty & 1 & 8 & 7 & 12 \\ -\infty & -\infty & 4 & 2 & 7 \\ -\infty & -\infty & -\infty & -\infty & 3 \\ -\infty & -\infty & 1 & -\infty & 5 \\ -\infty & -\infty & -\infty & -\infty & -\infty \end{bmatrix},$$

$$\mathbf{P}_4 = \mathbf{P}_5 = \begin{bmatrix} 0 & 2 & 4 & 4 & 4 \\ 0 & 0 & 3 & 4 & 3 \\ 0 & 0 & 0 & 0 & 5 \\ 0 & 0 & 3 & 0 & 5 \\ 0 & 0 & 0 & 0 & 0 \end{bmatrix}.$$

8.

M	$D(v_j)$						$P(v_j)$					
	v_1	v_2	v_4	v_5	v_6	v_7	v_1	v_2	v_4	v_5	v_6	v_7
$\{v_3\}$	∞	∞	1	5	7	∞			v_3	v_3	v_3	
$\{v_3, v_4\}$	∞	∞	1	4	7	∞			v_3	v_4	v_3	
$\{v_3, v_4, v_5\}$	∞	∞	1	4	5	7			v_3	v_4	v_5	v_5

no change now

9. (a)

$$\mathbf{D_0} = \mathbf{D_1} = \begin{bmatrix} -\infty & 1 & 2 & -\infty & -\infty & -\infty & -\infty \end{bmatrix}$$
$$\mathbf{D_2} = \begin{bmatrix} -\infty & 1 & 2 & 5 & 4 & -\infty & -\infty \end{bmatrix}$$
$$\mathbf{D_3} = \begin{bmatrix} -\infty & 1 & 2 & 5 & 7 & 9 & -\infty \end{bmatrix}$$
$$\mathbf{D_4} = \begin{bmatrix} -\infty & 1 & 2 & 5 & 8 & 13 & -\infty \end{bmatrix}$$
$$\mathbf{D_5} = \begin{bmatrix} -\infty & 1 & 2 & 5 & 8 & 13 & 11 \end{bmatrix}$$
$$\mathbf{D_6} = \begin{bmatrix} -\infty & 1 & 2 & 5 & 8 & 13 & 16 \end{bmatrix}$$

(b) The only allowable relabeling is $s = v_1$, $a = v_2$, $c = v_3$, $b = v_4$, $d = v_5$.

$$\mathbf{D_0} = \mathbf{D_1} = \begin{bmatrix} -\infty & 2 & -\infty & 6 & -\infty \end{bmatrix}, \quad \mathbf{D_2} = \begin{bmatrix} -\infty & 2 & 4 & 6 & 3 \end{bmatrix},$$

$$\mathbf{D_3} = \begin{bmatrix} -\infty & 2 & 4 & 7 & 3 \end{bmatrix}, \quad \mathbf{D_4} = \begin{bmatrix} -\infty & 2 & 4 & 7 & 8 \end{bmatrix}.$$

10. (a) Dijkstra's algorithm gives

M	$D(v_j)$		
	v_2	v_3	v_4
$\{v_1\}$	4	2	∞
$\{v_1, v_3\}$	4	2	6
$\{v_1, v_3, v_2\}$	4	2	5

when in fact $W^*(v_1, v_3) = 4 - 4 = 0$ and $W^*(v_1, v_4) = 0 + 4 = 4$.

(b) No. The algorithm would yield $W^*(v_1, v_3) = 0$ correctly, but still give $D(v_4) = 5$, rather than 4.

11. (a) The algorithm would give

M	$D(v_j)$		
	v_2	v_3	v_4
$\{v_1\}$	5	6	$-\infty$
$\{v_1, v_3\}$	5	6	9

no change

whereas $M(1, 3) = 9$ and $M(1, 4) = 12$.

(b) The algorithm would give

M	$D(v_j)$		
	v_2	v_3	v_4
$\{v_1\}$	6	4	$-\infty$
$\{v_1, v_3\}$	6	4	5

no change

whereas $M(1,3) = 10$ and $M(1,4) = 11$.

(c) Both algorithms would fail to give correct values of $M(1,4)$.

12. (a)

$$\mathbf{W}_0 = \begin{bmatrix} \infty & \infty & 1 & \infty & 1 & \infty \\ 1 & \infty & 1 & 1 & \infty & \infty \\ \infty & \infty & \infty & \infty & \infty & \infty \\ \infty & \infty & 1 & \infty & 1 & 1 \\ \infty & \infty & 1 & \infty & \infty & \infty \\ 1 & 1 & \infty & \infty & 1 & \infty \end{bmatrix}, \quad \mathbf{W}_1 = \begin{bmatrix} \infty & \infty & 1 & \infty & 1 & \infty \\ 1 & \infty & 1 & 1 & 2 & \infty \\ \infty & \infty & \infty & \infty & \infty & \infty \\ \infty & \infty & 1 & \infty & 1 & 1 \\ \infty & \infty & 1 & \infty & \infty & \infty \\ 1 & 1 & 2 & \infty & 1 & \infty \end{bmatrix},$$

$$\mathbf{W}_2 = \mathbf{W}_3 = \begin{bmatrix} \infty & \infty & 1 & \infty & 1 & \infty \\ 1 & \infty & 1 & 1 & 2 & \infty \\ \infty & \infty & \infty & \infty & \infty & \infty \\ \infty & \infty & 1 & \infty & 1 & 1 \\ \infty & \infty & 1 & \infty & \infty & \infty \\ 1 & 1 & 2 & 2 & 1 & \infty \end{bmatrix}, \quad \mathbf{W}_4 = \mathbf{W}_5 = \begin{bmatrix} \infty & \infty & 1 & \infty & 1 & \infty \\ 1 & \infty & 1 & 1 & 2 & 2 \\ \infty & \infty & \infty & \infty & \infty & \infty \\ \infty & \infty & 1 & \infty & 1 & 1 \\ \infty & \infty & 1 & \infty & \infty & \infty \\ 1 & 1 & 2 & 2 & 1 & 3 \end{bmatrix},$$

$$\mathbf{W}_6 = \mathbf{W}^* = \begin{bmatrix} \infty & \infty & 1 & \infty & 1 & \infty \\ 1 & 3 & 1 & 1 & 2 & 2 \\ \infty & \infty & \infty & \infty & \infty & \infty \\ 2 & 2 & 1 & 3 & 1 & 1 \\ \infty & \infty & 1 & \infty & \infty & \infty \\ 1 & 1 & 2 & 2 & 1 & 3 \end{bmatrix}, \quad \text{so} \quad \mathbf{M}_R = \begin{bmatrix} 0 & 0 & 1 & 0 & 1 & 0 \\ 1 & 1 & 1 & 1 & 1 & 1 \\ 0 & 0 & 0 & 0 & 0 & 0 \\ 1 & 1 & 1 & 1 & 1 & 1 \\ 0 & 0 & 1 & 0 & 0 & 0 \\ 1 & 1 & 1 & 1 & 1 & 1 \end{bmatrix}.$$

(b) No; $v_2 \, v_4 \, v_6 \, v_2$ is a cycle. If the digraph were acyclic, all diagonal entries in $\mathbf{M}_R$ would be 0.

13. (a)

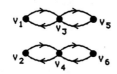

(b) No; for instance $v_1 \, v_3 \, v_1$ is a cycle.

(c)

$$\mathbf{M}_R = \begin{bmatrix} 1 & 0 & 1 & 0 & 1 & 0 \\ 0 & 1 & 0 & 1 & 0 & 1 \\ 1 & 0 & 1 & 0 & 1 & 0 \\ 0 & 1 & 0 & 1 & 0 & 1 \\ 1 & 0 & 1 & 0 & 1 & 0 \\ 0 & 1 & 0 & 1 & 0 & 1 \end{bmatrix}.$$

14. (a)

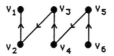

(b) Yes.

(c)

$$\mathbf{M}_R = \begin{bmatrix} 0 & 0 & 0 & 0 & 0 & 0 \\ 1 & 0 & 0 & 0 & 0 & 0 \\ 1 & 1 & 0 & 0 & 0 & 0 \\ 1 & 1 & 1 & 0 & 0 & 0 \\ 1 & 1 & 1 & 1 & 0 & 0 \\ 1 & 1 & 1 & 1 & 1 & 0 \end{bmatrix}.$$

15. (a) Create a row matrix $\mathbf{P}$, with $\mathbf{P}[j] = 1$ initially if there is an edge from v_1 to v_j and $\mathbf{P}[j] = 0$ otherwise. Add the line

$$\text{Replace } \mathbf{P}[j] \text{ by } k.$$

(b) Part of this exercise is solved in Example 4. The sequence of row matrices $\mathbf{P}_k$ is as follows. $\mathbf{P}_0 = \mathbf{P}_1 = \begin{bmatrix} 0 & 1 & 1 & 0 & 0 & 0 \end{bmatrix}$, $\mathbf{P}_2 = \begin{bmatrix} 0 & 1 & 1 & 2 & 2 & 0 \end{bmatrix}$, $\mathbf{P}_3 = \begin{bmatrix} 0 & 1 & 1 & 3 & 2 & 0 \end{bmatrix}$, $\mathbf{P}_4 = \mathbf{P}_5 = \begin{bmatrix} 0 & 1 & 1 & 3 & 2 & 4 \end{bmatrix}$.

16. (a) We claim that MaxWeight and the max-modified Warshall's algorithm produce the same final value of $\mathbf{W}[1,j]$, namely $M(v_1, v_j)$, for each j.

Consider the max-modified Warshall's algorithm applied to a digraph with a reverse sorted labeling. The algorithm guarantees that for every $k \geq 1$ and every $j \geq 1$

$$\mathbf{W}_k[1,j] = \max\{\mathbf{W}_{k-1}[1,j], \mathbf{W}_{k-1}[1,k] + \mathbf{W}_{k-1}[k,j]\}.$$

The proof that Warshall's algorithm works shows that $\mathbf{W}_{k-1}[k,j]$ is the largest weight of a path from v_k to v_j with intermediate vertices in $\{v_1, \ldots, v_{k-1}\}$. Since the digraph is reverse sorted, no path starting at v_k goes through any of $v_1, \ldots, v_{k-1}$, so $\mathbf{W}_{k-1}[k,j] = W(v_k, v_j)$. Thus for every j

$$\mathbf{W}_k[1,j] = \max\{\mathbf{W}_{k-1}[1,j], \mathbf{W}_{k-1}[1,k] + W(v_k, v_j)\}. \tag{$*$}$$

Assume inductively that $\mathbf{W}_{k-1}[1,j]$ and $\mathbf{W}_{k-1}[1,k]$ are the values of $\mathbf{W}[1,j]$ and $\mathbf{W}[1,k]$ produced by MaxWeight at the end of the loop for $k-1$. [Here it is convenient to include a loop for $k=1$ in MaxWeight, even though nothing happens then because $\mathbf{W}_0[1,1] = -\infty$.] Then $(*)$ says that for every j, $\mathbf{W}_k[1,j]$ is the value of $\mathbf{W}[1,j]$ produced by MaxWeight at the end of the loop for k. Thus, by induction, MaxWeight and the max-modified Warshall's algorithm produce the same values of $\mathbf{W}[1,j]$ at each stage, and hence give the same end results.

[In passing, we note that the k-loop in MaxWeight could just as well have been placed inside the j-loop.]

(b) The comparison and replacement steps take a fixed amount of time, and the j-loop repeats at most $n-2$ times for each of the $n-2$ passes through the k-loop.

17. Initially, $\mathbf{W}[i,j] = 1$ if there is an edge from v_i to v_j, and $\mathbf{W}[i,j] = 0$ otherwise. Change the update step to

> if $\mathbf{W}[i,j] < \min\{\mathbf{W}[i,k], \mathbf{W}[k,j]\}$, then
>   Replace $\mathbf{W}[i,j]$ by $\min\{\mathbf{W}[i,k], \mathbf{W}[k,j]\}$.

or to

$$\mathbf{W}[i,j] := \max\{\mathbf{W}[i,j], \min\{\mathbf{W}[i,k], \mathbf{W}[k,j]\}\}.$$

The pointer portion could be omitted.

Chapter 9

We view Boolean algebras as algebraic structures with operations $\wedge$, $\vee$ and $'$. $\mathcal{P}(S)$ is the familiar model and $\text{FUN}(S,\mathbb{B})$ is the example that we want to understand better. The natural order relation $\leq$ is derived from the operations in the same way that $\subseteq$ can be expressed in terms of $\cap$ or $\cup$. The key idea is the unique expression as joins of atoms, which we then exploit to talk about Boolean functions [i.e., switching functions]. After a brief digression to look at logical circuits [= networks] we describe the Karnaugh map procedures for finding Boolean expressions which are in some sense "optimal."

Section 9.1 contains the algebraic facts. At first it's not clear where all of this is leading. Tell the students that our aim is to describe logical circuits algebraically. Theorem 3 on page 507 shows why we care so much about atoms; they are the basic building blocks for [finite] Boolean algebras. The notion of Boolean function as illustrated in Example 8 will be important in what follows. The link with truth tables provides the connection with logic. Wright, the algebraist, thinks Hasse diagrams are extremely valuable. Exercise 9 gives a chance to discuss them if you don't plan to cover § 10.1.

The main message of § 9.2 is the theorem on page 513, which says that if you've seen one Boolean algebra with n atoms you've seen 'em all; they're all isomorphic to $\mathbb{B}^n$. We don't quite say it this directly, but instead get B isomorphic to $\mathcal{P}(A)$, where A is the set of atoms of B. Then the remark following the corollary finishes the job. You may want to belabor the point more. Exercise 11 is fairly tough for the students to do, but makes a reasonable classroom example. Ross, the analyst, likes it.

The key idea in § 9.3 is that Boolean expressions that look different may produce the same Boolean function. We want to choose a "good" representative expression for each Boolean function. Work out an example similar to Example 6 to illustrate terminology and the connection between the values in the literal columns and the values in the final column. Perhaps carry out the details of Example 7(b). See also the answer and comments below on Exercise 9.

Section 9.4 relates Boolean expressions to hardware. The challenge thus becomes: find the "best" hardware configuration to produce a given logical [= Boolean] function. We don't pretend to give a complete answer, since to do so would be dif-

149

ficult even if we knew all of the associated costs and constraints, but we hope to give the flavor of the problem. Students seem to find this material concrete and enjoyable. Many will have seen it in their computer science courses. The idea in Example 5 can be amplified to discuss time complexity versus space complexity in computation.

The idea behind the Karnaugh maps in § 9.5 seems easy for students to grasp. The difficulty lies in making sure that we've chosen the best set of blocks. The erroneous "solution" in Figure 4(b) was obtained using the method in some other discrete mathematics texts. This example illustrates the fact that the choice process is somewhat sophisticated.

9.1 Answers

1. (a) Since the operations $\vee$ and $\wedge$ treat 0 and 1 just as if they represent truth values, checking the laws 1Ba through 5Bb for all cases amounts to checking corresponding truth tables. Do enough until the situation is clear to you.

   (b) We illustrate laws 3Ba and 5Ba. For each $x \in S$

   $$(f \vee (g \wedge h))(x) = f(x) \vee (g \wedge h)(x) = f(x) \vee [g(x) \wedge h(x)]$$

   by definition of $\vee$ and $\wedge$ on $\text{FUN}(S, \mathbb{B})$. Likewise,

   $$((f \vee g) \wedge (f \vee h))(x) = [f(x) \vee g(x)] \wedge [f(x) \vee h(x)].$$

   Since $\mathbb{B}$ is a Boolean algebra, we have

   $$f(x) \vee [g(x) \wedge h(x)] = [f(x) \vee g(x)] \wedge [f(x) \vee h(x)] \text{ for all } x \in S.$$

   So $f \vee (g \wedge h) = (f \vee g) \wedge (f \vee h)$. For each $x \in S$, $(f \vee f')(x) = f(x) \vee f'(x) = f(x) \vee f(x)' = 1$ and so $f \vee f' = 1$, the function identically 1 on S.

2. For examples,

   $$(1, 0, 0, 1) \vee (1, 1, 0, 0) = (1 \vee 1, 0 \vee 1, 0 \vee 0, 1 \vee 0) = (1, 1, 0, 1)$$

   and

   $$(1, 0, 0, 1)' = (1', 0', 0', 1') = (0, 1, 1, 0).$$

3. We have
   $$
   \begin{aligned}
   (x \vee y) \wedge (x' \wedge y') &= [x \wedge (x' \wedge y')] \vee [y \wedge (x' \wedge y')] &&\text{distributivity} \\
   &= [y' \wedge (x \wedge x')] \vee [x' \wedge (y \wedge y')] &&\text{associativity and} \\
   & &&\text{commutativity} \\
   &= [y' \wedge 0] \vee [x' \wedge 0] = 0 \vee 0 = 0.
   \end{aligned}
   $$

4. We have $a = x \vee a$ from the first sentence of the proof. So

$$
\begin{aligned}
a &= a \wedge 1 && \text{identity law 4Bb} \\
&= (x \vee a) \wedge (x \vee x') && a = x \vee a \text{ and law 5Ba} \\
&= x \vee (a \wedge x') && \text{distributive law 3Ba.}
\end{aligned}
$$

And we have $a \wedge x' = a$ from the sentence of the proof preceding the following claim, so

$$
\begin{aligned}
x &= a \wedge x && \text{first sentence of the proof} \\
&= (a \wedge x') \wedge x && a \wedge x' = a \\
&= a \wedge (x' \wedge x) && \text{associative law 2Bb} \\
&= a \wedge 0 && \text{laws 1Bb and 5Bb} \\
&= 0 && \text{identity law 7Bb.}
\end{aligned}
$$

5. (a) $\{a, c, d\} = \{a\} \cup \{c\} \cup \{d\}$.

(b) $(1, 0, 1, 1, 0) = (1, 0, 0, 0, 0) \vee (0, 0, 1, 0, 0) \vee (0, 0, 0, 1, 0)$.

(c) $f = f_a \vee f_c \vee f_d$ where f_a, f_c, f_d are defined as follows

	a	b	c	d	e
f_a	1	0	0	0	0
f_c	0	0	1	0	0
f_d	0	0	0	1	0

Note the similarity among parts (a), (b) and (c).

6. They are the functions that take the value 1 at exactly one element in S. This is true whether S is finite or not.

7. (a) The atoms are given by the four columns on the right in the table.

x	y	a	b	c	d
0	0	1	0	0	0
0	1	0	1	0	0
1	0	0	0	1	0
1	1	0	0	0	1

(b) In the notation of the answer to (a), $g = c \vee d$.

(c) In the notation of the answer to (a), $h = a \vee b \vee d$.

8. (a) $2^4 = 16$. (b) 5. (c) $\binom{16}{5} = 4368$.

9. (a) (b)

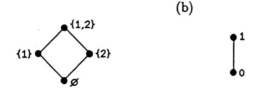

(c)   (d)

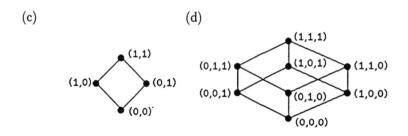

10. (a) The sets $\{n\}$, $n \in \mathbb{N}$.

   (b) No, since we only take the join of a finite collection of elements. In our case, the join (union!) of atoms will always be a finite subset of $\mathbb{N}$.

11. (a) If $a \leq x$ or $a \leq y$, then surely $a \leq x \vee y$ by Lemmas 4(a) and 3(a). Suppose $a \leq x \vee y$. Then $a = a \wedge (x \vee y) = (a \wedge x) \vee (a \wedge y)$. One of $a \wedge x$ and $a \wedge y$, say $a \wedge x$, must be different from 0. But $0 < a \wedge x \leq a$, so $a \wedge x = a$ and $a \leq x$.

   (b) If $a \leq x$ and $a \leq y$, then $a = a \wedge y = (a \wedge x) \wedge y = a \wedge (x \wedge y)$, so $a \leq (x \wedge y)$. If $a \leq (x \wedge y)$, then clearly $a \leq x$ and $a \leq y$.

   (c) $a \leq 1 = x \vee x'$, so $a \leq x$ or $a \leq x'$ by part (a). Both $a \leq x$ and $a \leq x'$ would imply $a \leq x \wedge x' = 0$ by part (b), a contradiction.

12. (a) $x \vee y = a_1 \vee \cdots \vee a_n \vee b_1 \vee \cdots \vee b_m$; remove duplicates. $x \wedge y$ is the join of the atoms used for both x and y. For example, in $\mathcal{P}(\{1, 2, 3\})$ we have $\{1, 2\} = \{1\} \cup \{2\}$ and $\{2, 3\} = \{2\} \cup \{3\}$, so $\{1, 2\} \cup \{2, 3\} = \{1\} \cup \{2\} \cup \{3\}$ and $\{1, 2\} \cap \{2, 3\} = \{2\}$.

   (b) Use exactly the set of atoms not used by x. For example, in $\mathbb{B}^4$, $(1, 1, 0, 0) = (1, 0, 0, 0) \vee (0, 1, 0, 0)$ so $(1, 1, 0, 0)' = (0, 0, 1, 0) \vee (0, 0, 0, 1) = (0, 0, 1, 1)$.

9.2   Answers

1. One solution is to set $S = \{1, 2, 3, 4, 5\}$ and define $\phi(x_1, x_2, x_3, x_4, x_5)$ to be the set $\{i \in S : x_i = 1\}$.

2. We have $\phi(\{a_1, a_2\} \cup \{a_1, a_3\}) = \phi(\{a_1, a_2, a_3\}) = (1, 1, 1)$, but $\phi(\{a_1, a_2\}) \vee \phi(\{a_1, a_3\}) = (1, 1, 0) \vee (1, 0, 1) = (1, 1, 1)$. Similarly $\phi(\{a_1, a_2\} \cap \{a_1, a_3\}) = \phi(\{a_1\}) = (1, 0, 0)$, whereas $\phi(\{a_1, a_2\}) \wedge \phi(\{a_1, a_3\}) = (1, 1, 0) \wedge (1, 0, 1) = (1, 0, 0)$. Also, $\phi(\{a_1, a_2\})' = (1, 1, 0)' = (0, 0, 1) = \phi(\{a_3\}) = \phi(\{a_1, a_2\}')$.

3. (a) No. A finite Boolean algebra has 2^n elements for some n.

   (b) No, since $|\text{BOOL}(n)| = 2^{2^n}$. For example, 8 does not have this form.

4. $\phi(\{a_1, a_2, a_3\} \cup \{a_3, a_5\}) = \phi(\{a_1, a_2, a_3, a_5\}) = a_1 \vee a_2 \vee a_3 \vee a_5 = a_1 \vee a_2 \vee a_3 \vee a_3 \vee a_5 = (a_1 \vee a_2 \vee a_3) \vee (a_3 \vee a_5) = \phi(\{a_1, a_2, a_3\}) \vee \phi(\{a_3, a_5\})$,
and
$(a_1 \vee a_2 \vee a_3) \wedge (a_3 \vee a_5) = (a_1 \wedge (a_3 \vee a_5)) \vee (a_2 \wedge (a_3 \vee a_5)) \vee (a_3 \wedge (a_3 \vee a_5)) = (a_1 \wedge a_3) \vee (a_1 \wedge a_5) \vee (a_2 \wedge a_3) \vee (a_2 \wedge a_5) \vee (a_3 \wedge a_3) \vee (a_3 \wedge a_5) = 0 \vee 0 \vee 0 \vee 0 \vee a_3 \vee 0 = a_3$.

5. In each part, each of the maps is a one-to-one correspondence; see Example 5 on page 168. Thus we only need to verify properties (1)–(3) defining a Boolean algebra isomorphism.

    (a) For $u, v \in B_2$, let $x = \phi^{-1}(u)$ and $y = \phi^{-1}(v)$. Then $\phi^{-1}(u \vee v) = \phi^{-1}(\phi(x) \vee \phi(y)) = \phi^{-1}(\phi(x \vee y)) = x \vee y = \phi^{-1}(u) \vee \phi^{-1}(v)$, and similarly $\phi^{-1}(u \wedge v) = \phi^{-1}(u) \wedge \phi^{-1}(v)$. Also $\phi^{-1}(u') = \phi^{-1}(\phi(x)') = \phi^{-1}(\phi(x')) = x' = \phi^{-1}(u)'$.

    (b) Let $\phi = \phi_2 \circ \phi_1$. Then

$\phi(x \vee y) = \phi_2(\phi_1(x \vee y))$	definition of $\phi = \phi_2 \circ \phi_1$
$= \phi_2(\phi_1(x) \vee \phi_1(y))$	property (1) for ϕ_1
$= \phi_2(\phi_1(x)) \vee \phi_2(\phi_1(y))$	property (1) for ϕ_2
$= \phi(x) \vee \phi(y)$	definition of $\phi = \phi_2 \circ \phi_1$.

Similarly $\phi(x \wedge y) = \phi(x) \wedge \phi(y)$. Finally

$$\phi(x)' = \phi_2(\phi_1(x))' = \phi_2(\phi_1(x)') = \phi_2(\phi_1(x')) = \phi(x'),$$

using property (3) first for ϕ_2 and then for ϕ_1.

6. (a) The 0 element is the integer 1; 6 is the 1 element.

    (b) The atoms are 2 and 3.

    (c) D_6 and $\mathcal{P}(\{2, 3\})$ are isomorphic, using ϕ defined by $\phi(1) = \varnothing$, $\phi(2) = \{2\}$, $\phi(3) = \{3\}$ and $\phi(6) = \{2, 3\}$. Any other 2-element set would work as well as $\{2, 3\}$, but the association with $\{2, 3\}$, which is the set of atoms of D_6, is especially obvious.

7. (a) $\phi(1) = 0$ and $\phi(7) = 1$ define a Boolean algebra isomorphism $\phi: D_7 \to \mathbb{B}$. One way to see that ϕ preserves the Boolean operations $\vee$ and $\wedge$ is to make tables for D_7 like those in Figure 1 on page 500 and compare. Also $1' = 7$ and $7' = 1$ in D_7, so

$$\phi(1') = \phi(7) = 1 = 0' = \phi(1)' \quad \text{and} \quad \phi(7') = \phi(1) = 0 = 1' = \phi(7)'.$$

Alternatively, if you show that D_7 is a Boolean algebra, then it must be isomorphic to $\mathbb{B}$, by the Remark after the Theorem. What are the atoms here?

    (b) $D_4 = \{1, 2, 4\}$ has 3 elements, while finite Boolean algebras must have 2^n elements for some $n \in \mathbb{P}$.

    (c) D_8 has 4 elements. However, 2 and 4 have no complements in D_8. For example, if $2' = z$ then $2 \wedge z = 1$ implies $z = 1$, while $2 \vee z = 8$ implies $z = 8$.

(d) Every product of three different primes will work—for example, $n = 2 \cdot 3 \cdot 5 = 30$.

8. Easily ϕ is also a one-to-one correspondence. For subsets C and D of S,

$$\phi(C \cup D) = f(C \cup D) = f(C) \cup f(D) = \phi(C) \cup \phi(D);$$

the middle equality holds for all functions. Also,

$$\phi(C \cap D) = f(C \cap D) = f(C) \cap f(D) = \phi(C) \cap \phi(D);$$

the middle equality doesn't hold in general, but it does for one-to-one functions. Finally

$$\phi(C^c) = f(C^c) = f(C)^c = \phi(C)^c,$$

the middle equality holding because f is one-to-one and maps S *onto* T.

9. (a) $x \leq y \Longleftrightarrow x \vee y = y \Longleftrightarrow \phi(x \vee y) = \phi(y) \Longleftrightarrow \phi(x) \vee \phi(y) = \phi(y) \Longleftrightarrow \phi(x) \leq \phi(y)$.

   (b) Suppose that a is an atom in B_1. Then $a \neq 0$ in B_1, and so $\phi(a) \neq 0$ in B_2 since ϕ is one-to-one. If $\phi(a)$ weren't an atom, then there would be z in B_2 with $0 < z < \phi(a)$. Since ϕ^{-1} is a Boolean algebra isomorphism [Exercise 5(a)], part (a) would yield

   $$\phi^{-1}(0) < \phi^{-1}(z) < \phi^{-1}(\phi(a)), \quad \text{i.e.,} \quad 0 < \phi^{-1}(z) < a,$$

   contradicting the assumption that a is an atom in B_1. For the converse, suppose that $\phi(a)$ is an atom in B_2. Then from above and Exercise 5(a), $\phi^{-1}(\phi(a)) = a$ is an atom in B_1.

10. As remarked in Example 3(b) and Exercise 11(c) below, $\mathcal{A}$ has no atoms. But $\mathcal{P}(\mathbb{N})$ has lots of atoms. A Boolean algebra isomorphism would map atoms to atoms [Exercise 9(b)] and that would be impossible for an isomorphism $\phi \colon \mathcal{P}(\mathbb{N}) \to \mathcal{A}$.

11. (a) It suffices to consider $\{[a_i, b_i)\}_{i \in \mathbb{P}}$ and show that each union $\bigcup_{i=1}^{n}[a_i, b_i)$ can be written as a finite *disjoint* union of such intervals. This is obvious for $n = 1$. Assume it has been done for $\bigcup_{i=1}^{n-1}[a_i, b_i)$; in fact, we can assume the intervals $[a_1, b_1), \ldots, [a_{n-1}, b_{n-1})$ are disjoint. If $[a_n, b_n)$ intersects none of these sets, we're done. Otherwise, let

   $I = \{i : 1 \leq i \leq n - 1 \text{ and } [a_i, b_i) \cap [a_n, b_n) \neq \varnothing\}$,
   $a^* = \min(\{a_i : i \in I\} \cup \{a_n\})$,
   $b^* = \max(\{b_i : i \in I\} \cup \{b_n\})$,
   and observe $[a_n, b_n) \cup \bigcup_{i \in I}[a_i, b_i) = [a^*, b^*)$ so that

$$[a^*, b^*) \cup \{[a_i, b_i) : i \notin I, 1 \leq i \leq n-1\}$$

expresses $\bigcup_{i=1}^{n} [a_i, b_i)$ as a disjoint union of intervals of the form $[a, b)$.

(b) Since $\mathcal{A}$ inherits the laws 1B, ..., 5B from the Boolean algebra $\mathcal{P}(S)$, we just need to show that if X and Y are in $\mathcal{A}$ then so are $X \cup Y$, $X \cap Y$ and X'. This is clear for $\cup$ and easy for $\cap$ since

$$[a, b) \cap [c, d) = [\max\{a, c\}, \min\{b, d\})$$

whenever the intersection is nonempty. For complementation, consider a disjoint union $\bigcup_{i=1}^{n} [a_i, b_i)$ and assume $a_1 < b_1 < a_2 < b_2 < \cdots < a_n < b_n$. Then the complement is

$$[0, a_1) \cup \left(\bigcup_{i=1}^{n-1} [b_i, a_{i+1}) \right) \cup [b_n, 1).$$

The union may be $[0, a_1)$ or $[b_n, 1)$.

(c) $\mathcal{A}$ has no atoms since nonempty members of $\mathcal{A}$ always contain smaller nonempty members of $\mathcal{A}$. For example, $[a, b)$ contains $[a, \frac{1}{2}(a+b))$.

12. This is like Example 2. $\phi(\emptyset) = (0, 0)$, $\phi(\{(1, 0)\}) = (1, 0)$, $\phi(\{(0, 1)\}) = (0, 1)$ and $\phi(A) = (1, 0) \vee (0, 1) = (1, 1)$.

13. (a) $\theta^{-1}(x \vee y) = \theta^{-1}(\theta(a) \vee \theta(b)) = \theta^{-1}(\theta(a \vee b)) = a \vee b = \theta^{-1}(x) \vee \theta^{-1}(y)$.

(b) Yes. Its inverse, of course, is θ.

(c) If $c \leq d$, then $d = c \vee d$, so $\theta(d) = \theta(c \vee d) = \theta(c) \vee \theta(d)$, and thus $\theta(c) \leq \theta(d)$.

(d) Repeat the argument for part (c) with θ^{-1} in place of θ, using part (a).

(e) Since θ maps onto B_2, there is an e in B_1 with $\theta(e) = 0_2$. Hence

$$\theta(0_1) = \theta(0_1) \vee 0_2 = \theta(0_1) \vee \theta(e) = \theta(0_1 \vee e) = \theta(e) = 0_2.$$

(f) Say $\theta(f) = 1_2$. Then

$$\theta(1_1) = \theta(1_1 \vee f) = \theta(1_1) \vee \theta(f) = \theta(1_1) \vee 1_2 = 1_2.$$

(g) We have $\theta(g) \wedge \theta(g') \leq \theta(g)$, so by part (d) $\theta^{-1}(\theta(g) \wedge \theta(g')) \leq \theta^{-1}(\theta(g)) = g$. Similarly, $\theta^{-1}(\theta(g) \wedge \theta(g')) \leq g'$. Thus $\theta^{-1}(\theta(g) \wedge \theta(g')) = 0$, so $\theta(g) \wedge \theta(g') = \theta(0) = 0$, by part (e).

(h) By part (f), $\theta(g) \vee \theta(g') = \theta(g \vee g') = \theta(1) = 1$.

(i) This follows from (g), (h) and Lemma 1 on page 503.

$$
\begin{aligned}
\text{(j)} \qquad \theta(a \wedge b) &= \theta((a' \vee b')') && \text{[DeMorgan in } B_1\text{]} \\
&= \theta(a' \vee b')' && \text{[part (i)]} \\
&= (\theta(a') \vee \theta(b'))' && \\
&= (\theta(a)' \vee \theta(b)')' && \text{[part(i)]} \\
&= \theta(a) \wedge \theta(b) && \text{[DeMorgan in } B_2\text{]}
\end{aligned}
$$

9.3 Answers

1. $x'y'z' \vee x'y'z \vee xyz'$.

2. From E's minterm canonical form we see that the corresponding $f \colon \mathbb{B}^3 \to \mathbb{B}$ maps $(0,0,1)$ and $(1,1,0)$ to 0 and all other triples to 1.

3.

			(a)	(b)	(c)	(d)
x	y	z	xy	z'	$xy \vee z'$	1
0	0	0	0	1	1	1
0	0	1	0	0	0	1
0	1	0	0	1	1	1
0	1	1	0	0	0	1
1	0	0	0	1	1	1
1	0	1	0	0	0	1
1	1	0	1	1	1	1
1	1	1	1	0	1	1

(a) $xyz' \vee xyz$.

(b) $x'y'z' \vee x'yz' \vee xy'z' \vee xyz'$.

(c) $x'y'z' \vee x'yz' \vee xy'z' \vee xyz' \vee xyz$.

(d) Use all eight minterms.

4. (a)

x	y	z	$x \vee yz$
0	0	0	0
0	0	1	0
0	1	0	0
0	1	1	1
1	0	0	1
1	0	1	1
1	1	0	1
1	1	1	1

(b) $x'yz \vee xy'z' \vee xy'z \vee xyz' \vee xyz$.

5. (a) $x_1 x_2 x_3' x_4 \vee x_1 x_2 x_3' x_4' \vee x_1' x_2 x_3 x_4'$.

   (b) $(x_1 \vee x_2) x_3' x_4 = x_1 x_3' x_4 \vee x_2 x_3' x_4 = x_1 x_2 x_3' x_4 \vee x_1 x_2' x_3' x_4 \vee x_1 x_2 x_3' x_4 \vee$
   $x_1' x_2 x_3' x_4 = x_1 x_2 x_3' x_4 \vee x_1 x_2' x_3' x_4 \vee x_1' x_2 x_3' x_4$.

6.

$$
\begin{array}{lll}
((x \vee y)' \vee z)' & = (x \vee y)'' z' & \text{DeMorgan} \\
& = (x \vee y) z' & \text{since } x'' = x \text{ in general} \\
& = xz' \vee yz' & \text{distributive law} \\
& = xyz' \vee xy'z' \vee xyz' \vee x'yz' & y \vee y' = 1, x \vee x' = 1 \\
& = xyz' \vee xy'z' \vee x'yz'.
\end{array}
$$

7. (a) $xz \vee y'$. Note $y' \vee y'z = y'z' \vee y'z \vee y'z = y'z' \vee y'z = y'$ and similarly $y' \vee xy'z' = y'$.

   (b) $xy \vee xyz = xy$ and $xz \vee z = z$, so the expression is equivalent to $xy \vee z$.

8. (a) $xyz \vee xy'z' \vee x'yz' \vee x'y'z$ (b) Same.

9. $x'y' \vee z \vee xyz \vee xy'z' = x'y'z \vee x'y'z' \vee z \vee xyz \vee xy'z'$. Now $x'y'z \vee z \vee xyz = z$ and $x'y'z' \vee xy'z' = y'z'$, so we get $z \vee y'z' = yz \vee y'z \vee y'z' = (yz \vee y'z) \vee (y'z \vee y'z') = z \vee y'$. This expression can also be obtained from a table of the corresponding Boolean function. The expression is not a single product of literals, by Exercise 12 [its function has the value 1 in more than 4 places], so any equivalent expression as a join of products of literals has at least two products, with at least one literal in each product. Thus the expression $z \vee y'$ is optimal. The purpose of Exercises 9 and 13 is to give students exercises in which they can find an optimal expression by brute force, recognize that it's optimal because the form is so simple, realize that they'd just gotten lucky and wonder if there's a general method. The exercises are intended to set them up to beg for Karnaugh maps.

10. $(xyz \vee xyz') \vee (xy'z \vee xyz) = xy \vee xz$.

11. (a) Find the minterm canonical form for E'. Then find $E = (E')'$ using DeMorgan laws, first on joins and then on products.

    (b) If $E = xy' \vee x'y$, then $E' = xy \vee x'y'$ in minterm canonical form. Thus

    $$E = (xy \vee x'y')' = (xy)'(x'y')' = (x' \vee y')(x \vee y).$$

12. We follow the hint: $E = E \cdot (w_1 \vee w_1') \cdots (w_{n-k} \vee w_{n-k}')$. Apply the distributive law $n - k$ times to get an expression for E as a join of 2^{n-k} minterms.

13. (a) The Boolean function for $x'z \vee y'z$ takes the value 1 at three elements in $\mathbb{B}^3$. The Boolean functions for products of literals take the value 1 at 1, 2 or 4 elements in $\mathbb{B}^3$ by Exercise 12.

    (b) The Boolean function for a single literal takes the value 1 at four elements in $\mathbb{B}^3$. Joining it with other products of literals will only increase the number of elements with value 1.

14. If f_1, f_2 are the Boolean functions for E_1, E_2, then $f_1 \vee f_2$ and $f_2 \vee f_1$ are the Boolean functions for $E_1 \vee E_2$ and $E_2 \vee E_1$, respectively. Boolean functions form a Boolean algebra, so $f_1 \vee f_2 = f_2 \vee f_1$. Hence $E_1 \vee E_2$ and $E_2 \vee E_1$ are equivalent.

9.4 Answers

1. (a) $\{[((xy)z)' \vee x'] \vee [(z \vee y')']\}'$ simplifies to xyz with a little work.

   (b)

   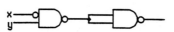

2. NOT $x' = (x \vee x)'$

   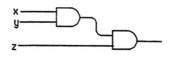

   OR $x \vee y = ((x \vee y)')'$

   AND $x \wedge y = (x' \vee y')'$

   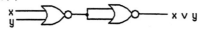

3. (a)

   (b)

4. (a) $(x \vee y)(z \vee w) = [(x \vee y)' \vee (z \vee w)']'$.

   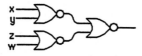

   (b) $(xy')' = x' \vee y$.

   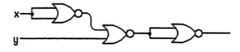

5. (a)

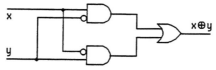

(b) $x \oplus y = (x' \vee y')(x \vee y)$.

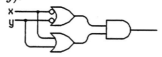

6. (a) $(x \oplus y \oplus z)(xyz)'$ corresponds to the network

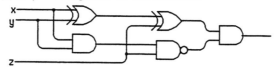

There are other possible answers, corresponding to different Boolean expressions, e.g., $(x \oplus y)z' \vee (x \vee y)'z$.

(b) $(x \vee y \vee z)w \vee (x \vee y)z \vee xy$ corresponds to the network

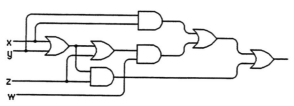

One alternative uses the Boolean expression $((xz)\vee(y\vee w))((yw)\vee(x\vee z))$.

7. (a) $S = 1, \quad C_O = 0$.

(b) $S = x \oplus y \oplus C_I = 1 \oplus 1 \oplus 0 = 0, \quad C_O = 11 \vee (0)0 = 1$.

(c) $S = 0, \quad C_O = 1$.

(d) $S = 1 \oplus 1 \oplus 1 = 1, \quad C_O = 1$.

8. (a) $x = y = C_I = 0$.

(b) Exactly two of x, y, C_I equal 1.

(c) $x = y = C_I = 1$.

9. (a)

(b) $xy = x(y')'$.

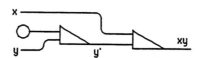

(c)

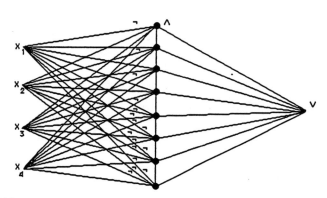

10. Since $x \oplus y = (xy \vee x'y')'$, input x' for z and y' for w.

11.

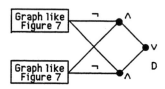

12. (a)

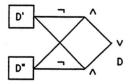

(b) $2^7 = 128$.

13. It is convenient to view the result as valid for $n = 1$. Apply the Second Principle of Mathematical Induction. A glance at a piece of Figure 7 shows that the result is valid for $n = 2$. Assume the result is true for all j with $1 \leq j < n$. Consider k with $2^{k-1} < n \leq 2^k$, and let $n' = 2^{k-1}$, $n'' = n - 2^{k-1}$. By the inductive assumption, there are digraphs D' and D'' for computing $x_1 \oplus x_2 \oplus \cdots \oplus x_{n'}$ and $x_{n'+1} \oplus \cdots \oplus x_n$. D' has $3(n'-1)$ $\wedge$ and $\vee$ vertices and D'' has $3(n''-1)$ $\wedge$ and $\vee$ vertices. Also, every path in D' and in D'' has length at most $2(k-1)$. Now create D as shown.

D has $3(n'-1) + 3(n''-1) + 3$ $\wedge$ and $\vee$ vertices, i.e., $3(n-1)$ such vertices. Moreover, every path in D has length at most $2(k-1) + 2 = 2k$.

14.

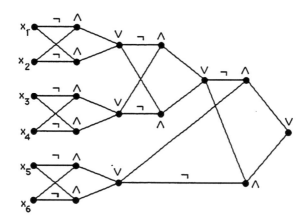

15. (a) The Boolean function for $E_1 \oplus E_2$ is $f = f_1 \oplus f_2$, where

$$f(a_1, a_2, \ldots, a_n) = f_1(a_1, a_2, \ldots, a_n) \oplus f_2(a_1, a_2, \ldots, a_n)$$

for each $(a_1, a_2, \ldots, a_n)$ in $\mathbb{B}^n$. This function has value 1 if exactly one of $f_1(a_1, a_2, \ldots, a_n)$ and $f_2(a_1, a_2, \ldots, a_n)$ does.

(b) The result is clear for the Boolean expression x_1, since the corresponding Boolean function is 1 at $(a_1, a_2, \ldots, a_n)$ if and only if $a_1 = 1$. Assume that the statement is true for $1 \le m < n$, and consider the Boolean function f for

$$(x_1 \oplus x_2 \oplus \cdots \oplus x_m) \oplus x_{m+1}.$$

By part (a), there are two cases where f takes the value 1. It happens if the Boolean function for $x_1 \oplus x_2 \oplus \cdots \oplus x_m$ takes the value 1 and the one for x_{m+1} takes the value 0, in which case $a_{m+1} = 0$ and an odd number of the values $a_1, a_2, \ldots, a_m$ are 1 [by the induction hypothesis]. It also happens if the Boolean function for $x_1 \oplus x_2 \oplus \cdots \oplus x_m$ takes the value 0 and the one for x_{m+1} takes the value 1, in which case $a_{m+1} = 1$ and an even number of the values $a_1, a_2, \ldots, a_m$ are 1 [again, by the induction hypothesis]. In both cases, an odd number of the values $a_1, a_2, \ldots, a_m, a_{m+1}$ are 1. A similar argument shows that f takes the value 0 when an even number of the values $a_1, a_2, \ldots, a_m, a_{m+1}$ are 1.

9.5 Answers

1. $xyz \vee xyz' \vee xy'z' \vee xy'z \vee x'yz \vee x'y'z = x \vee z.$

2. $xyz \vee xyz' \vee xy'z \vee x'yz \vee x'y'z' \vee x'y'z = xy \vee x'y' \vee z.$

3. $xyz \lor xyz' \lor xy'z \lor x'y'z' \lor x'y'z = xz \lor xy \lor x'y' = xy \lor y'z \lor x'y'$.

4. $xyz \lor xy'z \lor x'y'z' = xz \lor x'y'z'$.

5. (a)   (b)

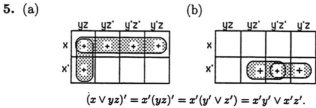

$$(x \lor yz)' = x'(yz)' = x'(y' \lor z') = x'y' \lor x'z'.$$

(c)   (d)

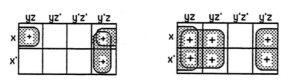

6. (a) E is a product of literals and F is a product of literals that includes the ones in E.

    (b) Consider E with Boolean expression z' and F with Boolean expression xz', say.

7. (a)   (b)

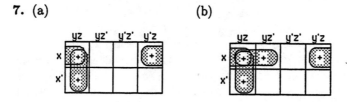

Each two-square block is essential.   Each two-square block is essential.

(c)

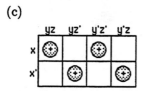

Each one-square block is essential.

8. (a)

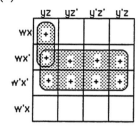

Both marked blocks are essential.

(b)

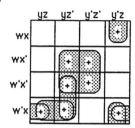

Blocks for $x'z'$, $w'xy$ and $xy'z$ are essential and they cover.

(c)

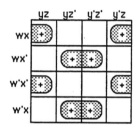

Each two-square block is essential.

9. (a) $z' \lor xy \lor x'y' \lor w'y$ or $z' \lor xy \lor x'y' \lor w'x'$.

(b) $w'x' \lor w'z' \lor w'y' \lor wxyz$.

(c) $w'x'z' \lor w'xy' \lor wxy \lor wx'z \lor y'z'$, not $w'x'z' \lor w'xy' \lor wx'y' \lor wyz \lor wxz'$, which also has five product terms but one more literal.

(d) $wz \lor xz \lor w'x'z'$.

10. (a) $wx \lor wy \lor wz \lor xy \lor xz \lor yz$. Each four-square block of the Karnaugh map is essential.

(b) $w(x \lor y \lor z) \lor x(y \lor z) \lor yz$ is one example.

Chapter 10

The first two sections of this chapter deal with partial orders. The last two look at properties of relations in general. One can skip over the partial orders to get to the material on matrices and relations. If time permits, though, we recommend covering order relations.

Section 10.1 introduces partial orders and the basic terminology of posets. Hasse diagrams are especially important as pictorial representations. It is a good idea to present a number of examples of posets by giving their Hasse diagrams. The theorem shows the link with digraphs. There is some unavoidable overlap with Chapter 9 in order to make the chapters independent. The material on lattices can be touched on lightly. Otherwise the section will probably need two days.

The main message of § 10.2 is that chains are often nice structures, and that if $S, T, \ldots, U$ are chains it's possible to make $S \times T \times \cdots \times U$ into a chain in a natural way. But **not** with the product order. The right order on $S \times T \times \cdots \times U$ is the filing order. It gives an order on $\Sigma^k = \Sigma \times \cdots \times \Sigma$ as well. There are two natural orders on Σ^*, the standard order and the lexicographic order, both of which agree with the filing order on each Σ^k. They differ in the way they relate words of different lengths. Give examples to illustrate both of these orders, and assign Exercise 6. Point out that lexicographic order can have infinitely many words between two given words, while standard order has only finitely many words before any given word. If this situation distresses your students, you can illustrate the same phenomenon with the set $\mathbb{Q}^+$ of positive rationals. Think of the usual order on the terminating decimals in the unit interval. Sections 10.1 and 10.2 have lots of interesting exercises. An extra day here is a good idea, if time permits.

Section 10.3 picks up from Chapter 3. The main themes are composition of relations, which is a surprisingly difficult concept for many students, and the connection between relations and Boolean matrices. Theorem 1 presents composition in matrix form. Students like to see how easily some properties can be read off at once from the matrices. One way to illustrate the trouble in spotting transitivity from a matrix is to take an example that is known to be transitive, such as a partial order, and to order its rows and columns awkwardly. Linking symmetric relations with graphs gives students a geometric handle to grasp.

The notions of transitive, reflexive and symmetric closures in § 10.4 may seem too intuitively obvious to be worth a whole section. The trick here is to raise doubts first. Look at Theorem 1, which gives the obviously correct answers, and then look at Theorem 3. Why should $tsr(R)$ be symmetric? After all, Example 5 shows that $st(R)$ need not be transitive. Something subtle is going on, which takes proof. Then go back to the beginning of the section for details. Exercise 9 is more trouble than fun for some students.

10.1 Answers

1. (a)   (b)

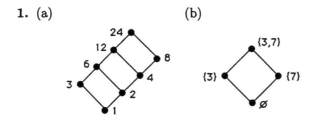

3. (a) h, o, p, q, r, z.

   (b) Posets A, B and C all have minimal elements.

   (c) B and C.   (d) f and g.   (e) f, z, p, does not exist.

   (f) Only C is a lattice. A lacks glb's and B lacks lub's.

4. They are the 2-element subsets, namely $\{a, b\}$, $\{a, c\}$ and $\{b, c\}$.

5. (a) $a \vee b = \text{lub}(a, b) = \max\{a, b\}$, $a \wedge b = \text{glb}(a, b) = \min\{a, b\}$.

   (b) $\mathbb{R}$ itself is an example.   (c) 73.

   (d) 73.   (e) $\sqrt{73}$.   (f) $-\sqrt{73}$.

6. There must be no chains A, B, $C, \ldots, D$, A in which A calls B, B calls $C, \ldots, D$ calls A. A chain of this sort yields $A \prec D \prec \cdots \prec C \prec B \prec A$. So $A \prec A$ by (T), which violates (AR).

7. (a) Suppose that $\preceq$ is a partial order on S and that $\succeq$ is defined by $x \succeq y$ if and only if $y \preceq x$. Then $x \preceq x$, so $x \succeq x$. If $x \succeq y$ and $y \succeq x$, then $y \preceq x$ and $x \preceq y$, so $x = y$. If $x \succeq y$ and $y \succeq z$, then $y \preceq x$ and $z \preceq y$, so $z \preceq x$ and thus $x \succeq z$. Thus $\succeq$ satisfies (R), (AS) and (T).

(b) Clearly $x \preceq x$, so (R) holds for $\preceq$. If $x \preceq y$ and $y \preceq z$ there are four possible cases:

$$x = y = z, \quad x = y \prec z, \quad x \prec y = z \quad \text{and} \quad x \prec y \prec z.$$

In the first case $x = z$. In the other three cases $x \prec z$. In any case $x \preceq z$. Thus (T) holds for $\preceq$.

If $x \preceq y$ and $y \preceq x$ the cases are:

$$x = y = x, \quad x = y \prec x, \quad x \prec y = x \quad \text{and} \quad x \prec y \prec x.$$

Only the first is possible. The other three cases violate (AR) for $\prec$. Thus $\preceq$ satisfies (AS).

8. Yes. See the answer for Exercise 10 for a model argument for (R) and (T). (AS) is easily checked also: If $w_1 \preceq w_2 \preceq w_1$, then $w_2 = ww_1w'$ and $w_1 = uw_2u'$ for w, w', u, u' in Σ^*. Then $w_1 = uww_1w'u'$ and this forces $u = w = w' = u' = \lambda$. So $w_1 = w_2$.

9. Not if Σ has more than one element. Show that antisymmetry fails.

10. Since $w = w\lambda$, $w \preceq w$ and (R) holds. If $w_1 \preceq w_2$ and $w_2 \preceq w_3$, there are words u and v with $w_2 = w_1u$ and $w_3 = w_2v$. Then $w_3 = w_1uv$ with $uv \in \Sigma^*$ and so $w_1 \preceq w_3$. Thus (T) holds.

11. (a) Use $x \vee y = y \vee x$ and $x \vee x = x$.

$\vee$	a	b	c	d	e	f
a	a	e	a	e	e	a
b	e	b	d	d	e	b
c	a	d	c	d	e	c
d	e	d	d	d	e	d
e	e	e	e	e	e	e
f	a	b	c	d	e	f

(b) e is the largest element and f is the smallest.

12. (a) Since $f \vee c = c$, $f \preceq c$. Since $c \vee d = d$, $c \preceq d$. Since $d \vee e = e$, $d \preceq e$.

(b)

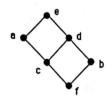

13. (a) No. Every finite subset of $\mathbb{N}$ is a subset of a larger finite subset of $\mathbb{N}$.

(b) $\varnothing$ is the unique minimal element.

(c) $\mathrm{lub}\{A, B\} = A \cup B$. Note that $A \cup B \in \mathcal{F}(\mathbb{N})$ for all $A, B \in \mathcal{F}(\mathbb{N})$.

(d) $\mathrm{glb}\{A, B\} = A \cap B$.   (e) Yes; see parts (c) and (d).

14. (a) $\mathbb{N}$ is the unique maximal element.

(b) $\mathcal{I}(\mathbb{N})$ has no minimal element. Each member S of $\mathcal{I}(\mathbb{N})$ contains members of $\mathcal{I}(\mathbb{N})$ obtained by deleting finite sets from S.

(c) $\mathrm{lub}\{A, B\} = A \cup B$.

(d) $\mathrm{glb}\{A, B\}$ need not exist, since $A \cap B$ may be finite for infinite A and B. *If $A \cap B$ is infinite*, then $\mathrm{glb}\{A, B\}$ exists and equals $A \cap B$.

(e) No, by part (d).

15. (a) Only $\leq$. $<$ is not reflexive and $\preceq$ is not antisymmetric.

(b) Only $<$. Neither $\leq$ nor $\preceq$ is antireflexive.

(c)   (d)

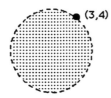

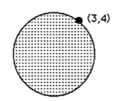

16. (a) Any subset of $\mathbb{N}$ that contains $\{1, 2, 3\}$ and has an even number of elements is an upper bound.

(b) No. For example, both $\{1, 2, 3, 4\}$ and $\{1, 2, 3, 5\}$ cover A and B. A lub of $\{A, B\}$ would have to be contained in $\{1, 2, 3, 4\} \cap \{1, 2, 3, 5\} = \{1, 2, 3\}$ and have an even number of elements.

(c) No, by part (b).

17. See Figures 2 and 7 or Exercise 16 for two different sorts of failure.

18. (a) Every poset with 1 member clearly has a minimal element. Assume inductively that every poset with $n \geq 1$ members has a minimal element, and consider a poset $(S, \preceq)$ with $n + 1$ members. Choose $x \in S$. The subposet $(S \setminus \{x\}, \preceq)$ has a minimal member, say m. Suppose first that $x \preceq m$. If $s \preceq x$ for some $s \in S \setminus \{x\}$, then $s \preceq m$ by (T). Then $s = m$ by minimality of m, so $x \preceq m$, $m \preceq x$ and $x = m$ by (AS), a contradiction. Thus if $x \preceq m$, then x is minimal in S. But if $x \preceq m$ fails, then since m is already minimal in $S \setminus \{x\}$, m is minimal in S. The claim follows by induction.

(b) For example, use $(0, 1]$ or $\{n \in \mathbb{Z} : n \leq 0\}$ with its natural order.

19. (a) Show that b satisfies the definition of $\text{lub}\{x, y, z\}$, i.e., $x \preceq b$, $y \preceq b$, $z \preceq b$, and if $x \preceq c$, $y \preceq c$, $z \preceq c$, then $b \preceq c$.

In detail: Since $\text{lub}\{x, y\} = a$, $x \preceq a$. Similarly $a \preceq b$, so $x \preceq b$ by (T). In the same way $y \preceq b$, and since $\text{lub}\{a, z\} = b$, we have $z \preceq b$.

Now suppose $x \preceq c$, $y \preceq c$ and $z \preceq c$. Then c is an upper bound for x and y, so $a = \text{lub}\{x, y\} \preceq c$. Then c is an upper bound for a and z, so $b = \text{lub}\{a, z\} \preceq c$. Thus $b \preceq c$ for every upper bound c of $\{x, y, z\}$, and we conclude that $b = \text{lub}\{x, y, z\}$.

(b) Show by induction on n that every n-element subset of a lattice has a least upper bound. This is clear for $n = 1$ and true for $n = 2$ by the definition of lattice. Suppose it is true for some $n \geq 2$, and consider a subset $\{a_1, \dots, a_n, a_{n+1}\}$. By assumption, $\{a_1, \dots, a_n\}$ has a least upper bound, say a. Then $\text{lub}\{a, a_{n+1}\}$ is the least upper bound for $\{a_1, \dots, a_{n+1}\}$ by an argument like the one in part (a). Here $a_1, \dots, a_n$ play the role that x, y played in part (a). By induction, every finite subset has a least upper bound. [This proof is an illustration of the observation that in many cases "2 = finite." That is, what can be done for 2 objects can be done for any finite number.]

(c) Use part (a) and commutativity of $\vee$: $(x \vee y) \vee z = \text{lub}\{x, y, z\} = \text{lub}\{y, z, x\} = (y \vee z) \vee x$ [by part (a) again] $= x \vee (y \vee z)$.

20. $w \vee (x \wedge y) = w \vee v = w$, $\quad (w \vee x) \wedge (w \vee y) = z \wedge z = z$,
$w \wedge (x \vee y) = w \wedge z = w$, $\quad (w \wedge x) \vee (w \wedge y) = v \vee v = v$.

10.2 Answers

1. (a) $(1,1)$, $(1,2)$, $(2,2)$, $(2,3)$, $(2,4)$, $(3,4)$, $(4,4)$ is one example.

(b) No. Each step in the chain increases either the first or second coordinate by at least 1, and only $3 + 3 = 6$ increases are possible.

2.

3. (a) $(0,0)$, $(0,1)$, $(0,2)$, $(1,0)$, $(1,1)$, $(1,2)$, $(2,0)$, $(2,1)$, $(2,2)$.

(b) $(0,3)$, $(0,4)$, $(1,3)$, $(1,4)$, $(2,3)$, $(2,4)$.

(c) $(3,0)$, $(3,1)$, $(3,2)$, $(4,0)$, $(4,1)$, $(4,2)$.

4. If S, say, contains elements s and s' that are not comparable under $\preceq_1$, then (s,t) and (s',t) are not comparable in $S \times T$ for any t in T, so $S \times T$ is not a chain. Thus we may assume S and T are themselves chains. Say $s <_1 s'$ in S and $t <_2 t'$ in T. Then the pairs (s,t') and (s',t) are not comparable in $S \times T$ with the product order.

5. (a) 000, 0010, 010, 10, 1000, 101, 11.

   (b) 10, 11, 000, 010, 101, 0010, 1000.

6. (a) in of the list this order words sentence standard increasing.

   (b) in increasing lexicographic list of order sentence the this words.

7. (a) No. If $w \in \Sigma^*$ then $w \preceq^* wu$ for every $u \in \Sigma^*$.

   (b) No, for the same reason.

8. They are the same only if Σ has exactly one member, since if $a \neq b$ then $ab \prec_L b$ but $b \prec^* ab$.

9. (a)   (b)   (c)

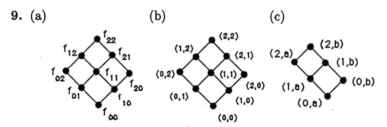

10. No. It need not be antisymmetric or transitive. For example, let $S = T = \mathbf{N}$ with the usual order $\leq$. Then $(0,2) \preceq (1,1)$ since $0 \leq 1$, but $(1,1) \preceq (0,2)$ since $1 \leq 2$. Thus $\preceq$ is not antisymmetric. The string $(2,2) \preceq (3,0) \preceq (1,1)$ shows that transitivity fails too.

11. Yes. If $a \preceq b$, then $\text{lub}(a,b) = b$ and $\text{glb}(a,b) = a$.

12. Here is one natural way. For $x \in C_i$ and $y \in C_j$ define $x \preceq y$ if $i < j$ or if $i = j$ and $x \preceq_i y$.

13. (a) Transitivity, for example. If $f \preceq g$ and $g \preceq h$, then $f(t) \preceq g(t)$ and $g(t) \preceq h(t)$ in S, for all t in T. Since $\preceq$ is transitive on S, $f(t) \preceq h(t)$ for all t, so $f \preceq h$ in $\text{FUN}(T,S)$.

    (b) Suppose $f_m \preceq g$ with $g \in \text{FUN}(T,S)$. Then $m = f_m(t) \leq g(t)$ for every $t \in T$. Since m is maximal in S, $m = g(t)$ for all t, so $g = f_m$. Thus f_m is maximal in $\text{FUN}(T,S)$.

    (c) $f(t) \preceq f(t) \vee g(t) = h(t)$ for all t, so $f \preceq h$. Similarly $g \preceq h$, so h is an upper bound for $\{f,g\}$. Show that if $f \preceq k$ and $g \preceq k$ then $h \preceq k$, so that h is the least upper bound for $\{f,g\}$.

    (d) $f \prec g$ in case $f(t) \preceq g(t)$ for every t, and $f(t) \prec g(t)$ for at least one t.

14. (a) $\{\varnothing, \{1\}, \{1,4\}, \{1,4,3\}, \{1,4,3,5\}, \{1,4,3,5,2\}\}$ is one.

(b) $5! = 120$.

15. (a) $501, 502, \ldots, 1000$.   (b) Some examples are:

$$\{2,4,8,16,32,64,128,256,512\}, \quad \{2,4,8,40,200,1000\}, \quad \{503\}.$$

(c) Yes. Think of primes or see Exercise 17.

16. (a) Yes. The poset $\mathcal{C}(S)$ of all chains in S is ordered by $\subseteq$, so a chain greater than the given one would have more members.

(b) Here are Hasse diagrams for some examples

Another example is $\{1,2,3,5,6,7,11,12,13\}$ with order relation $|$.

17. Consider a maximal chain $a_1 \prec a_2 \prec \cdots \prec a_n$ in S. There is no chain $b \prec a_1 \prec a_2 \prec \cdots \prec a_n$ in S, so there is no b with $b \prec a_1$. That is, a_1 is minimal. [Finiteness is essential. The chain $(\mathbb{Z}, \leq)$ is a maximal chain in itself.]

18. (a) If $(m_1, m_2) \preceq (s,t)$ in the filing order, then $m_1 \preceq_1 s$, so $m_1 = s$ because m_1 is maximal. Since $(s, m_2) \preceq (s,t)$, $m_2 \preceq_2 t$ and so $m_2 = t$ because m_2 is maximal. Thus $(m_1, m_2) = (s,t)$ whenever $(m_1, m_2) \preceq (s,t)$; i.e., (m_1, m_2) is maximal.

(b) No. If (s,t) is maximal in $S \times T$ and $s \preceq_1 s'$ then $(s,t) \preceq (s',t)$, which forces $(s,t) = (s',t)$ and thus $s = s'$. That is, s is maximal in S. If $t \preceq_2 t'$ then $(s,t) \preceq (s,t')$ forces $t = t'$, so t is maximal in T.

(c) Yes. Suppose (s,t) is the largest member of $S \times T$. Then for all $s' \in S$, $t' \in T$, we have $(s',t) \preceq (s,t)$ and $(s,t') \preceq (s,t)$, so $s' \preceq_1 s$ and $t' \preceq_2 t$. Thus s and t are largest members of S and T, respectively.

19. Antisymmetry is immediate. For transitivity consider cases. Suppose

$$(s_1, \ldots, s_n) \prec (t_1, \ldots, t_n) \text{ and } (t_1, \ldots, t_n) \prec (u_1, \ldots, u_n).$$

If $s_1 \prec_1 t_1$ then $s_1 \prec_1 t_1 \preceq_1 u_1$, so $(s_1, \ldots, s_n) \prec (u_1, \ldots, u_n)$. If $s_1 = t_1, \ldots, s_{r-1} = t_{r-1}$, $s_r \prec_r t_r$ and $t_1 = u_1, \ldots, t_{p-1} = u_{p-1}$, $t_p \prec_p u_p$ and if $r < p$, then $s_1 = u_1, \ldots, s_{r-1} = u_{r-1}$ and $s_r \prec_r t_r = u_r$, and again $(s_1, \ldots, s_n) \prec (u_1, \ldots, u_n)$. The remaining cases are similar.

10.3 Answers

1. (a) $A * A = \begin{bmatrix} 1 & 1 & 1 \\ 1 & 1 & 1 \\ 1 & 1 & 1 \end{bmatrix}$. Since $A * A \leq A$ is not true, R is not transitive.

   (b) $A * A = A$, so R is transitive.

   (c) Not transitive. Note that $A * A = \begin{bmatrix} 1 & 0 & 0 \\ 0 & 1 & 0 \\ 0 & 0 & 1 \end{bmatrix}$.

2. (a)　　　　(b)　　　　(c)

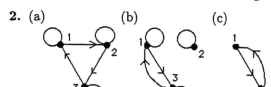

3. (a) The matrix for R is $A = \begin{bmatrix} 0 & 0 & 0 \\ 1 & 0 & 1 \\ 0 & 1 & 0 \end{bmatrix}$. The matrix for R^2 is $A * A =$

   $\begin{bmatrix} 0 & 0 & 0 \\ 0 & 1 & 0 \\ 1 & 0 & 1 \end{bmatrix}$.

   (b)

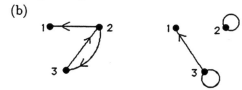

   (c) No; compare A and $A * A$ and note that $A * A \leq A$ fails.

   (d) Yes.　　　　　　　　　(e) Yes.

4. (a) $\begin{bmatrix} 1 & 1 & 1 \\ 0 & 0 & 0 \\ 0 & 1 & 0 \end{bmatrix}$, $\begin{bmatrix} 1 & 1 & 1 \\ 0 & 0 & 0 \\ 0 & 0 & 0 \end{bmatrix}$.

   (b)

   (c) Just observe that $A * A < A$.

   (d) $R^2 = R^3 = \cdots = \{(1,1),(1,2),(1,3)\}$.

5. (a) Matrix for R^0 is the identity matrix. Matrix for R^1 is $\mathbf{A}$, of course. Matrix for R^n is $\mathbf{A} * \mathbf{A}$ for $n \geq 2$, as should be checked by induction.

   (b) R is reflexive, but not symmetric or transitive.

6. (a) For $n \geq 2$ the matrix is $\begin{bmatrix} 1 & 1 & 1 \\ 1 & 1 & 1 \\ 1 & 1 & 1 \end{bmatrix}$.

   (b) R is symmetric but not reflexive or transitive.

7. (a) $\mathbf{A}_f = \begin{bmatrix} 0 & 0 & 1 & 0 \\ 0 & 1 & 0 & 0 \\ 0 & 1 & 0 & 0 \\ 0 & 1 & 0 & 0 \end{bmatrix}$ and $\mathbf{A}_g = \begin{bmatrix} 0 & 0 & 0 & 1 \\ 0 & 0 & 1 & 0 \\ 0 & 1 & 0 & 0 \\ 1 & 0 & 0 & 0 \end{bmatrix}$.

   (b) They will be different, since the Boolean matrix for $R_f R_g$ is $\mathbf{A}_f * \mathbf{A}_g = \begin{bmatrix} 0 & 1 & 0 & 0 \\ 0 & 0 & 1 & 0 \\ 0 & 0 & 1 & 0 \\ 0 & 0 & 1 & 0 \end{bmatrix}$; this is the Boolean matrix for $R_{g \circ f}$ but not for $R_{f \circ g}$. The

   Boolean matrix for $R_{f \circ g}$ is $\begin{bmatrix} 0 & 1 & 0 & 0 \\ 0 & 1 & 0 & 0 \\ 0 & 1 & 0 & 0 \\ 0 & 0 & 1 & 0 \end{bmatrix}$.

   (c) The Boolean matrix for $R_f^{\leftarrow}$ is $\begin{bmatrix} 0 & 0 & 0 & 0 \\ 0 & 1 & 1 & 1 \\ 1 & 0 & 0 & 0 \\ 0 & 0 & 0 & 0 \end{bmatrix}$. The Boolean matrix for $R_g^{\leftarrow}$

   is $\begin{bmatrix} 0 & 0 & 0 & 1 \\ 0 & 0 & 1 & 0 \\ 0 & 1 & 0 & 0 \\ 1 & 0 & 0 & 0 \end{bmatrix}$. $R_g^{\leftarrow}$ is a function and $R_f^{\leftarrow}$ is not.

8. (a) $\begin{bmatrix} 0 & 0 & 0 & 1 \\ 0 & 0 & 1 & 0 \\ 0 & 1 & 0 & 0 \\ 1 & 0 & 0 & 0 \end{bmatrix}$.   (b) $\begin{bmatrix} 1 & 0 & 1 & 0 \\ 0 & 1 & 0 & 1 \\ 1 & 0 & 1 & 0 \\ 0 & 1 & 0 & 1 \end{bmatrix}$.   (c) $\begin{bmatrix} 1 & 1 & 1 & 1 \\ 0 & 1 & 1 & 1 \\ 0 & 0 & 1 & 1 \\ 0 & 0 & 0 & 1 \end{bmatrix}$.

   (d) $\begin{bmatrix} 1 & 1 & 1 & 1 \\ 1 & 1 & 1 & 1 \\ 1 & 1 & 1 & 0 \\ 1 & 1 & 0 & 0 \end{bmatrix}$.   (e) $\begin{bmatrix} 0 & 0 & 0 & 1 \\ 0 & 0 & 0 & 1 \\ 0 & 0 & 0 & 1 \\ 1 & 1 & 1 & 1 \end{bmatrix}$.

9. (a) R_1 satisfies (AR) and (S).

   (b) R_2 satisfies (R), (S) and (T). It's an equivalence relation.

   (c) R_3 satisfies (R), (AS) and (T).

(d) R_4 satisfies only (S).

(e) R_5 satisfies only (S).

10. R_3 is the only partial order, and R_2 is the only equivalence relation. R_1, R_4 and R_5 are not transitive, so cannot be partial orders or equivalence relations.

11. (a) True. For each s, $(s,s) \in R_1 \cap R_2$, so $(s,s) \in R_1 R_2$.

(b) False. The example in part (c) below works. Since $\{(3,2),(2,1)\} \subseteq R_1 R_2$ but $(3,1) \notin R_1 R_2$, this relation is not transitive.

(c) False. Consider the equivalence relations R_1 and R_2 on $\{1,2,3\}$ with Boolean matrices

$$\mathbf{A}_1 = \begin{bmatrix} 1 & 1 & 0 \\ 1 & 1 & 0 \\ 0 & 0 & 1 \end{bmatrix} \quad \text{and} \quad \mathbf{A}_2 = \begin{bmatrix} 1 & 0 & 0 \\ 0 & 1 & 1 \\ 0 & 1 & 1 \end{bmatrix}.$$

Then $\mathbf{A}_1 * \mathbf{A}_2 = \begin{bmatrix} 1 & 1 & 1 \\ 1 & 1 & 1 \\ 0 & 1 & 1 \end{bmatrix}$. Since $(1,3) \in R_1 R_2$ but $(3,1) \notin R_1 R_2$, this relation is not symmetric.

12. The Boolean matrix is the identity matrix. E is clearly reflexive, symmetric and transitive. "Equality" is the simplest of all equivalence relations.

13. Don't use Boolean matrices; the sets S, T, U might be infinite.

(a) $R_1 R_3 \cup R_1 R_4 \subseteq R_1(R_3 \cup R_4)$ by Example 2(a). For the reverse inclusion, consider (s,u) in $R_1(R_3 \cup R_4)$ and show (s,u) is in $R_1 R_3$ or $R_1 R_4$.

(b) If $(s,u) \in (R_1 \cap R_2)R_3$, there is a t such that $(s,t) \in R_1 \cap R_2$ and $(t,u) \in R_3$. Since $(s,t) \in R_1$ we have $(s,u) \in R_1 R_3$, and since $(s,t) \in R_2$ we have $(s,u) \in R_2 R_3$. One example where equality fails is given by relations with Boolean matrices

$$\mathbf{A}_1 = \begin{bmatrix} 1 & 0 \\ 0 & 1 \end{bmatrix}, \quad \mathbf{A}_2 = \begin{bmatrix} 0 & 1 \\ 1 & 0 \end{bmatrix} \quad \text{and} \quad \mathbf{A}_3 = \begin{bmatrix} 1 & 1 \\ 1 & 1 \end{bmatrix}.$$

(c) Show that $R_1(R_3 \cap R_4) \subseteq R_1 R_3 \cap R_1 R_4$. Equality need not hold. For example, consider R_1, R_3, R_4 with Boolean matrices

$$\mathbf{A}_1 = \begin{bmatrix} 1 & 1 \\ 0 & 0 \end{bmatrix}, \quad \mathbf{A}_3 = \begin{bmatrix} 0 & 0 \\ 0 & 1 \end{bmatrix}, \quad \mathbf{A}_4 = \begin{bmatrix} 0 & 1 \\ 0 & 0 \end{bmatrix}.$$

14. If $(s,u) \in (R_1 R_2)^{\leftarrow}$ then $(u,s) \in R_1 R_2$ so there is a t in T with $(u,t) \in R_1$ and $(t,s) \in R_2$. Then $(s,t) \in R_2^{\leftarrow}$ and $(t,u) \in R_1^{\leftarrow}$, so $(s,u) \in R_2^{\leftarrow} R_1^{\leftarrow}$. This argument is reversible.

15. (R) R is reflexive if and only if $(s,s) \in R$ for every s, if and only if $\mathbf{A}[s,s] = 1$ for every s.

(AR) Similar to the argument for (R), with $(s, s) \notin R$ and $\mathbf{A}[s, s] = 0$.

(S) Follows from $\mathbf{A}^T[s, t] = \mathbf{A}[t, s]$ for every s, t.

(AS) R is antisymmetric if and only if $s = t$ whenever $(s, t) \in R$ and $(t, s) \in R$, i.e., whenever $\mathbf{A}[s, t] = \mathbf{A}^T[s, t] = 1$. Thus R is antisymmetric if and only if all of the off-diagonal entries of $\mathbf{A} \wedge \mathbf{A}^T$ are 0.

(T) This follows from Theorem 3 and (a) of the summary.

16. (a) $R_1 \subseteq R_2$ means that $(s, t) \in R_2$ whenever $(s, t) \in R_1$, i.e., that $\mathbf{A}_2[s, t] = 1$ whenever $\mathbf{A}_1[s, t] = 1$. Since $\mathbf{A}_2[s, t] \geq \mathbf{A}_1[s, t]$ whenever $\mathbf{A}_1[s, t] = 0$, $R_1 \subseteq R_2$ if and only if $\mathbf{A}_2[s, t] \geq \mathbf{A}_1[s, t]$ for every s, t.

(b) $(s, t) \in R_1 \cup R_2$ if and only if $(s, t) \in R_1$ or $(s, t) \in R_2$, if and only if $\mathbf{A}_1[s, t] = 1$ or $\mathbf{A}_2[s, t] = 1$, if and only if $\mathbf{A}_1 \vee \mathbf{A}_2[s, t] = 1$.

(c) Similar to (b).

17. Given $m \times n$, $n \times p$ and $p \times q$ Boolean matrices $\mathbf{A}_1$, $\mathbf{A}_2$, $\mathbf{A}_3$, they correspond to relations R_1, R_2, R_3 where R_1 is a relation from $\{1, 2, \ldots, m\}$ to $\{1, 2, \ldots, n\}$, etc. The matrices for $(R_1 R_2) R_3$ and $R_1 (R_2 R_3)$ are $(\mathbf{A}_1 * \mathbf{A}_2) * \mathbf{A}_3$ and $\mathbf{A}_1 * (\mathbf{A}_2 * \mathbf{A}_3)$ by four applications of Theorem 1.

18. (a) Suppose $(s, s') \in RR^{\leftarrow}$. Then there is a t with $(s, t) \in R$ and $(t, s') \in R^{\leftarrow}$. So $(t, s) \in R^{\leftarrow}$ and $(s', t) \in R$; hence $(s', s) \in RR^{\leftarrow}$.

(b) Replace R by $R^{\leftarrow}$ in part (a) to get $R^{\leftarrow}(R^{\leftarrow})^{\leftarrow}$ symmetric and note that $(R^{\leftarrow})^{\leftarrow} = R$.

(c) $RR^{\leftarrow}$ is reflexive if and only if each s in S is related to at least one t in T by R.

19. (a) To show that $R \cup E$ is a partial order, show

   (R) $(s, s) \in R \cup E$ for all $s \in S$,

   (AS) $(s, t) \in R \cup E$ and $(t, s) \in R \cup E$ imply $s = t$,

   (T) $(s, t) \in R \cup E$ and $(t, u) \in R \cup E$ imply $(s, u) \in R \cup E$.

   To verify (T), consider cases. The four cases for (T) are: $(s, t) \in R$ and $(t, u) \in R$; $(s, t) \in R$ and $(t, u) \in E$ [so $t = u$]; $(s, t) \in E$ and $(t, u) \in R$; $(s, t) \in E$ and $(t, u) \in E$. The last two can be grouped together, since if $(s, t) \in E$ and $(t, u) \in R \cup E$ then $(s, u) = (t, u) \in R \cup E$.

(b) $R \setminus E$ is antireflexive for every R. If $(s, t), (t, u) \in R \setminus E$, then $(s, t), (t, u)$ are in R, so $(s, u) \in R$. Suppose, if possible, that $(s, u) \in E$. Then $s = u$, so $(s, t), (t, s) \in R$, contradicting antisymmetry of R. Hence $(s, u) \in R \setminus E$.

10.4 Answers

1. (a) $\begin{bmatrix} 1 & 1 & 0 \\ 0 & 1 & 0 \\ 0 & 0 & 1 \end{bmatrix}$.　(b) $\begin{bmatrix} 0 & 1 & 0 \\ 1 & 0 & 0 \\ 0 & 0 & 1 \end{bmatrix}$.　(c) $\begin{bmatrix} 1 & 1 & 0 \\ 1 & 1 & 0 \\ 0 & 0 & 1 \end{bmatrix}$.

   (d) $\begin{bmatrix} 1 & 1 & 0 \\ 1 & 1 & 0 \\ 0 & 0 & 1 \end{bmatrix}$.　(e) $\begin{bmatrix} 1 & 1 & 0 \\ 1 & 1 & 0 \\ 0 & 0 & 1 \end{bmatrix}$.

2. (a) $\begin{bmatrix} 1 & 1 & 1 \\ 0 & 1 & 1 \\ 0 & 0 & 1 \end{bmatrix}$.　(b) $\begin{bmatrix} 0 & 1 & 1 \\ 1 & 0 & 1 \\ 1 & 1 & 0 \end{bmatrix}$.　(c) $\begin{bmatrix} 1 & 1 & 1 \\ 1 & 1 & 1 \\ 1 & 1 & 1 \end{bmatrix}$
   $= $ (d) $= $ (e).

3. $\{1, 2\}, \{3\}$.

4. $\{1, 2, 3\}$ is the only class.

5. (a) $\begin{bmatrix} 1 & 1 & 0 & 0 & 0 \\ 0 & 1 & 0 & 1 & 0 \\ 0 & 0 & 1 & 0 & 1 \\ 0 & 1 & 0 & 1 & 0 \\ 0 & 0 & 0 & 0 & 1 \end{bmatrix}$.　(b) $\begin{bmatrix} 0 & 1 & 0 & 0 & 0 \\ 1 & 1 & 0 & 1 & 0 \\ 0 & 0 & 0 & 0 & 1 \\ 0 & 1 & 0 & 0 & 0 \\ 0 & 0 & 1 & 0 & 0 \end{bmatrix}$.　(c) $\begin{bmatrix} 1 & 1 & 0 & 0 & 0 \\ 1 & 1 & 0 & 1 & 0 \\ 0 & 0 & 1 & 0 & 1 \\ 0 & 1 & 0 & 1 & 0 \\ 0 & 0 & 1 & 0 & 1 \end{bmatrix}$.

   (d) $\begin{bmatrix} 1 & 1 & 0 & 0 & 0 \\ 1 & 1 & 0 & 1 & 0 \\ 0 & 0 & 1 & 0 & 1 \\ 0 & 1 & 0 & 1 & 0 \\ 0 & 0 & 1 & 0 & 1 \end{bmatrix}$.　(e) $\begin{bmatrix} 1 & 1 & 0 & 1 & 0 \\ 1 & 1 & 0 & 1 & 0 \\ 0 & 0 & 1 & 0 & 1 \\ 1 & 1 & 0 & 1 & 0 \\ 0 & 0 & 1 & 0 & 1 \end{bmatrix}$.

6. $\{1, 2, 4\}, \{3, 5\}$.

7. (a) $r(R)$ is the usual order $\leq$.

   (b) $sr(R)$ is the universal relation.

   (c) $rs(R)$ is the universal relation on $\mathbb{P}$.

   (d) $tsr(R)$ is the universal relation.

   (e) R is already transitive.

   (f) $(m, n) \in st(R)$ if and only if $m \neq n$.

8. (a) R is already reflexive, so $r(R) = R$.

   (b) $sr(R) = \{(m, n) \in \mathbb{P} \times \mathbb{P} : m|n \text{ or } n|m\}$.

   (c) $rs(R) = sr(R)$ as in part (b).

   (d) For every $m, n \in \mathbb{P}$, both $(m, 1)$ and $(1, n)$ are in $sr(R)$, so (m, n) is in $tsr(R)$. Thus $tsr(R)$ is the universal relation.

(e) R is already transitive, so $t(R) = R$.

(f) Same as in part (b), since $st(R) = s(R) = sr(R)$.

9. $(h_1, h_2) \in st(R)$ if $h_1 = h_2$ or if one of h_1, h_2 is the High Hermit. On the other hand, $ts(R)$ is the universal relation on F.O.H.H.

10. (a) If $(x, y) \in \bigcup_{k=1}^{\infty} R_k$ then $(x, y) \in R_l$ for some l, and since R_l is symmetric

$$(y, x) \in R_l \subseteq \bigcup_{k=1}^{\infty} R_k.$$

(b) Use induction on n. Assuming that R^n is symmetric, if $(x, y) \in R^{n+1} = R^n R$ then there is a z with $(x, z) \in R^n$ and $(z, y) \in R$. So $(y, z) \in R$ and $(z, x) \in R^n$ by assumption, and thus $(y, x) \in RR^n = R^{n+1}$. Beware the trap of supposing that if R and S are symmetric, then RS must be, too; see Exercise 11(c) on page 578.

(c) Suppose R is symmetric. Then $R = R^\leftarrow$, so [by Exercise 16(a) on page 137] we have $(r(R))^\leftarrow = (R \cup E)^\leftarrow = R^\leftarrow \cup E^\leftarrow = R \cup E = r(R)$. The relation $t(R)$ is symmetric, by parts (b) and (a) with $R_k = R^k$.

11. (a) Since $R \subseteq r(R)$, $t(R) \subseteq tr(R)$. Since $E \subseteq r(R)$, $E \subseteq tr(R)$. Thus $rt(R) = t(R) \cup E \subseteq tr(R)$. For the reverse containment $tr(R) \subseteq rt(R)$ it is enough to show that $r(R) \subseteq rt(R)$ and that $rt(R)$ is transitive, since then $rt(R)$ contains the transitive closure of $r(R)$. Now $r(R) = E \cup R \subseteq E \cup t(R) = rt(R)$, and $rt(R)$ is transitive by part (c) of the lemma to Theorem 3 on page 584. Thus $tr(R) \subseteq rt(R)$.

(b) Compare $(R \cup E) \cup (R \cup E)^\leftarrow$ and $(R \cup R^\leftarrow) \cup E$; see Exercise 16 on page 137.

12. (a) $(R_1 \cup R_2) \cup E = R_1 \cup E \cup R_2 \cup E$.

(b) $s(R_1 \cup R_2) = (R_1 \cup R_2) \cup (R_1 \cup R_2)^\leftarrow = R_1 \cup R_2 \cup R_1^\leftarrow \cup R_2^\leftarrow$ [Exercise 16 on page 137] $= (R_1 \cup R_1^\leftarrow) \cup (R_2 \cup R_2^\leftarrow) = s(R_1) \cup s(R_2)$.

(c) Yes. $(R_1 \cap R_2) \cup E = (R_1 \cup E) \cap (R_2 \cup E)$.

(d) No. For example, let R_1 and R_2 have Boolean matrices $\mathbf{A}_1 = \begin{bmatrix} 0 & 1 \\ 0 & 0 \end{bmatrix}$ and $\mathbf{A}_2 = \begin{bmatrix} 0 & 0 \\ 1 & 0 \end{bmatrix}$, respectively.

13. (a) By Exercise 12(a) and (b) $sr(R_1 \cup R_2) = sr(R_1) \cup sr(R_2) = R_1 \cup R_2$. Thus $tsr(R_1 \cup R_2) = t(R_1 \cup R_2)$. Apply Theorem 3.

(b) It is $R_1 \cap R_2$ because of Exercise 13 on page 137.

14. It was shown in Example 5 that $R = t(R)$ but $s(R) \neq ts(R)$. Hence $st(R) = s(R) \neq ts(R)$. Alternatively,

$$\mathbf{st(A)} = \begin{bmatrix} 1 & 1 & 1 \\ 1 & 1 & 0 \\ 1 & 0 & 1 \end{bmatrix} \neq \begin{bmatrix} 1 & 1 & 1 \\ 1 & 1 & 1 \\ 1 & 1 & 1 \end{bmatrix} = \mathbf{ts(A)}.$$

15. Any relation that contains R will include the pair $(1,1)$, so will not be antireflexive.

16. The relation given by $\begin{bmatrix} 1 & 1 \\ 1 & 0 \end{bmatrix}$ and the one given by $\begin{bmatrix} 1 & 0 \\ 1 & 1 \end{bmatrix}$ are onto relations containing R whose intersection is R. So if there were a smallest onto relation containing R, it would have to be R itself. But R is not an onto relation.

17. (a) The intersection of all relations that contain R and have property p is the smallest such relation.

    (c) (i) fails. $S \times S$ is not antireflexive.

    (d) (ii) fails. See the answer to Exercise 16.

18. Here is one possibility.

        {Input: $n \times n$ Boolean matrix $\mathbf{A}$}
        {Output: matrix $\mathbf{t(A)}$}
        Set $\mathbf{W} := \mathbf{A}$.
        for $k = 1$ to n do
           for $i = 1$ to n do
              for $j = 1$ to n do
                 set $\mathbf{W}[i,j] := \mathbf{W}[i,j] \vee (\mathbf{W}[i,k] \wedge \mathbf{W}[k,j])$.
        Set $\mathbf{t(A)} := \mathbf{W}$. ∎

Chapter 11

This chapter contains topics that lead off in different directions from the main themes of Chapters 1 and 2. Many people would argue that basic predicate calculus is an essential part of any account of logic, as important and useful as truth tables and formal proofs. We have put the material at the end of the book because many teachers don't feel the need to cover this material and because it isn't explicitly needed in other chapters. Its level of sophistication matches that of Chapter 2. Sections 11.1 and 11.2 can be covered after Chapter 2, while § 11.3 could be covered after Chapter 1, though it would be more natural after Chapter 5. Some students will enjoy studying § 11.3 on their own.

Section 11.1 introduces predicates as proposition-valued functions defined on sets called universes. The quantifiers ∀ and ∃ that were introduced informally in § 2.1 are now the key objects. One of the main messages here and in § 11.2 is that order matters for quantifiers. Exercise 17 is a tough one. We always assign it, but expect to help the students with it.

Section 11.2 illustrates the concept of tautology with the important example of DeMorgan's laws. Emphasize counterexamples as a way to disprove alleged tautologies, even though examples don't prove tautologies. Discuss how one **can** go about proving tautologies. Exercises 7 - 9 are good applications of DeMorgan's laws, as is Exercise 11. Exercises 6 and 10 give practice with counterexamples.

The purpose of § 11.3 is to expose students to the difference between countable and uncountable sets. There is not enough time or space to get very deeply into the subject, but students who have digested this section are ready to go on to more general questions about cardinal numbers. A good follow-up reference is *Set Theory—An Intuitive Approach*, by You-Feng Lin and Shwu-Yeng T. Lin, Houghton Mifflin Company, 1974. Exercise 9 is basic and should be assigned or gone over in class.

11.1 Answers

1. "Some person x is a mother of everybody," which is false.

2. (a) 1 (true). (b) 0 (false).

(c) 1 (true), though this was false for the universe of discourse $\mathbb{N}$.

(d) 0 (false), so order of quantifiers matters; see part (c).

3. (a) 0. Consider m odd.

(b) 0. Consider two different values of m.

(c) 1.

(d) 0. Consider m odd or two different values of m.

(e) 0. Consider $m = n = 0$.

4. (a) 0. Consider $x = 0$.

(b) 0. Consider $x = 0$ or any two different values of x.

(c) 1.   (d) 0. Consider $x = y = 1$.

(e) 1. Consider $y = 0$.   (f) 1. Consider $y = 0$.

(g) 1. $x = 8/5$ and $y = 6/5$.

(h) 0. By algebra $x^2 + y^2 + 1 = 2xy$ if and only if $(x - y)^2 = -1$.

5. (a) $\forall x \, \forall y \, \forall z [((x < y) \land (y < z)) \to (x < z)]$; universes $\mathbb{R}$.

(b) $\forall x \, \exists n [(n > x) \land (x > 1/n)]$; universe $(0, \infty)$ for x, universe $\mathbb{N}$ for n.

(c) $\forall m \, \forall n \, \exists p [(m < p) \land (p < n)]$; universes $\mathbb{N}$.

(d) $\exists u \, \forall n [un = n]$; universes $\mathbb{N}$.

(e) $\forall n \, \exists m [m < n]$; universes $\mathbb{N}$.

(f) $\forall n \, \exists m [(2^m \leq n) \land (n < 2^{m+1})]$; universes $\mathbb{N}$.

6. (a) 1.   (b) 1.

(c) 0. Consider $m \geq n - 1$.

(d) 1. Consider $n = 1$.   (e) 0. Consider $n = 0$.

(f) 0. Consider $n = 0$.

7. (a) $\forall w_1 \, \forall w_2 \, \forall w_3 [(w_1 w_2 = w_1 w_3) \to (w_2 = w_3)]$.

(b) $\forall w [(\text{length}(w) = 1) \to (w \in \Sigma)]$.

(c) $\forall w_1 \, \forall w_2 [w_1 w_2 = w_2 w_1]$.

8. (a) 1.   (b) 1.

(c) If $a, b \in \Sigma$ with $a \neq b$, then $ab \neq ba$. The truth value is 0 if Σ has at least 2 elements and is 1 otherwise. In the English language, panfry $\neq$ frypan.

9. (a) x, z are bound; y is free.   (b) x is bound; y and z are free.

(c) Same answers as part (a).

10. (a) Both x and y are free.

   (b) and (c) In fact, all expressions with one or two quantifiers, such as $\exists x \, \forall y[x + y = y + x]$, are true.

11. (a) x, y are free; there are no bound variables.

   (b) $\forall x \, \forall y[(x - y)^2 = x^2 - y^2]$ is false. Consider $x = 0 \neq y$, for instance.

   (c) $\exists x \, \exists y[(x - y)^2 = x^2 - y^2]$ is true.

12. (a) No. The proposition $\exists n[m + n = 7]$ is false for $m > 7$ and universe $\mathbb{N}$.

   (b) Yes.

13. (a) No. $\exists m[m + 1 = n]$ is false for $n = 0$.

   (b) Yes.

14. (a) No, since $1/(x^2 + 1) \notin \mathbb{N}$ for $x > 0$.

   (b) Yes. Note that if x is rational, so is $1/(x^2 + 1)$.

   (c) Yes.

15. (a) $\exists!x \, \forall y[x + y = y]$.   (b) $\exists!x[x^2 = x]$.

   (c) $\exists!A \, \forall B[A \subseteq B]$. Here A, B vary over the universe of discourse $\mathcal{P}(\mathbb{N})$. Note that $\forall B[A \subseteq B]$ is true if and only if $A = \varnothing$.

   (d) "$f: A \to B$" $\to \forall a \, \exists!b[f(a) = b]$. Here a ranges over A and b ranges over B. Alternative form: "$f: A \to B$" $\to \forall a \in A \; \exists!b \in B[f(a) = b]$.

   (e) "$f: A \to B$ is a one-to-one function" $\to \forall b \, \exists!a[f(a) = b]$. Here a ranges over A and b ranges over B. One way to make this clear is to write $\forall b \in B \; \exists!a \in A[f(a) = b]$.

16. (a) 1. Use $x = 0$.

   (b) 0. Both 0 and 1 are solutions.

   (c) 1. Consider the empty set.

   (d) 1. This follows from the definition of a function.

   (e) 0. f need not map A **onto** B.

17. (a) True.

   (b) False. The notation $\{0, 2, 4, 6, \ldots\}$ is deficient but is clearly meant to describe the set of all even nonnegative integers.

   (c) False; e.g., 3 is in the right-hand set.

   (d) False. The set described contains all odd positive integers as well as integers in A.

   (e) False; the right-hand set is empty.

   (f) False. The set described is $\mathbb{N}$ since $[2m = n \to m < 6]$ is trivially true for $m < 6$.

(g) True.　　(h) True.　　(i) True.　　(j) True.　　(k) True.

(l) Vacuously true.　　　　　　(m) True.

18. (a) There is an m in $\mathbb{N}$ such that, for every n in $\mathbb{N}$, if n is even, then $m + n$ is prime. In other words, there is an m in $\mathbb{N}$ such that $m + n$ is prime whenever n is an even nonnegative integer.

    (b) For every n in $\mathbb{N}$ there is an m in $\mathbb{N}$ such that if n is not even, then $m + n$ is even.

    (c) $\exists m\, \exists n[p(m) \wedge p(n) \wedge e(m + n) \wedge \neg\,(m = n)]$. Here the assumption that the two integers are different is implicit.

    (d) $\forall m\, \forall n[(p(m) \wedge p(n) \wedge e(m + n)) \rightarrow (\neg\,(m = 2) \wedge \neg\,(n = 2))]$.

    (e) $\forall m\, \forall n[(p(m) \wedge p(n)) \rightarrow \neg\, e(m + n)]$.

19. (a) 0. One of $m, m + 2$ and $m + 4$ is always a multiple of 3.

    (b) 1. Consider any odd m.　　　　(c) 1.

    (d) 1.　　　　　　　　　　　　(e) 0. Consider $3 + 5$.

11.2　Answers

1. (a) Every club member has been a passenger on every airline if and only if every airline has had every club member as a passenger.

   (b) Some club member has been a passenger on some airline if and only if some airline has had some club member as a passenger.

   (c) If there is a club member who has been a passenger on every airline, then every airline has had a club member as a passenger.

2. (a) $\neg\,\forall x\, p(x)$.　　　　　　　　　(b) $\forall x\,\neg\, p(x)$.

   (c) As shown in Example 4(b), $\forall x\,\neg\, p(x)$ always implies $\neg\,\forall x\, p(x)$ for a nonempty universe. Thus (b) $\Longrightarrow$ (a). (a) doesn't imply (b) since some, but not all, college students like broccoli.

   (d) There is no college student who likes broccoli if and only if every college student does not like broccoli.

   (e) Some college student likes broccoli if and only if not all college students dislike broccoli.

3. Rule 37b says that "There does not exist a yellow car" is logically equivalent to "Every car is not yellow." In fact, both are false. Rule 37c says that "Every car is yellow" is logically equivalent to "There does not exist a non-yellow car." Both are false. Rule 37d says that "There exists a yellow car" is logically equivalent to "Not every car is non-yellow." Both are true.

4. (a) 0. $\forall n\,[m \neq n]$ is false for every m but $\forall n\,\exists m\,[m \neq n]$ is true.

   (b) 1. This is the contrapositive of the predicate in Example 3(a).

   (c) 0 for each m; $p(m,n)$ is false for $n = m$.

   (d) 1.

5. (a) Rule 37d becomes $p(a) \vee p(b) \Longleftrightarrow \neg\,(\neg p(a) \wedge \neg p(b))$. This is rule 8c of Table 1 on page 85.

   (b) Rule 37b becomes $\neg\,(p(a) \vee p(b)) \Longleftrightarrow (\neg p(a)) \wedge (\neg p(b))$, which is Rule 8a of Table 1 on page 85.

6. (a) Arrange for $p(x)$ and $q(x)$ to be true for disjoint sets of x's. For example, let $p(x)$ be "x is even" and $q(x)$ be "x is odd" with universe $\mathbb{N}$.

   (b) Since $\neg\,(\forall x\,\exists y\,p(x,y)) \Longleftrightarrow \exists x\,\forall y\,\neg p(x,y)$, the predicate $p(x,y)$ should be such that if U is nonempty there is some x for which $p(x,y)$ is true for all y, and some x for which $p(x,y)$ is false for all y. For example, let $p(x,y)$ be "$x + y = y$" with universes $\mathbb{N}$.

7. $\exists n[\neg\,\{p(n) \rightarrow p(n+1)\}]$ or $\exists n[p(n) \wedge \neg p(n+1)]$.

8. $\forall x\,\exists y\,\forall z[(z > y) \wedge (z \geq x^2)]$.

9. (a) $\exists x\,\exists y[(x < y) \wedge \forall z\{(z \leq x) \vee (y \leq z)\}]$.

   (b) 1. For instance, let $z = (x+y)/2$.

   (c) 0; for example, $[x < y \rightarrow \exists z\{x < z < y\}]$ is false for $x = 3$ and $y = 4$.

10. (a) Any integer of the form $4n + 2$, such as 2 or 6.

    (b) Any example with $S \cap T \neq \emptyset$.

    (c) Let $k = 6$, for example.

    (d) A graph with 1 edge will suffice:

    (e) Actually, this statement is true.

11. $\exists N\,\forall n[p(n) \rightarrow (n < N)]$.

12. (a) Let the universe of discourse for the variable x be the set of negative integers, the universe of discourse for z be the set of positive integers, and let $\mathbb{Z}$ be the universe of discourse for y.

    (b) Let $\mathbb{Z}$ or $\mathbb{R}$ be the universe of discourse for all three variables x, y and z.

13. One can let $q(x,y)$ be the predicate "$x = y$." Another way to handle $\exists x\,p(x,x)$ is to let $r(x)$ be the 1-place predicate $p(x,x)$. Then $\exists x\,r(x)$ is a compound predicate.

14. If U has one member, then $\forall x\,p(x)$ and $\exists x\,p(x)$ are either both true or both false.

11.3 Answers

1. (a) True (b) False. (c) False. (d) False.
   (e) True. Compare Exercise 1 on page 63.

2. (a) True. (b) True. (c) False.
   (d) False. It's countable, but it might not be infinite. It might even be empty.
   (e) True.

3. (a) A function of the form $f(x) = ax + b$ will work if you choose a and b so that $f(0) = -1$ and $f(1) = 1$. Sketch your answer to see that it works. [For example, $f(x) = 2x - 1$ works.]
   (b) Use g where $g(x) = 1 - x$.
   (c) Modify suggestion for part (a). For example, $f(x) = 13x - 5$ works.
   (d) Use $x \to 1/x$.
   (e) Map $(1, \infty)$ onto $(0, \infty)$ using $h(x) = x - 1$ and compose with your answer from part (d) to obtain $h(1/x) = (1/x) - 1$.
   (f) $f(x) = 2^x$, say. Sketch f to see that it works.

4. $f(n) = 2n - 2$ and $g(n) = 2n - 1$ work.

5. (a) Use a graphing calculator or the data

x	.1	.2	.3	.4	.5	.6	.7	.8	.9
$f(x)$	-8.89	-3.75	-1.90	$-.83$	0	.83	1.90	3.75	8.89

   (b) The derivative is $\dfrac{2x^2 - 2x + 1}{x^2(1 - x)^2}$, which is positive on the interval $(0, 1)$ since $2x^2 - 2x + 1 = 2(x - \frac{1}{2})^2 + \frac{1}{2}$.

6. (a) - (f) are countable. (c), (e) and (f) are countably infinite. (g) is uncountable.

7. Only the sets in (b) and (c) are countably infinite.

8. If $m \le n$ there are $\dfrac{n!}{(n - m)!}$ one-to-one functions. If $m > n$ there are none.

9. (a) We may assume that S is infinite. Let $f \colon S \to T$ be a one-to-one correspondence where T is a countable set. There is a one-to-one correspondence $g \colon T \to \mathbb{P}$ since T is countable. Then $g \circ f$ is a one-to-one correspondence of S onto $\mathbb{P}$.
   (b) Suppose f is a one-to-one correspondence of S onto the uncountable set T. If S were countable, then $f^{\leftarrow}$ would be a one-to-one correspondence of T onto the countable set S, so that T would be countable by part (a), a contradiction.

10. By construction, $f(n+1) \neq f(k)$ for $1 \leq k < n+1$, so no two values of f are equal, and f is one-to-one.

    To show that f maps $\mathbb{P}$ onto A, consider $m \in A$. Some member of the infinite set $\{f(1), f(2), \dots\}$ of positive integers is larger than m; say $m < f(n)$ for some $n \in \mathbb{P}$. Then m is in $\{f(1), \dots, f(n-1)\}$, since otherwise $f(n)$ would not be the smallest member of $A \setminus \{f(1), \dots, f(n-1)\}$. Thus $m = f(k)$ for some $k \in \mathbb{P}$. That is, every member of A is in the image of f.

11. (a) Apply part (b) of the theorem to $S \times T = \bigcup_{t \in T} (S \times \{t\})$. Each $S \times \{t\}$ is countable, since it is in one-to-one correspondence with the countable set S.

    (b) For each $t \in T$, let $g(t)$ be an element in S such that $f(g(t)) = t$. Show that g is one-to-one and apply part (a) of the theorem.

    (c) By part (a), $\mathbb{Z} \times \mathbb{P}$ is countable. Since f maps $\mathbb{Z} \times \mathbb{P}$ onto $\mathbb{Q}$, $\mathbb{Q}$ is countable by part (b).

12. If S and T have the same size, there is a one-to-one function f from S onto T. Use f to define a function $f^* : \mathcal{P}(S) \to \mathcal{P}(T)$ by the rule $f^*(A) = f(A) = \{f(a) : a \in A\}$ for each subset A of S. The inverse of f defines the inverse of f^* similarly, so f^* is a one-to-one function mapping $\mathcal{P}(S)$ onto $\mathcal{P}(T)$.

13. (a) For each f in $\mathrm{FUN}(\mathbb{P}, \{0, 1\})$, let $\phi(f)$ be the set $\{n \in \mathbb{P} : f(n) = 1\}$. If $f, g \in \mathrm{FUN}(\mathbb{P}, \{0, 1\})$ and $f \neq g$, then there exists $k \in \mathbb{P}$ so that $f(k) \neq g(k)$. Then k belongs to $\{n \in \mathbb{P} : f(n) = 1\}$ or $\{n \in \mathbb{P} : g(n) = 1\}$ but **not** both. Hence $\phi(f) \neq \phi(g)$; this shows that ϕ is one-to-one. ϕ maps onto $\mathcal{P}(\mathbb{P})$ because given $A \in \mathcal{P}(\mathbb{P})$ its characteristic function χ_A belongs to $\mathrm{FUN}(\mathbb{P}, \{0, 1\})$ and $\phi(\chi_A) = A$.

    (b) Use Example 3(a) and Exercise 9.

14. Choose a member from each subset in the family. The set of chosen elements is in one-to-one correspondence with the family and is countable by part (a) of the theorem. Apply Exercise 9(a).

15. For the inductive step, use the identity $S^n = S^{n-1} \times S$.

16. (a) $8 = 2^3$, so $f(\frac{1}{8}) = 2^5 = 32$. $9 = 3^2$, so $f(\frac{1}{9}) = 3^3 = 27$. $10 = 2 \cdot 5$, so $f(\frac{1}{10}) = 2 \cdot 5 = 10$. $100 = 2^2 \cdot 5^2$, so $f(\frac{1}{100}) = 2^3 \cdot 5^3 = 1000$. $f(\frac{21}{20}) = 3^2 \cdot 7^2 \cdot 2^3 \cdot 5 = 17{,}640$.

    (b) $f(\frac{1}{23}) = 23$. $f(\frac{1}{12}) = 24$. $f(5) = 25$. $f(\frac{1}{26}) = 26$. $f(\frac{1}{9}) = 27$. $f(\frac{2}{7}) = 28$.

    (c) Consider a positive integer N and write it as a product of primes: $N = p_1^{2m_1} \cdots p_k^{2m_k} \cdot q_1^{2n_1 - 1} \cdots q_l^{2n_l - 1}$ where we have written the even powers of primes first. All p_i's are distinct, all q_j's are distinct, and no p_i equals any q_j. If $m = p_1^{m_1} \cdots p_k^{m_k}$ and $n = q_1^{n_1} \cdots q_l^{n_l}$, then $f(\frac{m}{n}) = N$. Moreover, this is the only fraction in $\mathbb{Q}^+$ that maps to N because the factorization of a positive integer into a product of primes is unique (except for order); see Theorem 5 on page 260.